An Illustrated Pocl

SHARKS
OF THE
WORLD

Illustrated by Marc Dando

Text by
David A. Ebert and Sarah Fowler

WILD
NATURE
PRESS

Leonard Compagno (Glencairn, South Africa)

Dedicated to our dear friend Leonard, one of the world's
foremost shark taxonomists, and a prolific author, who named
many of the species in this book and is particularly famous for
his 1984 *FAO Species Catalogue of Sharks of the World.*

FSC
www.fsc.org
MIX
Paper from
responsible sources
FSC® C110418

Published in 2014 by
Wild Nature Press
Winson House, Church Road
Plympton St. Maurice, Plymouth PL7 1NH

A CIP catalogue record for this book is available from the British Library.

ISBN 978-0-9573946-6-7

Printed and bound in Slovenia on behalf of Latitude Press

10 9 8 7 6 5 4 3 2 1

www.wildnaturepress.com

CONTENTS

ACKNOWLEDGEMENTS

We wish to thank all of those who have been extremely helpful and generous with their time in responding to our numerous questions, providing data and information from their own research (some of it unpublished), and much needed literature. We extend our particular thanks to the following individuals for general discussions, contributions and information on various aspects of this project:

David Catania (California Academy of Sciences, San Francisco, USA)
Demian Chapman (Stony Brook University, New York, USA)
Clinton Duffy (Department of Conservation, New Zealand)
Jon Fong (California Academy of Sciences, San Francisco, USA)
Malcolm Francis (NIWA, New Zealand) and Clinton Duffy (Department of Conservation, New Zealand)
Mark Harris
Hsuan-Ching (Hans) Ho (National Museum of Marine Biology and Aquarium, Taiwan)
Rob Leslie (Department Agriculture Forestry and Fisheries, Cape Town, South Africa)
Gavin Naylor (College of Charleston, Charleston, South Carolina, USA)
Andrew Stewart (Te Papa Museum, New Zealand)
William White (CSIRO Marine Laboratories, Hobart, Tasmania, Australia)
Marianne Taylor

INTRODUCTION

This pocket guide has been published in response to the many requests for a smaller, easily portable book describing all the shark species included in *Sharks of the World: A Fully Illustrated Guide* (Ebert, Fowler and Compagno 2013). This book hopefully does just that, with 501 species (including 77 new shark species named since 2005) depicted in colour, concise descriptions, key guide and much more essential information; this book is designed to be the shark guide you take with you everywhere.

The reason we have produced these guides is not just because we and so many other people love sharks, but also because the identification of whole sharks and high-value parts, such as teeth and fins, is an essential tool to support shark conservation, fisheries management and international trade regulation, prevent further depletion of stocks, and enable their recovery. As an example, the teeth or jaws of protected species, such as the White Shark, are still offered for sale or traded between countries as curios or trophies. Shark fins of many species are still traded in huge quantities, to meet demand for one of the most highly prized seafood dishes in the world: shark fin soup. It is estimated that the fins of up to 73 million sharks may have entered international trade annually in recent years. The role of the shark fin trade in driving unsustainable shark fisheries is now being addressed through shark finning bans (which outlaw the removal of fins and discard of shark carcasses at sea), prohibiting the capture and retention of some threatened species, and the legal regulation of international trade in products derived from sharks listed in the Appendices of the Convention on International Trade in Endangered Species (CITES) – this guide will support the implementation of these measures.

We also hope that this guide will encourage more people to become involved in field studies of sharks – in the sea and onshore; at fish landing sites and in fish markets; in armchairs, libraries and classrooms. It is not just for scientists and managers, but also for divers, anglers, naturalists and anyone else interested in wildlife and the sea. What is more, because knowledge of shark biodiversity and biology is still sparse in many parts of the world, those who use this book in the field might uncover new information, or even completely new shark species. We all still have a lot to learn about these fascinating animals, which are sadly more seriously threatened with extinction and in greater need of conservation and management action than any other higher taxon of vertebrate animals. We aim, through these pages, to spread our enthusiasm for sharks and encourage readers to improve their future chances of survival by supporting national and international efforts to end over-exploitation in fisheries and allow populations to recover.

The cartilaginous fishes – Chondrichthyes

There are about 1200 known living species of chondrichthyans (sharks, rays and chimaeras): jawed fishes with multiple gill openings and simple, flexible cartilaginous skeletons. Elasmobranchs, the sharks (~500 species) and their close cousins the batoid fishes (~650 species, most of them skates and rays), are the most common living chondrichthyans. There are also about 50 species of the rarely seen, deep sea chimaeras, or holocephalans. This is a tiny remnant of the numbers that dominated the seas 300 million years ago; more than 3000 predecessors of today's chondrichthyans have been identified in the fossil record (likely only a small proportion of extinct species). Today, sharks and their relatives are in the minority: more than 30,000 of living fishes are teleosts, with bony skeletons.

Biology and ecology

Since the first shark appeared almost 400 million years ago, these animals have occupied a wide range of habitats and adopted a variety of lifestyles and reproductive strategies. Shark species occur in the deep ocean, coastal and intertidal habitats, equatorial waters, frigid Arctic and Antarctic seas, and a few in freshwater. Some are very poor swimmers and clamber around on muscular fins; they may spend their entire lives within a relatively small area of seabed. Others never stop swimming, reach very high speeds and cover huge distances across the world's oceans, moving between warm tropical surface waters and the colder waters of the deepsea or boreal zones.

Water temperature is one of the most important environmental factors governing shark distribution. Most sharks are cold-blooded (ectotherms); their body temperature is similar to the water in which they swim because any warmth generated by muscle activity rapidly diffuses away

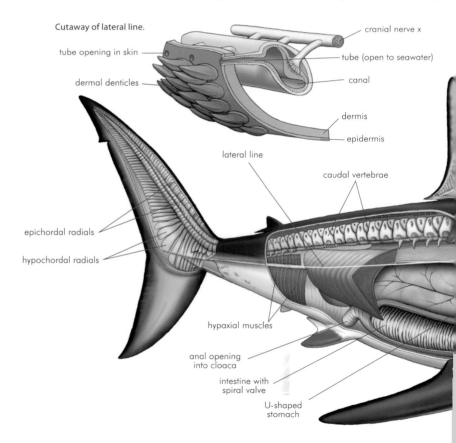

Shark general anatomy (for topography see pages 11–13).

across their gills. Many cold-blooded species live in warm seas, where they can retain a high enough body temperature to function effectively, and some migrate north and south with the changing seasons. Coldwater ectotherms (e.g. deepsea sharks) have a very low metabolic rate, are often small-bodied, and feed and grow very slowly; they probably die if they enter warm water.

Some mackerel sharks have evolved a complex heat-exchange system that maintains their core body temperature significantly above that of the cold water in which they live. These warm-bodied sharks (endotherms) are faster, more efficient predators, grow rapidly, and have a much higher metabolic rate than ectotherms. However, they also need up to ten times as much food as a similar sized cold-blooded shark, and mostly feed in colder, more productive waters. White Sharks returning from long journeys into tropical waters may be very much thinner than they were when they left their cold-water hunting grounds.

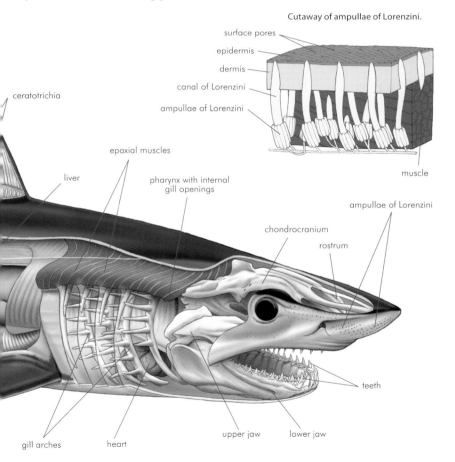

Cutaway of ampullae of Lorenzini.

surface pores
epidermis
dermis
canal of Lorenzini
ampullae of Lorenzini
muscle

ceratotrichia

ampullae of Lorenzini

epaxial muscles
liver
pharynx with internal gill openings
chondrocranium
rostrum

teeth

gill arches
heart
upper jaw
lower jaw

Reproduction

Unlike most bony fishes (which broadcast-spawn huge numbers of tiny eggs, few of which reach adulthood), sharks have internal fertilisation and produce a small number of large young with high survival rates. This reproductive strategy is similar to that of birds and mammals, except that shark pups are born fully-developed and require no further care from their mother.

About 40% of sharks are egg-laying. Each egg has a large reserve of yolk to feed the developing pup, is protected by a tough capsule and develops anchored to the seabed. Some shark eggs may take a year or more to hatch, while species that lay their eggs shortly before hatching reduce the risk that they may be eaten by predators.

All other sharks are viviparous; they give birth to live young. In some species, unborn pups are attached to a yolk sac, with no direct maternal supply of nutrition. Others may have a placental attachment and, like mammals, receive nutrition directly from the mother. A small percentage of sharks exhibit oviphagy, whereby they feed on infertile eggs produced by their mother; the first pups to develop may even feed on their siblings in the uterus.

So much maternal investment means that several species need one or two 'resting' years between litters, to rebuild their energy reserves. Astonishingly, parthenogenesis or 'virgin birth' is known in some captive female sharks, which produced daughters without a father.

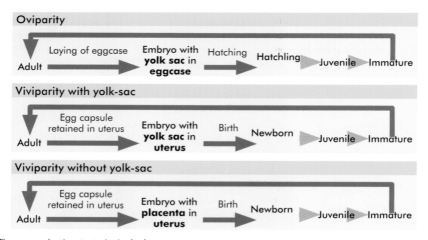

Three reproductive strategies in sharks.

Shark senses

Sharks include some of the world's most intelligent and efficient predators, with highly sophisticated social behaviours. Brain size and complexity of behaviour does, however, vary significantly between species. Less intelligence is needed to ambush crabs, crunch molluscs, or slurp plankton, than to locate, stalk and outwit highly intelligent prey animals, or to engage in complex migratory, social and mating behaviours. Carcharhinid sharks have larger brains (relative to body size) than angelsharks. The White Shark's brain is larger than that of the filter-feeding Basking Shark. Hammerheads have the largest brains of all sharks (but are outclassed by manta and devil rays).

All sharks have the same range of senses, although some species use them in a more sophisticated manner. Smell and taste, used to locate prey over long distances, are outstanding. Sight is very important, particularly for clear-water species, with the largest eyes found in top visual predators (e.g. White Shark) and the deepwater sharks. The latters' eyes are designed to capture as much light as possible in deep ocean darkness, and appear to glow green at the surface. In contrast, species that live in murky rivers have tiny eyes, and rely heavily upon their other senses. As well as good hearing, sharks can perceive changes in pressure and electric fields, using sensory cells scattered around their head and mouth, and along their lateral lines. A variety of numerous tiny receptor cells detect changes in pressure caused by other animals moving nearby. Minute organs known as 'ampullae of Lorenzini' pick up the tiny changes in electric fields that are given off by living animals (even when buried in the seabed), inanimate objects, and water moving through the earth's magnetic field. These help sharks to detect and locate prey, to orient themselves during migration, and to follow magnetic highways between feeding and aggregation sites.

Globally threatened species

A global analysis of the conservation status of the world's sharks, batoids and chimaeras used the IUCN Red List categories and criteria to highlight our lack of knowledge of many stocks and the high extinction risk faced by many sharks and their relatives. These large marine predators, which include some of the latest-maturing and slowest-reproducing of all animals, are under greater threat than even the amphibians (formerly thought to be the world's most threatened vertebrates) and mammals. Large sharks are more likely to be threatened than smaller species. Almost a quarter of all chondrichthyan species is threatened with extinction, and only one third is safe.

Unsustainable, unregulated target and bycatch fisheries, often driven by global trade demand for meat and fins, are the greatest threat to sharks. Habitat damage is also a problem in coastal waters and rivers, and population control or persecution of large sharks has depleted some stocks.

Sharks of shallow water habitats, on the coast and in the open ocean, are the most seriously threatened; sharks longer than 1m have a more than 50% chance of being threatened, compared with about 12% for deepwater species of a similar size. Small deepwater species, like the lanternsharks, have the lowest risk. The angelsharks and thresher sharks are the two groups with the highest level of extinction risk to their entire families.

Geographically, coastal species in the Indo-Pacific Biodiversity Triangle, the Red Sea and the Mediterranean Sea/West Africa are at greatest risk.

For more information, see Dulvy *et al.* (2014), **www.iucnredlist.org**, and **www.iucnssg.org**

	IUCN Red List category of threat		No. of shark sp.	%
CR	Critically Endangered	Threatened categories	11	2.4%
EN	Endangered		15	3.2%
VU	Vulnerable		48	10.4%
NT	Near Threatened		67	14%
LC	Least Concern		115	25%
DD	Data Deficient		209	45%

The global Red List status of sharks.

HOW TO USE THIS BOOK

If you have not studied sharks before, you might want to start by checking that you are definitely looking at a shark.

All sharks have multiple pairs of gill openings (5–7 pairs). Sharks have gill slits on the sides of their heads and their pectoral fins are never fused to the head along their entire length (pages 11–12), unlike skates and rays whose gills always lie beneath their pectoral fins, and these fins are fused to the sides of their heads. Sharks' body shape varies considerably, depending upon their habitat and their feeding strategy – there are some flat sharks (e.g. angelsharks and wobbegongs) and some shark-like rays (e.g. guitarfishes and sawfishes). The position of the gill openings and the shape of the pectoral fins are the most important and consistent characteristics.

Once you are sure you have a shark, turn to the illustrated key to orders and families on page 28 and follow the sequence indicated until you have identified the taxon within which the shark occurs. We recommend always using this key, even if you already think that you know what species it is. Then turn to the page number provided to study the detailed illustrations, confirm your identification, and read more about the species. If you intend to make regular field or fish market observations, consult Field Observations on pages 231 to 234 to ensure that you collect the most useful written and photographic records of each animal.

Each taxonomic section starts with a very brief description of the order, key identification features (e.g. number and shape of fins, fin spines, gills, position of mouth etc. – please refer back to the labeled drawings on pages 11–13), biology, and their fisheries and conservation status. This is followed by similar information for each family. It is a good idea to read these basic descriptions first, to ensure that they match the animal you are trying to identify, before moving on to trying to identify the species from the plates that follow. The colour illustrations show the appearance in life of every species, scaled according to their relative maximum size, while the size of one named species relative to an average person is also provided.

The text opposite the plate provides for each species one widely used English name, its scientific name and the maximum total length (cm) recorded (which could be less than the maximum to which the species may grow). Beneath this are its geographic distribution **DN** (see also page 230), habitat **HT** (see also Oceans and seas pages 229 to 230), key identification features **ID**, coloration **CR**, and its **Status** in the IUCN Red List of Threatened Species (see cover flap and page 9 for categories).

Teeth (pages 14–19) and jaw size and shape are useful supplementary indicators of shark species identification, and may even be used alone to determine family or genus, occasionally even species. Because sharks shed so many teeth during their life-time, and these survive extremely well in the fossil record, most people see far more shark teeth than they ever encounter whole sharks – but this also means that it is possible to mistake a fossil tooth in very good condition as a tooth from a living species.

Pages 20–27 reproduce a key to the identification of some of the most common shark fins and those whose trade is regulated under CITES. These are followed, on page 30, by an illustrated key to the identification of orders and families of sharks from whole animals.

As this is a pocket guide, with its obvious limitations of space, more information may be required. Please refer to *Sharks of the World: A Fully Illustrated Guide* (Ebert *et al.* 2013) for more detailed descriptions, further taxonomic illustrations and distribution maps. Or the most recent *FAO Species Catalogue of Sharks of the World* and *Regional Identification Guides* (download from www.fao.org/fishery).

TOPOGRAPHY

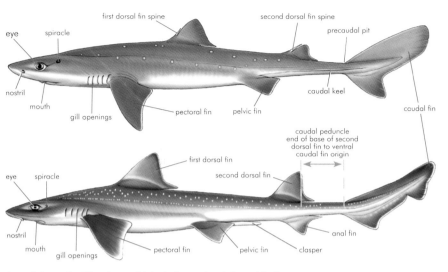

Lateral views – (top) female squalid shark; (bottom) male houndshark.

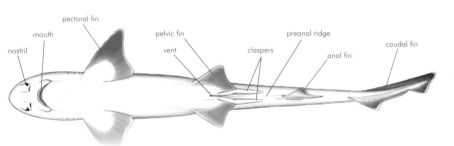

Ventral view – male houndshark.

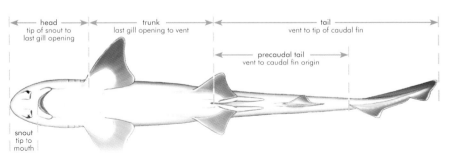

Ventral view – showing body regions referred to in text.

Caudal fin topography.

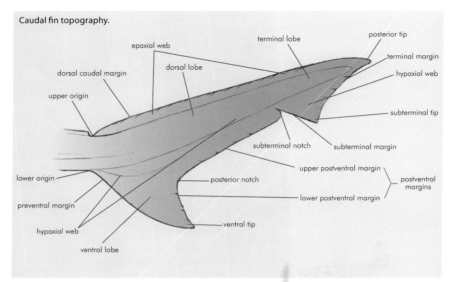

epaxial web

terminal lobe

posterior tip

dorsal caudal margin

dorsal lobe

terminal margin

hypaxial web

upper origin

subterminal tip

subterminal notch

subterminal margin

upper postventral margin

postventral margins

lower origin

posterior notch

lower postventral margin

preventral margin

hypaxial web

ventral tip

ventral lobe

Dorsal fin topography.

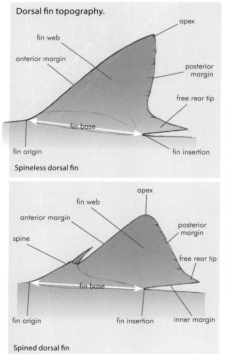

apex

fin web

anterior margin

posterior margin

free rear tip

fin base

fin origin

fin insertion

Spineless dorsal fin

apex

fin web

anterior margin

posterior margin

spine

free rear tip

fin base

fin origin

fin insertion

inner margin

Spined dorsal fin

Pectoral fin topography.

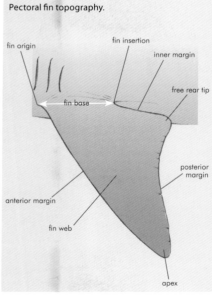

fin origin

fin insertion

inner margin

free rear tip

fin base

posterior margin

anterior margin

fin web

apex

Head (ventral) topography.

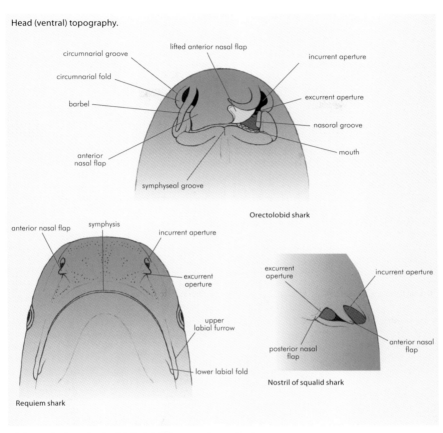

circumnarial groove

circumnarial fold

barbel

anterior
nasal flap

lifted anterior nasal flap

incurrent aperture

excurrent aperture

nasoral groove

mouth

symphyseal groove

Orectolobid shark

anterior nasal flap

symphysis

incurrent aperture

excurrent
aperture

upper
labial furrow

lower labial fold

Requiem shark

excurrent
aperture

incurrent aperture

posterior nasal
flap

anterior nasal
flap

Nostril of squalid shark

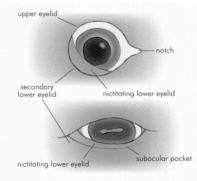

upper eyelid

notch

secondary
lower eyelid

nictitating lower eyelid

nictitating lower eyelid

subocular pocket

Eyes of (top) requiem sharks and (bottom) catsharks.

TOOTH GUIDE

Tooth types and tooth count

The size, shape and arrangement of sharks' teeth (their 'dental morphology') have been used to distinguish between different species since the earliest documented taxonomic studies of sharks. Different tooth forms are associated with catching and eating different prey animals: sharks that bite chunks out of very large prey need big serrated teeth; catching small slippery fishes and squid is easier with needle-like teeth, and crunching hard-shelled animals requires flat tooth plates. However, tooth shape often changes with age in some species, because their diet changes as they grow (e.g. mako sharks mostly eat squid and small fishes, but the very largest adults develop triangular teeth for tackling larger prey). It is also very common for teeth with completely different shapes to be found in each jaw (broader, more distinctive teeth often in the upper jaw and narrower, less robust teeth in the lower jaw), or in different parts of the same jaw. This is known as 'heterodonty'. In nearly all species, the largest, most functional teeth are located in the front (anterior) section of the jaw and smaller, lower crowned teeth further back (posterior). Below illustrates how each jaw quadrant can be broken down into sections of rows (or files) of teeth that include one or more of the following tooth types: symphyseal, anterior, intermediate, anterolateral (where there is no differentiation between anterior and lateral teeth), lateral, anteroposterior (teeth in the symphyseal region where there is no differentiation between anterior and posterior teeth) and posterior teeth.

Tooth count can also be used to distinguish between species when tooth type alone cannot. There are several different ways to take tooth counts, from recording the total per quadrant of the upper and lower jaw, to counting the number and location of teeth of different types within each section of the jaw (the most widely used method). The latter counts are usually broken down into the upper left side total, centrally located teeth and right side total, followed by a similar count of the lower jaw. Each jaw is divided in half at the centre, called the symphysis, by small groups of 'symphyseal teeth' (or sometimes as even smaller teeth known as alternates and medials). In general, those teeth at the centre of a jaw that are one half the size or smaller of adjacent teeth provide the 'symphyseal count'. For example, the jaw illustrated in below would likely be counted as 24-2-24/16-3-16 (this is its meristic formula), or simply as 50/35. However, in some genera (e.g. smoothhounds *Mustelus*) the tooth count varies so much within each species that it may not be diagnostic. In any event, if a specimen is being documented for scientific purposes and the jaws cannot be kept, it is advisable to record the tooth count as part of the reference.

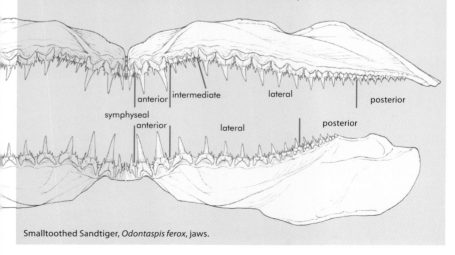

Smalltoothed Sandtiger, *Odontaspis ferox*, jaws.

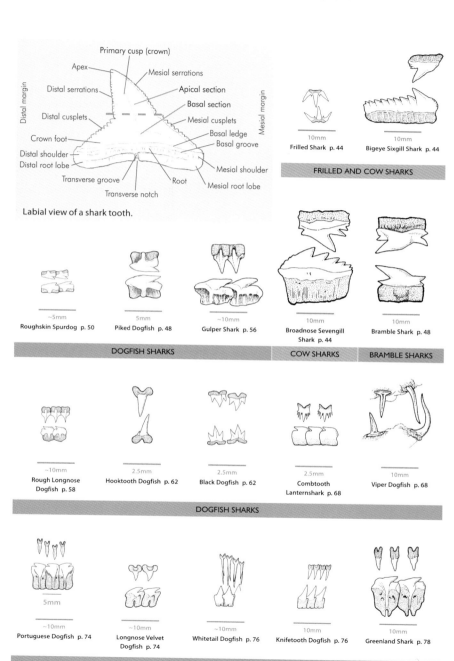

Labial view of a shark tooth.

Primary cusp (crown)
Apex
Mesial serrations
Distal serrations
Apical section
Distal margin
Distal cusplets
Basal section
Mesial margin
Crown foot
Mesial cusplets
Distal shoulder
Basal ledge
Distal root lobe
Basal groove
Transverse groove
Mesial shoulder
Transverse notch
Root
Mesial root lobe

10mm
Frilled Shark p. 44

10mm
Bigeye Sixgill Shark p. 44

FRILLED AND COW SHARKS

~5mm
Roughskin Spurdog p. 50

5mm
Piked Dogfish p. 48

~10mm
Gulper Shark p. 56

10mm
Broadnose Sevengill Shark p. 44

10mm
Bramble Shark p. 48

DOGFISH SHARKS

COW SHARKS

BRAMBLE SHARKS

~10mm
Rough Longnose Dogfish p. 58

2.5mm
Hooktooth Dogfish p. 62

2.5mm
Black Dogfish p. 62

2.5mm
Combtooth Lanternshark p. 68

10mm
Viper Dogfish p. 68

DOGFISH SHARKS

5mm

~10mm
Portuguese Dogfish p. 74

~10mm
Longnose Velvet Dogfish p. 74

~10mm
Whitetail Dogfish p. 76

10mm
Knifetooth Dogfish p. 76

10mm
Greenland Shark p. 78

DOGFISH SHARKS

| ~5mm | 10mm | ~2.5mm | ~2.5mm | 5mm | ~10mm |
| Prickly Dogfish p. 80 | Kitefin Shark p. 80 | Taillight Shark p. 82 | Pygmy Shark p. 82 | Cookiecutter Shark p. 82 | Pocket Shark p. 82 |

DOGFISH SHARKS

| ~2.5mm | 2.5mm | ~2.5mm | 2.5mm | 10mm |
| Smalleye Pygmy Shark p. 82 | Sixgill Sawshark p. 86 | Longnose Sawshark p. 86 | Japanese Angelshark p. 92 | Horn Shark p. 100 |

DOGFISH SHARKS | **SAWSHARKS** | **ANGELSHARKS** | **BULLHEAD SHARKS**

| 10mm | 10mm | 10mm |
| Goblin Shark p. 104 | Sandtiger Shark p. 104 | Smalltooth Sandtiger p. 104 |

MACKEREL SHARKS

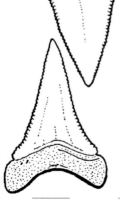

| 10mm | 10mm | 10mm | 10mm | 10mm |
| White Shark p. 110 | Crocodile Shark p. 104 | Thresher Shark p. 108 | Shortfin Mako p. 110 | Porbeagle Shark p. 110 |

MACKEREL SHARKS

~2.5mm
Taiwan Saddled
Carpetshark p. 116

~2.5mm
Collared
Carpetshark p. 114

~2.5mm
Bluegrey
Carpetshark p. 116

~10mm
Tasselled
Wobbegong p. 118

~10mm
Western
Wobbegong p. 120

~10mm
Cobbler
Wobbegong p. 118

CARPETSHARKS

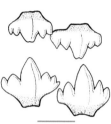

~5mm
Brownbanded
Bambooshark p. 124

~10mm
Epaulette Carpetshark
p. 126

~5mm
Zebra Shark p. 130

10mm
Nurse Shark p. 130

10mm
Tawny Nurse Shark p. 130

CARPETSHARKS

10mm
Basking Shark p. 106

10mm
Megamouth Shark p. 106

5mm
Whale Shark p. 106

~2.5mm
Brown Catshark p. 140

~2.5mm
Dwarf Catshark p. 142

MACKEREL SHARKS   **CARPET SHARKS**   **GROUND SHARKS**

~2.5mm
Coral Catshark p. 144

~2.5mm
Blackspotted Catshark
p. 144

~2.5mm
Spotless Catshark p. 146

~5mm
Swellshark p. 148

~2.5mm
Northern Sawtail
Catshark p. 154

GROUND SHARKS

5mm
Blackmouth Catshark
p. 152

~2.5mm
Rusty Catshark p. 156

~2.5mm
Filetail Catshark p. 162

5mm
Redspotted Catshark
p. 166

~2.5mm
Chain Catshark p. 170

GROUND SHARKS

~2.5mm
Harlequin Catshark p. 172

~2.5mm
**African Ribbontail
Catshark p. 172**

~2.5mm
**Slender Smoothhound
p. 172**

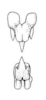

2.5mm
False Catshark p. 176

~2.5mm
**Pygmy False Catshark
p. 176**

GROUND SHARKS

2.5mm
**Barbeled Houndshark
p. 176**

5mm
Tope p. 176

~2.5mm
**Sicklefin Houndshark
p. 178**

2.5mm
**Blacktip Topeshark
p. 177**

2.5mm
**Longnose Houndshark
p. 180**

GROUND SHARKS

~2.5mm
**Dusky Smoothhound
p. 182**

2.5mm
**Flapnose Houndshark
p. 180**

~5mm
Leopard Shark p. 180

~2.5mm
**Sicklefin Weasel Shark
p. 190**

10mm
Snaggletooth Shark p. 190

GROUND SHARKS

4 times size

~2.5mm

Atlantic Weasel Shark
p. 190

10mm

Silvertip Shark p. 198

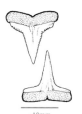

~10mm

Blacktip Shark p. 204

10mm

Oceanic Whitetip Shark
p. 194

10mm

Night Shark p. 208

GROUND SHARKS

10mm

Tiger Shark p. 194

~10mm

Speartooth Shark p. 210

2 times size

5mm

Daggernose Shark p. 212

10mm

Broadfin Shark p. 216

GROUND SHARKS

10mm

Sliteye Shark p. 218

10mm

Whitenose Shark p. 216

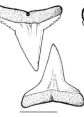

10mm

Lemon Shark p. 206

2.5mm

Blue Shark p. 196

10mm

Milk Shark p. 214

GROUND SHARKS

~5mm

New Spadenose Shark
p. 218

10mm

Whitetip Reef Shark
p. 200

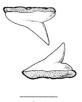

5mm

Winghead Shark p. 220

10mm

Scalloped Hammerhead
p. 222

10mm

Great Hammerhead
p. 222

GROUND SHARKS

FIN GUIDE

This guide covers the fins of many shark species that are listed in various regional and international agreements, including CITES Appendix II, and/or that are common in the international dried fin trade. These are: Porbeagle Shark, Oceanic Whitetip, Scalloped Hammerhead, Smooth Hammerhead, Great Hammerhead, Blue Shark and Shortfin Mako.

Primary/Secondary Fin Set

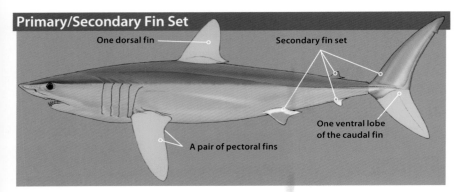

One dorsal fin

Secondary fin set

One ventral lobe of the caudal fin

A pair of pectoral fins

The following pages focus on dried, unprocessed first dorsal fins because these are the most easily identified of the traded fins for the species covered here. Caution is suggested when using this guide to identify dorsal fins less than 20cm across the base, to avoid possible misidentification of samples from very small sharks. Pectoral fins descriptions help to confirm identification.

The key characteristics that can be used to separate the first dorsal fins of the above seven species from other types of shark fins in trade are described. Porbeagle and Oceanic Whitetip first dorsal fins can be rapidly identified to the species level based on the diagnostic white markings detailed here. The first dorsal fins of the three largest hammerhead sharks, as a group, which are the only hammerhead species that are common in trade, can also rapidly be separated from all other large sharks using two simple measurements that describe their characteristic shape (much taller than they are broad) and colour (dull brown or light grey). Identification of hammerhead shark fins to species requires examination of dorsal and pectoral fin sets or genetic testing. Blue Shark and Shortfin Mako fins are also described.

How to use this guide

Step 1. Distinguish first dorsal fins from other highly valued traded fins: pectoral fins and lower caudal lobes (see below).

Step 2. Look for white first dorsal fin markings, and use the flowchart to identify either Porbeagle or Oceanic Whitetip Sharks or exclude many species with black fin markings.

Step 3. Take several simple measurements (opposite) to help identify hammerhead first dorsal fins, which are much taller than they are broad and are dull brown or light grey.

Step 4. Check for Blue Shark and Shortfin Mako fins.

STEP 1 Distinguish first dorsal fins from pectoral fins and lower caudal lobes

a. Check the fin colour on each side

Dorsal fins are the same colour on both sides (see both side views below). Pectoral fins are darker above (dorsal view) than underneath (ventral view), see below.

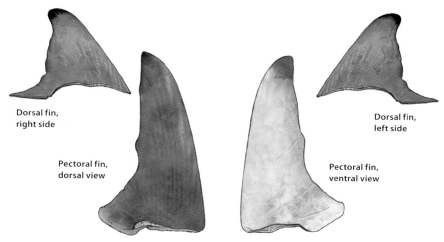

Dorsal fin, right side

Dorsal fin, left side

Pectoral fin, dorsal view

Pectoral fin, ventral view

b. Check the base of the fin

Dorsal fins (D) have a continuous row of closely spaced cartilaginous blocks running along almost the entire fin base. When looking at a cross section of the base of a lower caudal lobe (LC1), there is typically only a yellow, 'spongy' material called ceratotrichia, which is the valuable part of the lower caudal lobe. In some lower caudal lobes (LC2) there may be a small number of the cartilaginous blocks, but they are usually widely spaced and/or occur only along part of the fin base. Usually the lower caudal lobe has been cut along its entire base when removed from the shark; in contrast, dorsal fins frequently have a free rear tip that is fully intact.

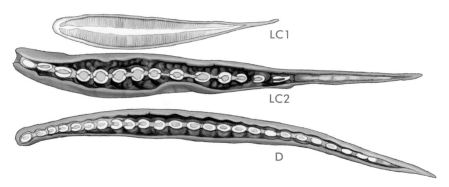

LC1

LC2

D

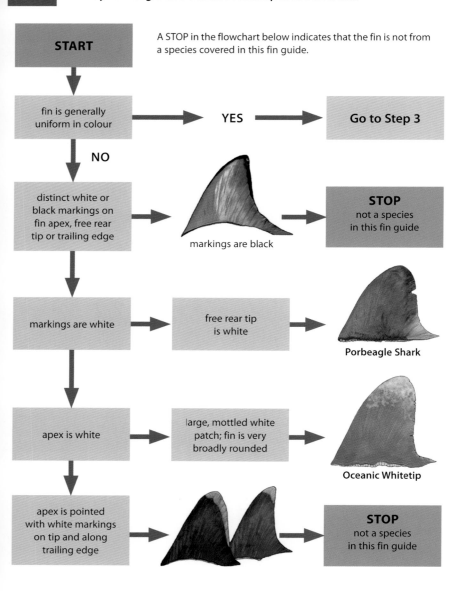

START

A STOP in the flowchart below indicates that the fin is not from a species covered in this fin guide.

fin is generally uniform in colour

YES → **Go to Step 3**

NO

distinct white or black markings on fin apex, free rear tip or trailing edge

markings are black

STOP not a species in this fin guide

markings are white → free rear tip is white →

Porbeagle Shark

apex is white → large, mottled white patch; fin is very broadly rounded →

Oceanic Whitetip

apex is pointed with white markings on tip and along trailing edge →

STOP not a species in this fin guide

Take fin measurements

1 Measure fin origin to apex (O–A) with a flexible tape measure.
2 Measure the fin width (W) at the halfway point of O–A (i.e., if O–A is 10cm, measure W at 5cm along O–A).
3 Divide O–A by W (O–A/W).

Origin, apex and fin width (measured from leading edge to trailing edge) are the landmarks found to be the most useful for species identification purposes, as measurements based on fin height, fin base and free rear tip are often too variable and dependent on cut and condition of the fin.

fin is 'short'
(O–A divided by W is less than 2.6)

YES

NO

STEP 4

shape of trailing edge

straight or concave

convex (curves outward)

check whether mako (page 25)

fin is 'tall'
(O–A divided by W is greater than 2.6)

Fin is slate grey-blue or greyish-brown

Blue or Silky Shark

fin is brown or light in colour
(see below)

hammerhead species
(see pages 26–27)

probably a thresher

Distinguishing hammerhead dorsals from other tall fins (mako and thresher sharks)

Thresher and hammerhead shark first dorsal fins are very tall and slender, mako slightly shorter. Thresher and mako fins are slate grey or dark greyish-brown. Great Hammerhead first dorsal fins have a distinctive curved shape and are much lighter. Scalloped and Smooth Hammerhead first dorsal fins are similar in shape to thresher shark dorsal fins, but much lighter in colour and usually light brown not grey. Shortfin Mako first dorsal fins are dark greyish-brown or slate grey, with a steep-angled leading edge, smooth texture and short free rear tip.

Great Hammerhead
Sphyrna mokarran

Scalloped Hammerhead
Sphyrna lewini

Shortfin Mako
Isurus oxyrinchus

Thesher Shark
Alopias vulpinus

Distinguishing hammerhead dorsals from other tall fins (guitarfish and Blacktip Sharks)

Dorsal fins that are tall and slender and dull brown or light greyish-brown are probably one of three species of hammerhead sharks: Great *Sphyrna mokarran*, Scalloped *S. lewini* or Smooth *S. zygaena*. See descriptions on the pages 26–27.

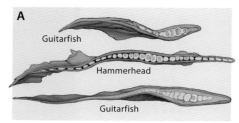

A

Guitarfish

Hammerhead

Guitarfish

Tall dorsal fins can also come from several species of guitarfish, or Blacktip Sharks *Carcharhinus limbatus*. In guitarfish first dorsal fins, cartilaginous blocks do not extend across the entire fin base (Image **A**). In hammerheads, these cartilaginous blocks are present along almost the entire fin base (Image **A**). Guitarfish dorsal fins also exhibit a glossy sheen (Image **B**), and some species also have white spots, unlike the dull brown, uniform coloration of hammerhead dorsal fins.

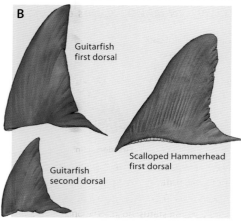

B

Guitarfish
first dorsal

Scalloped Hammerhead
first dorsal

Guitarfish
second dorsal

Some Blacktip Shark first dorsal fins exhibit O–A/W that is close to or slightly greater than 2.5. However, they often (but not always) have a black spot on the dorsal fin apex, and the fin has a glossy appearance that is unlike the dull surface of the hammerheads (Image **C**).

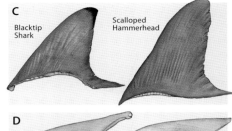

If fins from a single shark have been kept together in sets and are available for comparison, Blacktip Shark pectoral fins are also longer and more slender than the short, broad fins of the hammerheads (Image **D**).

PORBEAGLE SHARK *Lamna nasus* page 110

First dorsal fin: dark blue/black to dark greyish brown, rounded apex with white patch on lower trailing edge onto free rear tip.

First dorsal fin

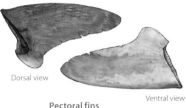

Dorsal view

Ventral view

Pectoral fins

Pectoral fins: short, rounded at apex; ventral surface has dusky coloration from apex throughout midsection of fin and along leading edge.

Conservation status: CITES Appendix II and other international and regional Agreements.

SHORTFIN MAKO *Isurus oxyrinchus* page 110

First dorsal fin: dark greyish-brown or slate grey; very erect steep-angled leading edge, moderately straight trailing edge, short free rear tip, thick base; smooth texture.

First dorsal fin

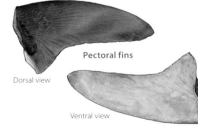

Pectoral fins

Dorsal view

Ventral view

Pectoral fins: dorsal surface dark greyish-brown or slate grey, white margin on edge of free rear tip, ventral surface white unmarked; rounded apex, moderately short and broad from leading edge to trailing edge.

Conservation status: no international or regional regulations or catch limits (in 2013).

OCEANIC WHITETIP *Carcharhinus longimanus*

page 194

First dorsal fin: large and broadly rounded paddle-like); mottled white colour at apex.

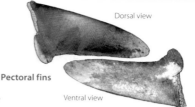

First dorsal fin

Pectoral fins

Dorsal view

Ventral view

Pectoral fins: long, broadly rounded at apex; dorsal surface has mottled white colour at apex, ventral surface is typically white but can have mottled brown coloration.
- mottled white colour also present on caudal fin (upper and lower lobe)
- very small juveniles may have mottled black coloration on dorsal, pectoral and caudal fins.

Conservation status: CITES Appendix II, prohibited in many Atlantic and Pacific pelagic fisheries.

BLUE SHARK *Prionace glauca*

page 196

First dorsal fin: dark grey-blue to greyish-brown; rounded apex, trailing edge convex, leading edge with rather a shallow angle; moderate free rear tip. Silky Shark dorsal is same shape but light grey; its pectoral fins are much shorter.

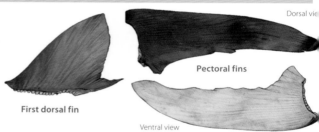

First dorsal fin

Pectoral fins

Dorsal view

Ventral view

Pectoral fins: dorsal surface dark grey-blue or dark greyish-brown, ventral white and unmarked; long and slender from leading edge to trailing edge, radial cartilage visible under skin.

Conservation status: no regulations or catch limits (in 2013); the most abundant species in trade.

SCALLOPED HAMMERHEAD *Sphyrna lewini*

page 222

First dorsal fin: tall, flattening out toward apex; straight to moderately curved trailing edge (similar to Smooth Hammerhead, less slender than Great Hammerhead first dorsal fin).

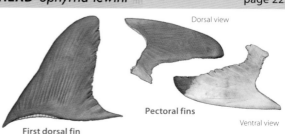

First dorsal fin

Pectoral fins

Dorsal view

Ventral view

Pectoral fins: short and broad with black tips visible at the apex on ventral side.

Conservation status: CITES Appendix II and prohibited by some international and regional fisheries Agreements.

GREAT HAMMERHEAD *Sphyrna mokarran*   page 222

First dorsal fin: tall, slender from leading edge to trailing edge; elongated and pointed at apex.

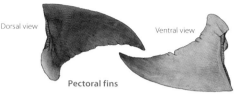

Dorsal view

Ventral view

Pectoral fins

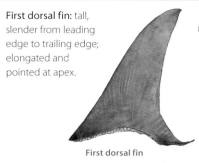

First dorsal fin

Note: Small to moderate-sized *S. mokarran* first dorsal fins are similar to those of the Winghead Shark *Eusphyra blochii* (page 220), but the latter are extremely rare in trade and only landed in the northern Indo-Pacific.

Pectoral fins: Pointed apex, moderately curved along trailing edge with dusky colour at apex on ventral side and often along trailing edge.

Conservation status: CITES Appendix II and a prohibited species in some regional fisheries agreements.

SMOOTH HAMMERHEAD *Sphyrna zygaena*   page 222

First dorsal fin: tall, sloping more at apex; moderately curved trailing edge (similar to Scalloped Hammerhead, less slender than Great Hammerhead first dorsal fin).

Dorsal view

Pectoral fins

Ventral view

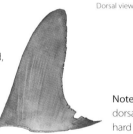

First dorsal fin

Note: Scalloped and Smooth Hammerhead first dorsal fins are so similar they are often extremely hard to differentiate. However, it is not uncommon for valuable fins from an individual to be traded as a set (first dorsal, paired pectoral fins and lower caudal lobe). If this is the case, the two species can be distinguished using the pectoral fins.

Pectoral fins: short and broad with faint to no markings on ventral side.

Conservation status: CITES Appendix II and a prohibited species in some regional fisheries agreements.

For terminology used in this section, please see page 12. This information is reproduced from *Identifying Shark Fins: Oceanic Whitetip, Porbeagle and Hammerheads* (Stony Brook University/Pew Environment group, D.L. Abercrombie and D.D. Chapman authors) and Abercrombie *et al.* 2013. For more information on fin identification, see www.sharkfinid.org and http://www.nmfs.noaa.gov/ia/species/sharks/fin_guide.pdf

KEY TO ORDERS AND FAMILIES OF LIVING SHARKS

1a Anal fin absent, *drawing 1.* → **2**

1b Anal fin present, *drawing 2.* → **10**

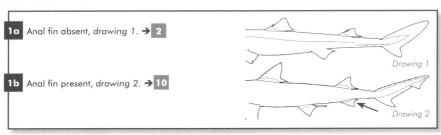

Drawing 1

Drawing 2

2a [1a] Mouth at end of head; body flat and ray-like; very large pectoral fins with anterior triangular lobes that overlap gill slits; caudal fin with base slanted ventrally (hypocercal) see *drawing 3.*

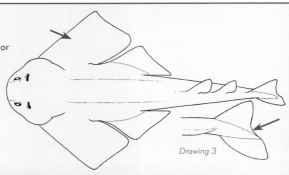

Drawing 3

▶ Family Squatinidae. Angelsharks: pages 85; **90–94**

2b [1a] Mouth beneath head; body cylindrical, compressed, or slightly flattened, not ray-like; pectoral fins smaller, without anterior lobes; caudal fin with base slanted dorsally (heterocercal) see drawing 4 or horizontal (diphycercal). → **3**

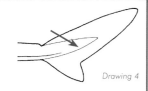

Drawing 4

3a [2b] Very long flattened saw-like snout, with rows of large and small sharp-pointed tooth-like denticles on sides and underside; a pair of long, tape-like barbels on lower surface of snout in front of nostrils.

▶ Family Pristiophoridae. Sawsharks: pages 84; **86–88**

3b [2b] Snout normal, not saw-like. Order Squaliformes. Dogfish sharks. → **4**

4a [3b] Spiracles small and well behind eyes; fifth gill slits much longer than first four; body covered with moderately large and close set, thorn-like denticles or sparse, large, plate-like denticles; pelvic fins much larger than second dorsal fin; first dorsal fin origin over or behind pelvic fin origins.

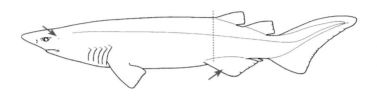

➡ Echinorhinidae. Bramble sharks: pages 46; **48**

4b [3b] Spiracles larger and close behind eyes; fifth gill slits not abruptly larger than first to fourth; denticles variable in shape but small to moderately large; pelvic fins usually as large as second dorsal fin or smaller; first dorsal fin origin well in front of pelvic origins. ➡ **5**

5a [4b] Body very high and compressed, triangular in cross-section with heavy lateral keels between pectoral and pelvic bases; dorsal fins extremely high.

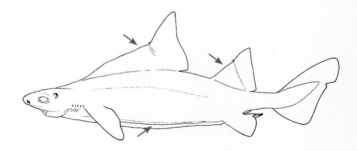

➡ Family Oxynotidae. Roughsharks: pages 61; **80**

5b [4b] Body low and more cylindrical in cross-section, with a low lateral keels between pectoral and pelvic bases or no keels; dorsal fins low. ➡ **6**

6a [5b] Teeth similar and blade-like in both jaws, with a deflected horizontal cusp, a low blade, and no cusplets see *drawing 5*; caudal peduncle usually with an upper precaudal pit (weak or absent in *Cirrhigaleus*); strong lateral keels present on caudal peduncle see *drawing 6*; dorsal fin spines without grooves; subterminal notch absent from caudal fin.

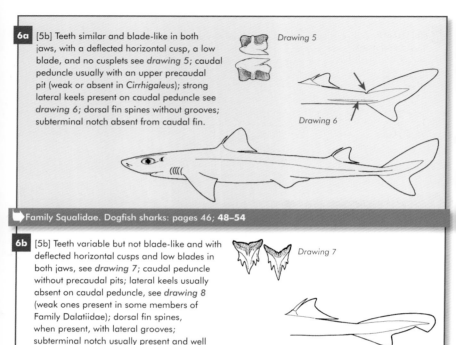

Drawing 5

Drawing 6

▶ Family Squalidae. Dogfish sharks: pages 46; **48–54**

6b [5b] Teeth variable but not blade-like and with deflected horizontal cusps and low blades in both jaws, see *drawing 7*; caudal peduncle without precaudal pits; lateral keels usually absent on caudal peduncle, see *drawing 8* (weak ones present in some members of Family Dalatiidae); dorsal fin spines, when present, with lateral grooves; subterminal notch usually present and well developed on caudal fin. → **7**

Drawing 7

Drawing 8

7a [6b] Teeth either hook-like or with cusps and cusplets in both jaws, or upper teeth with cusps and cusplets and lower teeth compressed, blade-like and more or less overlapping; underside of body, flanks, and tail usually with more or less conspicuous dense black markings (photomarks) with light organs (photophores).

▶ Family Etmopteridae. Lanternsharks: pages 60; **62–72**

7b [6b] Upper teeth with strong cusps but without cusplets; lower teeth laterally expanded, compressed, blade-like, and overlapping, much larger than uppers see *drawing 9*; underside of body, flanks, and tail without conspicuous dense black markings that have light organs, though light-producing organs may be present elsewhere. → **8**

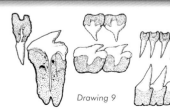

Drawing 9

8a [7b] Upper teeth relatively broad and blade-like, lower teeth low and wide and blade-like, see *drawing 10* below.

Drawing 10

➤ Family Centrophoridae. Gulper sharks: pages 47; **56–58**

8b [7b] Upper teeth relatively narrow and not blade-like, lower teeth high and wide and blade-like. ➜ **9**

9a [8b] Head moderately broad and somewhat flattened or conical; snout flat and narrowly rounded to elongate-rounded in dorsoventral view; abdomen usually with lateral keels; both dorsal fins either with or without (*Somniosus, Scymnodalatias*) fin spines.

➤ Family Somniosidae. Sleeper sharks: pages 60; **74–78**

9b [8b] Head narrow and rounded-conical; snout conical and narrowly rounded to elongate-rounded in dorsoventral view; abdomen without lateral ridges; most genera lacking dorsal fin spines (*Squaliolus* with a small first dorsal spine only).

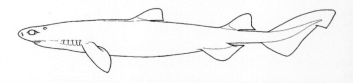

➤ Family Dalatiidae. Kitefin sharks: pages 61; **80–82**

10a [1b] 6 or 7 gill slits on each side of head; one dorsal fin present, this set far back. Order Hexanchiformes; cow and frilled sharks. → **11**

10b [1b] Two dorsal fins (except the scyliorhinid *Pentanchus profundicolus* with one dorsal fin); 5 gill slits on each side of head. → **12**

11a [10a] Mouth terminal on head; teeth tricuspidate, see *drawing 12*, and similar in both jaws; 6 pairs of gill slits, first pair connected across the underside of the throat; body elongated and eel-like.

Drawing 12

▶ Family Chlamydoselachidae. Frilled sharks: pages 43; **44**

11b [10a] Mouth subterminal on head; front teeth unicuspidate in upper jaw and comb-shaped and blade-like in lower jaw, see *drawing 13*; 6 or 7 pairs of gill slits, first not connected across underside of throat; body fairly stocky, not eel-like.

Drawing 13

▶ Family Hexanchidae. Cow sharks: pages 43; **44**

12a [10b] A strong spine on each dorsal fin.

▶ Family Heterodontidae. Bullhead sharks: pages 96; **100–102**

12b [10b] Dorsal fins without spines. → **13**

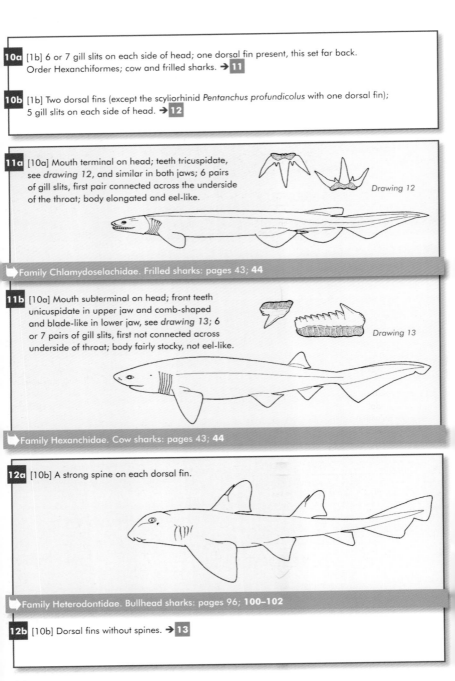

13a [12b] Eyes behind mouth; deep nasoral grooves connecting nostrils and mouth; a pair of barbels just medial to incurrent apertures of nostrils, see *drawing 14* (rudimentary in Family Rhincodontidae). Order Orectolobiformes. Carpet sharks. ➜ **14**

Drawing 14

13b [12b] Eyes partly or entirely over mouth; nasoral grooves usually absent, when present (a few members of the Family Scyliorhinidae) broad and shallow; barbels, when present, developed from anterior nasal flaps of nostrils, not separate from them, see *drawing 15*. ➜ **20**

Drawing 15

14a [13a] Mouth huge and nearly at end of head; external gill slits very large; caudal peduncle with strong lateral keels; caudal fin with a strong ventral lobe, but with a vestigial terminal lobe and subterminal notch.

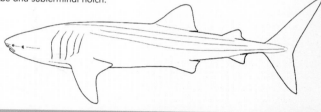

▶ Family Rhincodontidae. **Whale sharks: page 129; 106**

14b [13a] Mouth smaller and subterminal; external gill slits small; caudal peduncle without strong lateral keels; caudal fin with a weak ventral lobe or none, but with a strong terminal lobe and subterminal notch, see *drawing 16*. ➜ **15**

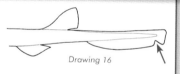

Drawing 16

15a [14b] Caudal fin about as long as rest of shark.

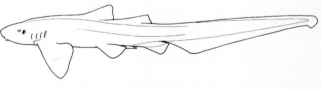

▶ Family Stegostomatidae. **Zebra sharks: page 128; 130**

15b [14b] Caudal fin much shorter than rest of shark. ➜ **16**

16a [15b] Head and body greatly flattened, head with skin flaps on sides; two rows of large, fang-like teeth at symphysis of upper jaw and 3 in lower jaw.

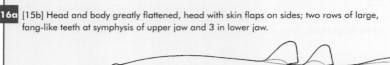

Family Orectolobidae. Wobbegongs: pages 113; 118–122

16b [15b] Head and body cylindrical or moderately flattened, head without skin flaps; teeth small. **→ 17**

17a [16b] No circumnarial lobe and groove around outer edges of nostrils, see *drawing 17*.

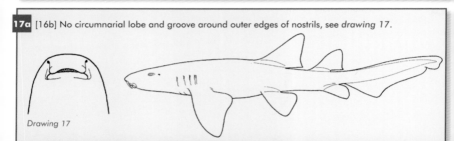

Drawing 17

Family Ginglymostomatidae. Nurse sharks: pages 128; 130

17b [16b] A circumnarial lobe and groove around outer edges of nostrils, see drawing 18. **→ 18**

Drawing 18

18a [17b] Spiracles minute; origin of anal fin well in front of second dorsal origin, separated from lower caudal origin by space equal or greater than its base length.

Family Parascylliidae. Collared carpetsharks: pages 112; 114–116

18b [17b] Spiracles large; origin of anal fin well behind second dorsal origin, separated from lower caudal origin by space less than its base length. **→ 19**

19a [18b] Nasal barbels very long; distance from vent to lower caudal-fin origin shorter than distance from snout to vent; anal fin high and angular.

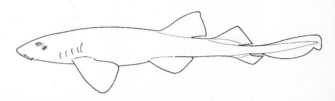

▶ Family Brachaeluridae. Blind sharks: pages 112; **116**

19b Nasal barbels short; distance from vent to lower caudal-fin origin longer than distance from snout to vent; anal fin low, rounded and keel-like.

▶ Family Hemiscyllidae. Longtailed carpetsharks: pages 113; **124–126**

20a [13b] No nictitating eyelids; largest teeth in mouth usually are 2 or 3 rows of anteriors on either side of upper and lower jaw symphyses; upper anterior teeth separated from large lateral teeth at sides of jaw by a gap that may have one or more rows of small intermediate teeth, *drawing 19*; plankton-feeding species (Families Megachasmidae and Cetorhinidae) have reduced teeth with anterior, intermediate, and lateral teeth poorly differentiated; intestine with ring valve.
Order Lamniformes. Mackerel sharks. ➔ **21**

Drawing 19

20b [13b] Nictitating eyelids present; largest teeth in mouth are well lateral on dental band, not on either side of symphysis; no gap or intermediate teeth separating large anterior teeth from still larger teeth in upper jaw, see *drawing 20*; intestine usually with spiral or scroll valve.
Order Carcharhiniformes. Ground sharks. ➔ **27**

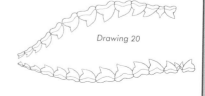

Drawing 20

21a [20a] A strong keel present on each side of caudal peduncle; caudal fin crescentic and nearly symmetrical, with a long lower lobe, see *drawing 21*. → **22**

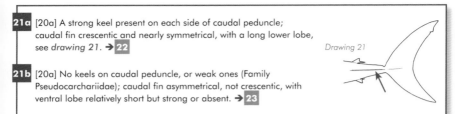

Drawing 21

21b [20a] No keels on caudal peduncle, or weak ones (Family Pseudocarchariidae); caudal fin asymmetrical, not crescentic, with ventral lobe relatively short but strong or absent. → **23**

22a [21a] Teeth large and few, sharp-edged; gill openings large but not extending onto upper surface of head; no gill rakers on internal gill arches.

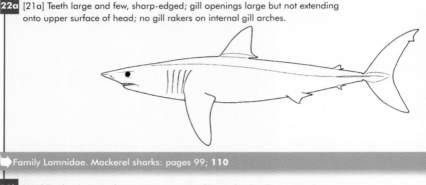

Family Lamnidae. Mackerel sharks: pages 99; **110**

22b [21a] Teeth minute and very numerous, not sharp-edged; gill openings huge, extending onto upper surface of head; gill rakers present on internal gill arches, sometimes absent after shedding.

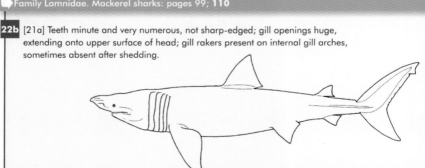

Family Cetorhinidae. Basking sharks: page 98; **106**

23a [21b] Snout elongated and blade-like; anal fin much larger than dorsal fins; no precaudal pits; caudal fin without ventral lobe.

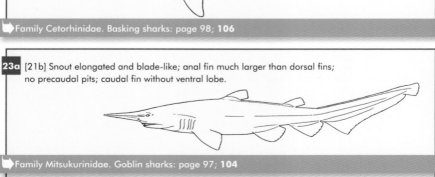

Family Mitsukurinidae. Goblin sharks: page 97; **104**

23b [21b] Snout conical or flattened, short and not blade-like; anal fin subequal to dorsal fins in size or smaller than them; upper and sometimes lower precaudal pits present; caudal fin with strong ventral lobe. ➔ **24**

24a [23b] Caudal fin about as long as rest of shark.

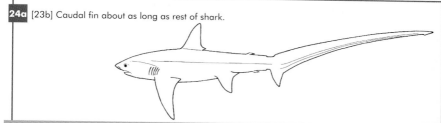

➡ Family Alopiidae. Thresher sharks: pages 99; **108**

24b [23b] Caudal fin less than half the length of rest of shark. ➔ **25**

25a [24b] Mouth huge, terminal on head, level with snout; teeth small, very numerous, and hook-shaped; internal gill openings screened by numerous long papillose gill rakers.

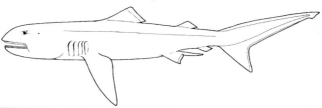

➡ Family Megachasmidae. Megamouth sharks: page 98; **106**

25b [24b] Mouth smaller, subterminal on head, behind snout tip; teeth blade-like with large anterior teeth, intermediate teeth, and lateral teeth in upper jaw; internal gill openings without gill rakers. ➔ **26**

26a [25b] Eyes very large; gill slits extending onto upper surface of head; both upper and lower precaudal pits present; a low keel on each side of caudal peduncle.

➡ Family Pseudocarchariidae. Crocodile sharks: page 98; **104**

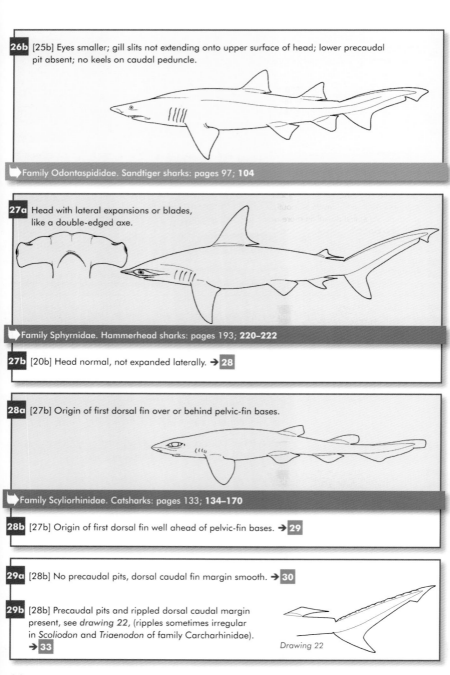

26b [25b] Eyes smaller; gill slits not extending onto upper surface of head; lower precaudal pit absent; no keels on caudal peduncle.

▶ Family Odontaspididae. Sandtiger sharks: pages 97; **104**

27a Head with lateral expansions or blades, like a double-edged axe.

▶ Family Sphyrnidae. Hammerhead sharks: pages 193; **220–222**

27b [20b] Head normal, not expanded laterally. ➔ **28**

28a [27b] Origin of first dorsal fin over or behind pelvic-fin bases.

▶ Family Scyliorhinidae. Catsharks: pages 133; **134–170**

28b [27b] Origin of first dorsal fin well ahead of pelvic-fin bases. ➔ **29**

29a [28b] No precaudal pits, dorsal caudal fin margin smooth. ➔ **30**

29b [28b] Precaudal pits and rippled dorsal caudal margin present, see *drawing 22*, (ripples sometimes irregular in *Scoliodon* and *Triaenodon* of family Carcharhinidae). ➔ **33**

Drawing 22

30a [29a] Labial furrows very short or absent, when present confined to mouth corners; posterior teeth on dental bands comb-like, see drawing 23. → **31**

Drawing 23

30b [29a] Labial furrows relatively long with uppers extending partway or all the way anterior to level of symphysis, see *drawing 24*; posterior teeth on dental bands not comb-like. → **32**

Drawing 24

31a [30a] Snout bell-shaped in dorso-ventral profile, with a deep groove in front of eye, see *drawing 25*; internarial space over 1.5 times nostril width; inside of mouth and edges of gill arches without papillae; first dorsal fin more or less elongated, base closer to pectoral fins than pelvic fins.

Drawing 25

➡ Family Pseudotriakidae. False catsharks: pages 174; **172, 176**

31b [30a] Snout rounded-parabolic or subangular in dorso-ventral profile, see *drawing 26*, without a deep groove in front of eye; internarial space less than 1.3 times nostril width; inside of mouth and edges of gill arches with papillae; first dorsal short, base closer to pelvic fins than pectoral fins.

Drawing 26

➡ Family Proscylliidae. Finback catsharks: pages 174; **172**

32a [30b] Anterior nasal flaps formed as slender barbels; upper labial furrows extremely long, nearly equal to internarial width and over half mouth width, see *drawing 27*; intestinal valve with 14 to 16 turns; no supraorbital crests on cranium.

Drawing 27

➡ Family Leptochariidae. Barbeled houndsharks: page 175; **176**

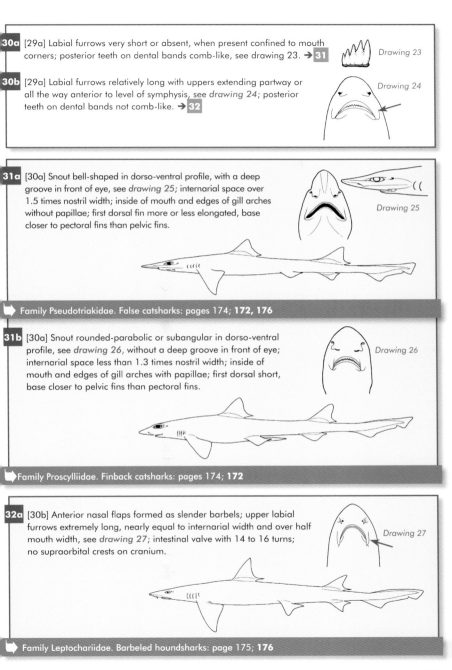

32b [30b] Anterior nasal flaps usually not barbel-like (except for *Furgaleus*); upper labial furrows shorter, considerably less than internarial and less than half of mouth width; intestinal valve with 4 to 10 turns; supraorbital crests present on cranium.

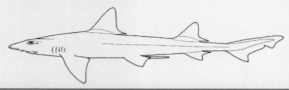

▶ Family Triakidae. Houndsharks: pages 175; **176–188**

33a [29b] Posterior nasal flaps well developed on rear edges of excurrent apertures of nostrils, see drawing 28; symphysial tooth rows well developed in upper and lower jaws; second dorsal fin height about 0.4 to 0.7 times first dorsal height; intestine with a spiral valve having 4 to 6 turns.

Drawing 28

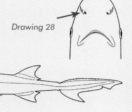

▶ Family Hemigaleidae. Weasel sharks: pages 175; **190**

33b [29b] Posterior nasal flaps poorly developed on rear edges of excurrent apertures of nostrils; symphysial tooth rows usually poorly developed in upper and lower jaws; second dorsal fin height from 0.2 to 1.0 times first dorsal height, but most species with fin than 0.4 times first dorsal height; intestine with a scroll valve.

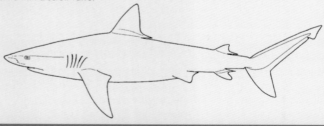

▶ Family Carcharhinidae. Requiem sharks: pages 192, **194–218**

SPECIES ACCOUNTS

This order contains the most primitive shark species surviving today. There are two families of extremely distinctive sharks: Chlamydoselachidae, now known to contain at least two species, very similar in appearance; and Hexanchidae, with four species.

Identification Six or seven pairs of gill slits in front of the pectoral fins; one spineless dorsal fin over or behind the pelvic fins; one anal fin. The vertebral column extends into the caudal fin's long dorsal lobe, the ventral lobe is short or absent. Large mouth. Eyes on the side of the head, spiracles very small, located well behind and above eyes. Medium to large sized.

Biology Most species are widespread worldwide, from tropical to temperate and boreal waters. Generally found in deep cold water in the tropics, but also inshore in temperate seas.

Status Taken as bycatch and in targeted fisheries (with trawls, nets, lines and by sports anglers). All are assessed either as Data Deficient or Near Threatened in the IUCN Red List of Threatened Species.

THE EVOLUTION OF SHARKS

The common ancestor of all modern vertebrates, from fishes to mankind, was a tiny, leaf-like, eyeless animal that probably first swam in the oceans more than 500 million years ago (500mya). Over the next few tens of millions of years, this proto-fish evolved a cartilaginous spine, eyes, simple fins and protective bony plates. Jaws and paired fins followed, and a wide range of vertebrates gradually evolved, including some that began breathing air and eventually crawled out onto land.

In the oceans, some fish species developed bones and hard flattened scales, but the sharks and their relatives (the chondrichthyans) retained the ancestral cartilaginous skeleton. Because cartilage does not fossilise well, the earliest known remains of sharks are scales and spines that were deposited in sediments more than 400mya, during the Devonian Period. (The Devonian is also known as the 'Age of Fishes' because of the extraordinary diversity of fishes that evolved then, more than 200 million years before the first dinosaurs appeared.) The ancestors of the modern sharks, rays and chimaeras subsequently became incredibly common; more than 3000 ancient chondrichthyan fish species have been recognised, making up 60% of all fish species preserved as fossils in shallow-water Carboniferous limestone deposits. However, this diversity ended abruptly with a mass extinction event about 252mya, which was probably caused by massive volcanic eruptions, leading to acid rain, catastrophic sediment run-off, global warming and ocean de-oxygenation.

Although the surviving chondrichthyan fishes evolved and diversified into animals that closely resemble those described in this book, they never regained their former domination of the world's oceans. Today the bony fishes are by far the most abundant of all vertebrates, with more than 30,000 species known. In contrast, only about 500 living shark species and 700 of the closely related rays and chimaeras are known to scientists today. This number is, however, rising steadily as scientists discover 'new' species in poorly explored tropical seas and deep ocean waters. About 200 species of sharks and their relatives have been described during the past 15 years alone. It is highly likely that future editions of this book will illustrate yet more newly discovered species, but we are sadly now entering another extinction event, this time caused mainly by mankind (primarily excessive fishing effort, coastal habitat destruction and climate change).

FRILLED SHARKS: Chlamydoselachidae – page 44

All frilled sharks are very similar externally (with some local variability) and were thought to be one wide-ranging living species. Internally, specimens from the southern African coast (southeast Atlantic and southwest Indian Ocean) differ from frilled sharks from Japan and Taiwan (northwest Pacific) and the two populations are now described as distinct species. More anatomical information (e.g. chondrocranium, vertebral counts and fin structure) is needed from east and northwest Atlantic and eastern Pacific specimens to determine where these are also distinct.

Identification Dark chocolate-brown, brownish-grey or brownish-black. Elongated eel-shape. Flattened snake-like head. Very short snout. Widely spaced, needle-sharp, slender three-cusped teeth in the large terminal mouth. Six pairs of curved gill slits, lower ends of first pair connected under throat. Dorsal fin low and much smaller than anal fin, pectoral fins smaller than pelvic fins.

Biology Widely but patchily distributed in offshore soft bottom habitats on continental and insular shelves and upper slopes. Sometimes enter shallow cold water. Swim in captivity with large mouth open, possibly to lure actively swimming fish and squid towards the teeth. Viviparous; pups feed on huge uterine eggs during long gestation.

Status Uncommon to rare and poorly known. Bycatch in deep bottom trawls and gillnets may be used for fishmeal and meat. Kept in some public aquaria. Harmless to man.

COW SHARKS: Hexanchidae – page 44

Three genera and four species: *Hexanchus* (two species), *Heptranchias* (one species) and *Notorynchus* (one species). Cow sharks are mostly found in cold water: usually in deep water in warm temperate and tropical regions, but may also enter shallow water in cool temperate areas. Only one species, the Broadnose Sevengill Shark, is apparently a permanent resident of shallow coastal areas.

Identification Moderately slender to stocky cylindrical sharks, with six or seven pairs of gill slits (the first pair not connected across the throat) in front of pectoral fins. Ventral mouth. Large compressed comb-like teeth in the lower jaw, smaller cuspidate teeth in the upper jaw. Single spineless dorsal fin, relatively high, angular and short. Pectoral fins angular, larger than pelvic fins. Anal fin smaller than dorsal fin. Caudal fin has marked sub-terminal notch.

Biology Viviparous, giving birth to large litters of relatively large pups. Some species are migratory, moving inshore seasonally to feed or give birth. Cow sharks are powerful predators; large Bluntnose Sixgill and Broadnose Sevengill Sharks are known to catch and eat cetaceans and pinnipeds. The latter species, in particular, appears to be highly social and may hunt cooperatively, in packs; it has even been observed 'spy-hopping' and has taken domestic dogs swimming and wading in shallow water.

Status Taken as a bycatch and in some target commercial and sports fisheries. Some populations have declined significantly following target commercial and sports fisheries and, like several other large deepwater species, these slow-growing sharks require careful management. They are important for dive tourism in a few shallow water locations in the USA, Canada and South Africa. A few large individuals have been implicated in non-fatal attacks on divers. Some species are kept in public aquaria.

Plate 1: FRILLED AND COW SHARKS

1 Southern African Frilled Shark *Chlamydoselachus africana*   ♀ at least 117cm

DN South Africa. **HT** Benthic, epibenthic and pelagic; 300–1400m. **ID** Large terminal mouth with widely spaced slender three-cusped needle sharp teeth. Six pairs of gills. Low dorsal fin smaller than anal fin; pectoral fins smaller than pelvic fins. Similar to species *C. anguineus*, difficult to distinguish externally. Head usually longer and body shorter than *C. anguineus*. **CR** Dark grey, but covered with a thin membrane that gives it a uniform dark brown colour. **Status:** NE.

2 Frilled Shark *Chlamydoselachus anguineus*   ♀196cm

DN Patchy worldwide. **HT** Benthic, epibenthic and pelagic; 20–1500m. **ID** Large terminal mouth with widely spaced slender three-cusped needle-sharp teeth. Six pairs of gills. Low dorsal fin smaller than anal fin; pectoral fins smaller than pelvic fins. **CR** Dark chocolate-brown, brownish-grey or brownish-black. **Status:** NT.

3 Sharpnose Sevengill Shark *Heptranchias perlo*   139cm

DN Patchy tropical and temperate waters, not in North-east Pacific. **HT** Mainly deepwater; 27–720m, to a maximum depth of 1000m. **ID** Slender body. Acutely pointed head with narrow mouth and large eyes. **CR** Above brownish-grey to olive, lighter below. Juvenile with black dorsal fin apex which fades with growth. **Status:** NT.

4 Bluntnose Sixgill Shark *Hexanchus griseus*   at least 482cm

DN Patchy worldwide, possibly absent polar regions. **HT** Juveniles found inshore in cold water, adults in shallow waters near submarine canyons; 200–1100m, down to 2500m or more. **ID** Large heavy body. Broad head with wide mouth. Soft supple fins. **CR** Grey or tan to blackish, sometimes darker spots on sides. Small white-ringed eyes; pale lateral line and posterior fin edges. **Status:** NT.

5 Bigeye Sixgill Shark *Hexanchus nakamurai*   180cm

DN Patchy warm temperate and tropical waters, possibly absent in East Pacific. **HT** On or near the seabed; 90–621m, occasionally near the surface or inshore. **ID** Slender body. Narrow head with narrow mouth and large eyes. Caudal fin with deep subterminal notch. **CR** Sharply divided between dark dorsal and light ventral surface. Fins with white posterior edges and tips. **Status:** DD.

6 Broadnose Sevengill Shark *Notorynchus cepedianus*   296cm

DN Patchy inshore cool temperate waters. **HT** Coastal, common in shallow bays and close to shore; surfline–50m, large sharks down to 136m or more. **ID** Bluntly pointed broad head with wide mouth and small eyes. **CR** Grey to brown body with numerous small black spots (some plain or white-spotted). Newborn's black dorsal fin apex fades with growth. **Status:** DD.

Hexanchus griseus

1

2

3

juvenile

4

colour variants

4

5

6

young

BRAMBLE SHARKS Echinorhiniformes – page 48

BRAMBLE SHARKS: Echinorhinidae – page 48

Two species of large, sluggish, deepwater sharks.

Identification Skin denticles very large and thorn-like. Stout cylindrical body, five gill openings in front of pectoral fin, fifth larger than others. Broad flat head and snout, very small spiracles far behind the eyes. Two similar-sized small dorsal fins, no spines, set close together and close to the caudal fin, origin of first dorsal slightly behind pelvic fin origin. No anal fin. Ventral caudal lobe poorly developed in adults, absent in young, subterminal caudal notch lacking or not obvious.

Biology Widely distributed on soft bottom habitats on temperate and tropical continental and insular shelves and upper slopes, sometimes entering shallow cold water. Large mouth and pharynx may be used to suck in prey (bony fishes, small chondrichthyans and invertebrates) as it comes within range.

Status Uncommon to rare and poorly known.

DOGFISH SHARKS Squaliformes – pages 48–82

A large and varied order with about 130 species in six families: Squalidae, dogfish sharks (28 described species); Centrophoridae, gulper sharks (17 species); Etmopteridae, lanternsharks (46 described species, others undescribed); Somniosidae, sleeper sharks (17 species); Oxynotidae, roughsharks (five species); and Dalatiidae, kitefin sharks (ten species).

Identification Two dorsal fins (with or without spines); no anal fin. Caudal fin with vertebral column elevated into a moderately long dorsal lobe; ventral lobe absent to strong. Five gill slits, all in front of pectoral fin origins. Nostrils not connected to the mouth by grooves. Spiracles behind and about opposite or above level of eyes. Eyes on side of head, no nictitating lower eyelids. Size ranges from dwarf to huge.

Status Dogfish sharks occur in a wide range of marine and estuarine habitats and depths in all oceans worldwide and include the only sharks found in high latitudes close to the poles. Their greatest diversity occurs in deepwater (many species occur nowhere else). Many species are fished commercially for meat or liver oil. Those with slow growth and low reproductive capacity are highly vulnerable to depletion by overfishing.

DOGFISH SHARKS: Squalidae – pages 48–54

Two genera, *Cirrhigaleus,* with three species, and *Squalus,* with at least 25 species; several recently discovered and not yet described. Dogfish sharks are recorded almost worldwide in boreal, temperate and tropical seas, except in the tropical eastern Pacific.

Identification Two dorsal fins with strong ungrooved spines. No anal fin. Snout short to moderately long, mouth short and transverse, low blade-like cutting teeth in both jaws. Spiracles large and close to eyes. Body cylindrical in cross-section. First dorsal origin opposite or slightly behind the pectoral fins, second dorsal fin strongly falcate. Pelvic fins smaller than pectoral fins.

Caudal peduncle with strong lateral keels, caudal fin without subterminal notch. Colour light grey to medium brown, not black, no luminous organs.

Status Despite the considerable (original) abundance and wide range of some species, they are highly vulnerable to overfishing because of their late maturity, longevity, low fecundity and long intervals between litters (*S. acanthias* and *S. suckleyi* have the longest known gestation period of any vertebrate: 18 to 24 months). Several stock declines have occurred and recovery of depleted populations is very slow. Rare species of no little or no commercial value that occur in heavily fished areas are taken as bycatch in fisheries for more common and abundant species. They may become threatened if restricted to small endemic or localised populations or isolated habitats, such as seamounts, targeted by fishing operations. Their abundance and ease of capture make some species of *Squalus*, particularly *S. acanthias*, among the most important species targeted by commercial shark fisheries. They are landed by up to 50 countries in directed fisheries or as utilised bycatch, mostly taken in bottom trawl fisheries, but also by hook and line, gill nets, seines, pelagic trawls and fish traps. They are of high value for their meat, liver oil, fins and occasionally leather. Sports anglers target some species, but they are not important game fish. A few species are regularly displayed in aquaria. Some species use their mildly toxic fin spines and teeth for defence; a hazard to human handlers. Some are considered 'trash fish' because they can cause damage to fishing gear and prey on or drive away more valuable fisheries species.

GULPER SHARKS: Centrophoridae – pages 56–58

About 17 mainly deepwater, bottom-dwelling species in two genera, *Centrophorus* and *Deania*, recorded almost worldwide from cold temperate to tropical seas, except in northeast Pacific and very high latitudes. Most diverse in warm waters and in the Indo-west Pacific, where some localised endemic species occur (although many species may be more widely distributed than currently recorded). Main depth range about 200–1500m, but a few records from as shallow as 50m and one *Centrophorus* photographed below 4000m.

Identification Short- to long-nosed cylindrical sharks with huge green or yellowish eyes. Two dorsal fins with grooved spines, first dorsal slightly smaller to much larger than second and originating in front of pelvic fin origins; second dorsal fin with a straight to weakly concave posterior margin. No anal fin.

Status Poorly sampled and identified, and imperfectly known, despite their importance in commercial target and bycatch fisheries where they are caught by longlines, trawls and gill nets. Their meat is valuable (gulper sharks are among the deepwater species known as 'siki shark' and highly valued in European markets); so too are their large, oily, squalene-rich livers, which are used in cosmetics, health supplements and for machine oil. Although the conservation status of gulper sharks is poorly known, they are of considerable concern because rapidly expanding and largely unmanaged and unmonitored deepwater fisheries have taken large numbers of these species and caused extremely rapid population depletion, particularly among *Centrophorus* species. Gulper sharks have a very limited reproductive capacity, with small litters, long gestation periods, slow growth and late maturity; recovery from overexploitation may therefore be extremely slow. The genus *Centrophorus* has been the subject of considerable scientific review; recent genetic analyses indicate that three of the species illustrated on page 56 (*C. acus*, *C. granulosus* and *C. niaukang*, which were originally described from different regions) are apparently all the same species.

Plate 2: BRAMBLE SHARKS AND DOGFISH SHARKS

1 Bramble Shark *Echinorhinus brucus*   310cm

DN Atlantic, Mediterranean and Indo-west Pacific. **HT** On or near the bottom; usually 200–900m, but may occur inshore on occasion. **ID** Irregular scattered whitish conspicuous denticles, which can fuse into plates. **CR** Uniformly grey or brownish to black on back and sides. Fin edges blackish; usually light below. **Status:** DD.

2 Prickly Shark *Echinorhinus cookei*   450cm

DN Pacific. **HT** Close to bottom; 4–1100m. **ID** Light-coloured inconspicuous denticles numerous and regularly spaced, but few below snout. **CR** Uniformly brown to slaty grey or black. Lighter colouring around mouth and ventral surface. Posterior fin edges blackish. **Status:** NT.

Dogfish sharks

Head with moderately long snout and large spiracle close behind eye; cylindrical body; two dorsal fins, each with a strong ungrooved spine preceding it, no anal fin; many *Squalus* species difficult to distinguish.

3 Piked Dogfish *Squalus acanthias*   160–200cm

DN Worldwide except tropical waters and near poles, and absent from North Pacific. **HT** Boreal to warm-temperate continental and insular shelves, occasionally slopes; 0–600m, possibly deeper, in epipelagic cold water 0–200m. **ID** Slender. Narrow head, long pointed snout, no barbel. First dorsal fin low. First dorsal spine slender and very short. **CR** Grey to bluish-grey above, lighter to white below often with white spots on back and sides. Black dorsal fin tips in young. Caudal fin with no blackish marks. **Status:** Globally: **V**, NE Atlantic: **CE**, Australasia and S Africa: **LC**.

4 Shortspine Spurdog *Squalus mitsukurii*   125cm

DN Western North Pacific. **HT** On or near the bottom; 4–954m. **ID** Fairly slender. Broad head, relatively long broad snout, large barbels. First dorsal fin spine stout and short. **CR** Grey or grey-brown, pale below, no white spots. Dorsal fin apices dusky; pectoral, pelvic and caudal fins with white posterior margins; posterior caudal notch dusky. **Status:** DD.

5 North Pacific Spiny Dogfish *Squalus suckleyi*   possibly 150cm

DN North Pacific. **HT** 0–1236m. **ID** Similar to *S. acanthias* except distance from snout to first dorsal origin shorter, less than 10% total length compared to more than 13% in *S. acanthias*. **CR** Greyish, lighter below flanks usually with conspicuous white spots which may be absent in larger individuals. **Status:** NE.

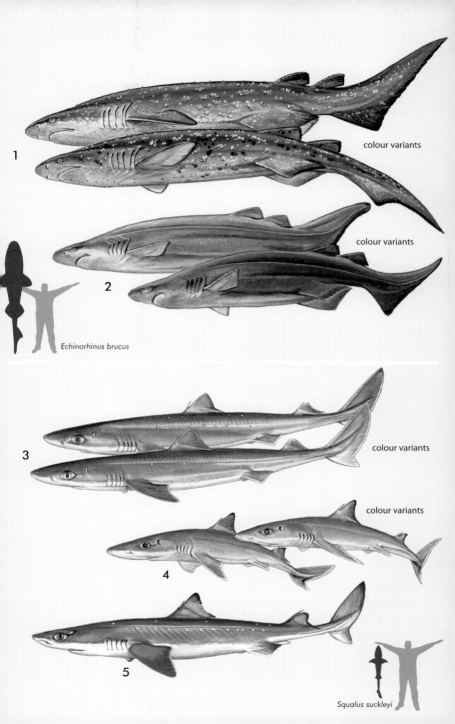

1

colour variants

2

colour variants

Echinorhinus brucus

3

colour variants

colour variants

4

5

Squalus suckleyi

Plate 3: DOGFISH SHARKS II

1 Roughskin Spurdog *Cirrhigaleus asper* — 118cm

DN Warm temperate to tropical West Atlantic to Indian Ocean and central Pacific (may be different species). **HT** On or near the bottom; 73–600m, sometimes off bays and river mouths. **ID** Stocky rough-skinned body. Broad flat head with short broadly rounded snout; large stubby barbels do not reach mouth. Two high, stout dorsal spines. **CR** Dark grey or brown above, lighter below. Conspicuous white-edged fin margins. **Status:** DD.

2 Southern Mandarin Dogfish *Cirrhigaleus australis* — at least 123cm

DN East coast of Australia from New South Wales to Tasmania. **HT** On or near the bottom; 360–640m. **ID** Similar to *C. asper*, but barbels on anterior nasal flaps less than 2.5 times prenasal length and reaching to mouth. **CR** Grey-brown above and pale below. Conspicuous white-edged fin margins. **Status:** DD.

3 Mandarin Dogfish *Cirrhigaleus barbifer* — at least 122cm

DN Patchy southern Japan, possibly to New Zealand. **HT** On or near the bottom; 360–640m. **ID** Similar to *C. australis*, but barbels greater than 2.5 times prenasal length and distinguished by long moustache-like barbels which reach mouth. **CR** Grey-brown above, whitish below. Conspicuous white-edged fin margins. **Status:** DD.

4 Eastern Highfin Spurdog *Squalus albifrons* — ♀ at least 86cm

DN Eastern Australia. **HT** 131–450m. **ID** Similar to *S. notocaudatus*, distinguished by small barbel; shorter first dorsal, thicker second dorsal spine; broad triangular pectoral fins, caudal fin shorter. **CR** Dorsal surface dark, sharply demarcated from paler ventral surface on side of head. Dusky dorsal fin apices and edges; caudal fin with light posterior margins and ventral lobe; no dark marks on caudal fin. **Status:** DD.

5 Western Highfin Spurdog *Squalus altipinnis* — at least 59cm

DN West Australia. **HT** 298–305m. **ID** Similar to *S. albifrons*, distinguished by slightly longer snout; slender second dorsal spine; slightly lower than fin apex; greyish dorsal fins with pale apices. **CR** Similar to *S. albifrons* apart from greyish dorsal fins with pale tips. **Status:** DD.

6 Fatspine Spurdog *Squalus crassispinus* — ♀58cm

DN Australia. **HT** 187–262m. **ID** Slender. Broad head with broad short snout and small medial barbels. First dorsal fin moderately high; dorsal fin spines stout, first dorsal spine lower than fin apex, second dorsal spine same height as fin apex. Pale fins. **CR** Light grey body, paler below. Dusky dorsal fin apices; caudal fin with dusky dorsal margin and almost white ventral lobe, posterior margins and posterior tip. **Status:** DD.

7 Eastern Longnose Spurdog *Squalus grahami* — ♀73cm ♂57cm

DN East Australia. **HT** 148–504m. **ID** Distinguished by short snout. First dorsal fin spine long, but less than second dorsal fin spine. Low first dorsal fin; large caudal fin. **CR** Pale greyish, paler below with dark bar along dorsal and ventral caudal base. Caudal fin white-tipped. **Status:** NT.

8 Western Longnose Spurdog *Squalus nasutus* — at least ♀77cm ♂57cm

DN West Australia. **HT** 300–850m. **ID** Slender. Narrow head with long narrow snout and small medial barbels. First dorsal fin moderately high. Slender dorsal fin spines; first dorsal low, second dorsal high same height as fin apex. **CR** Pale grey body, white below. Dorsal fins with dusky apices and posterior margins free tips white; caudal fin with dark dorsal margin and dark blotch on upper ventral margin (fades in adult). **Status:** DD.

9 Bartail Spurdog *Squalus notocaudatus* — at least 62cm

DN North-east Australia. **HT** Offshore; 220–450m. **ID** Fairly slender. Broad head, short broad snout with large medial barbel. High short first dorsal fin with spine lower than apex, second dorsal fin smaller with spine higher than apex; pectoral fins posterior margin deeply concave with narrow tip. **CR** Greyish-brown above, white below. Dorsal fin apices dusky; caudal fin with dark dorsal margin and white posterior margins; obvious dark bar along caudal base. **Status:** DD.

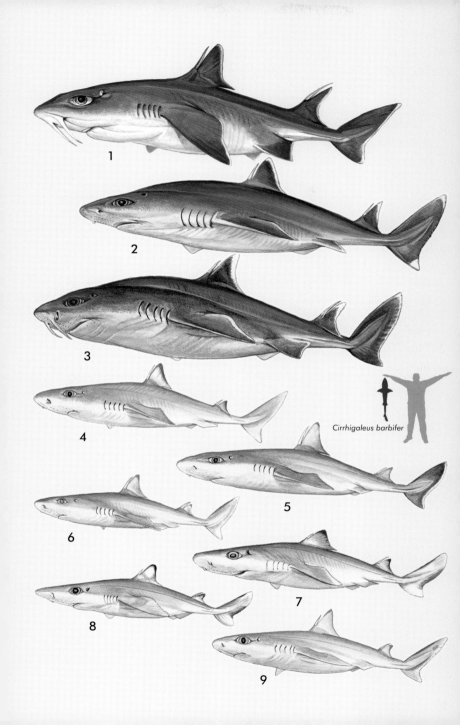

Cirrhigaleus barbifer

Plate 4: DOGFISH SHARKS III

1 Bighead Spurdog *Squalus bucephalus*   90cm

DN Western Pacific, New Caledonia and northern Tasman Sea. **HT** Upper continental slopes; 405–880m. **ID** Large stout body. Broad head; short snout. Dorsal fin spines slender, tapering towards tip. **CR** Uniform dark brown above lighter below. First dorsal fin apex darker along margins, most prominent at fin tip; second dorsal fin lighter coloured, free rear tip greyish with a narrow white margin. **Status:** DD.

2 Greeneye Spurdog *Squalus chloroculus*   ♀99cm ♂86cm

DN Southern Australia. **HT** Continental upper slopes; 216–1360m. **ID** Moderately elongated snout, bluntly rounded at tip. Dorsal fin spines prominent, slender, tapering to tip. **CR** Uniform grey above, paler below. Dorsal fins mostly grey except for blackish margins extending from above fin spine and along the outer margin to the notch in posterior margin; posterior edge of caudal fin at notch and centre of lobe usually dark. **Status:** NT.

3 Edmund's Spurdog *Squalus edmundsi*   87cm

DN Western Australia. **HT** Upper continental slopes; 200–850m. **ID** Similar to *S. albifrons* (page 50), distinguished by slightly longer snout and slender second dorsal fin spine that is slightly less than fin apex. **CR** Grey to greyish-brown above, lighter grey below. Greyish dorsal fins with pale apices; caudal fin dusky with narrow pale posterior margins. **Status:** NT.

4 Taiwan Spurdog *Squalus formosus*   81cm

DN Western North Pacific. **HT** Continental shelves and upper slopes; less than 300m. **ID** Medium-sized; slender-bodied. Short, narrow snout; prominent, robust, erect dorsal fin spines. **CR** Uniform greyish-brown above; white below which is strongly demarcated on head through to gill openings; dorsal fins blackish on posterior margin and caudal fin with posterior white margin. **Status:** NE.

5 New Zealand Dogfish *Squalus griffini*   ♀110cm ♂90cm

DN Waters around New Zealand. **HT** Outer continental shelf to upper continental slope; 15–700m. **ID** Large slender body. Long, narrowly rounded snout. First dorsal fin nearly triangular; fin spine about half the height of dorsal fin; second dorsal fin spine height about equal to second dorsal fin height. **CR** Uniform grey-brown above, white below. Dorsal and caudal fins grey with first dorsal fin margin base and free rear tip lighter than rest of fin; second dorsal fin base uniformly coloured except for posterior margin which has a narrow black margin. **Status:** LC.

6 Indonesian Shortsnout Dogfish *Squalus hemipinnis*   ♀74cm ♂52cm

DN Endemic to eastern Indonesia. **HT** Virtually unknown; greater than 100m. **ID** Moderate, slender body. Narrow, short, bluntly pointed snout. Dorsal fins unequal in size, first much larger than second. **CR** Slate grey above sharply demarcated with light and dark areas on head and extending through to above gills; first dorsal fin grey except darker apex; caudal fin mostly grey except for broad white posterior margin. **Status:** NT.

7 Seychelles Spurdog *Squalus lalannei*   ♀79cm ♂62cm

DN Western Indian Ocean, Seychelles. **HT** Virtually unknown; 1000m. **ID** Moderate, slender body. Short head with rounded snout tip. Dorsal fins rounded at apices; dorsal fin spines tapering toward tips; first dorsal fin spine height less than fin height; second dorsal fin height about equal to fin height. **CR** Uniformly grey with blackish dorsal fins. **Status:** DD.

8 Philippines Spurdog *Squalus montalbani*   ♀101cm ♂72cm

DN Western Pacific, Philippines to Australia. **HT** Outer continental shelf and upper continental slopes; 154–1370m. **ID** Body moderately elongated. Snout narrow and pointed at tip. Dorsal fin spines prominent; slender first dorsal fin spine, three-quarters height of first dorsal fin; second dorsal fin spine about equal to fin height. **CR** Greyish, paler below. Caudal fin notch and upper lobe usually darker. **Status:** V.

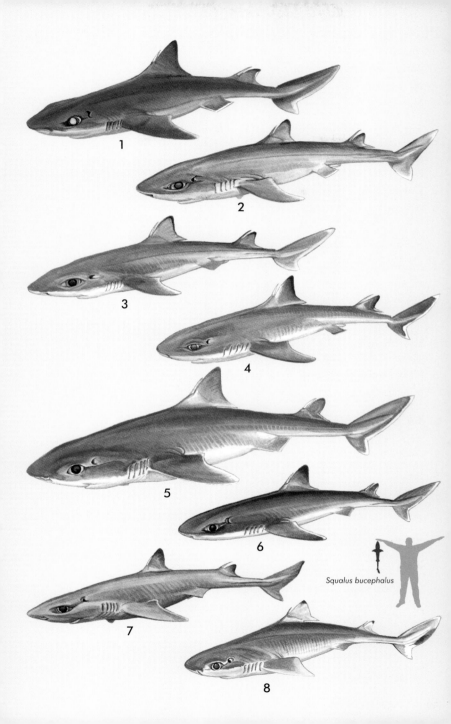

Squalus bucephalus

Plate 5: DOGFISH SHARKS IV

1 Longnose Spurdog *Squalus blainville* ♀89cm ♂74cm

DN Temperate to tropical east Atlantic. **HT** On or near the muddy bottom 16 to deeper than 440m. **ID** Heavy body. Broad head, relatively short broad snout; large barbels. Erect high first dorsal fin and heavy tall first dorsal spine. **CR** Greyish-brown without white spots. Dorsal fins white-edged. **Status:** DD.

2 Japanese Shortnose Spurdog *Squalus brevirostris* ♀59cm ♂45cm

DN Western North Pacific, possibly more widespread but needs confirmation. **HT** 150m and deeper. **ID** Small stout body. Head short. Dorsal fins unequal in size. Dorsal fin spines slender, tapering towards tip. **CR** Reddish above without white spots or other obvious dark fin markings. **Status:** DD.

3 Cuban Dogfish *Squalus cubensis* maybe 110cm

DN Warm temperate to tropical western Atlantic. **HT** On or near the bottom; 60–380m. **ID** Slender; broad head, short rounded snout and small barbels; first dorsal moderately high, dorsal spines slender and high, pectoral fins deeply concave. **CR** Grey without white spots. Pectoral fins with white tip and posterior margin; dorsal fins black patch at tips; pectoral and caudal fins with white posterior margins. **Status:** DD.

4 Japanese Spurdog *Squalus japonicus* 95cm

DN Northwest Pacific. **HT** On or near the bottom; 120–340m. **ID** Fairly slender. Long narrow tapering snout,; small barbels. First dorsal fin moderately high with long slender spine. **CR** Grey, reddish-grey or bluish-brown body without white spots. Dorsal fin apices dusky; dorsal caudal margin dusky; pectoral and caudal fins white posterior margins. **Status:** DD.

5 Shortnose Spurdog *Squalus megalops* 77cm

DN Indo-Pacific (eastern Atlantic form is a different species). **HT** On or near the bottom; 0–732m. **ID** Small, slender. Broad head, short broad snout; small barbels. First dorsal fin moderately high with short slender spine. **CR** Grey-brown to dark brown without white spots. Dorsal fin apices dark; dorsal caudal margin dark; pectoral and caudal fins white posterior margins. **Status:** DD.

6 Blacktail Spurdog *Squalus melanurus* at least 75cm

DN Southwest Pacific, New Caledonia. **HT** Upper insular slopes; 320–340m. **ID** Slender; broad head, very long broad snout, small barbels; first dorsal fin high, long slender spine. **CR** Dark grey-brown without white spots. Dorsal fin apices black. Dorsal caudal margin partial black and ventral lobe with black patch. **Status:** LC.

7 Cyrano Spurdog *Squalus rancureli* 77cm

DN Southwest Pacific, New Hebrides. **HT** Insular slopes; 320–400m. **ID** Slender. Broad head, very long broad snout; small barbels. First dorsal fin high with long slender spine. **CR** Dark grey-brown above, abruptly light grey below without white spots. Dorsal fin webs dusky, apices blackish; pectoral and pelvic fins with white posterior margins; caudal fin web dusky; upper post ventral margin and ventral tip white. **Status:** NT.

8 Kermadec Spiny Dogfish *Squalus raoulensis* 73cm

DN Western South Pacific. **HT** Insular slopes; to 320m. **ID** Small bodied. Short, narrow head, bluntly pointed at tip. Dorsal fin spines slender, moderately robust at base, tapering towards apices; first dorsal fin spine height shorter than fin apex, second dorsal fin spine height slightly less than fin height. **CR** Reddish- brown colour strongly demarcated from snout tip through gill openings. First dorsal fin with narrow black margin on apex; second dorsal fin with darker edge on fin apex and with posterior margin edge white; caudal fin with well defined white border extending along posterior fin margin. **Status:** LC.

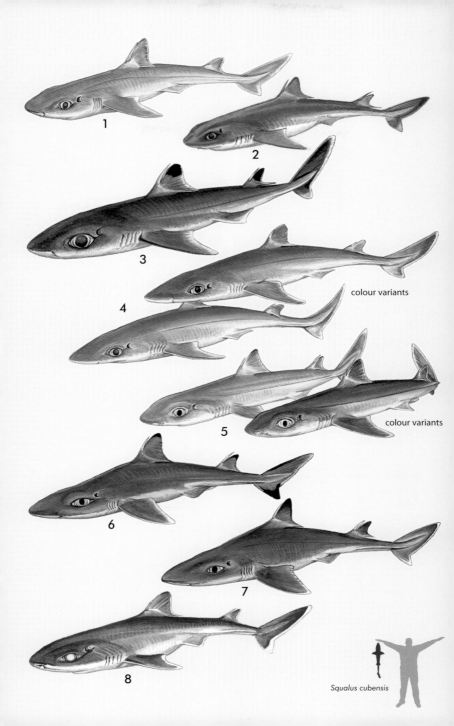

colour variants

colour variants

Squalus cubensis

Plate 6: GULPER SHARKS I

Cylindrical; huge green or yellowish eyes; two dorsal fins with grooved spines, no anal fin.

1 **Needle Dogfish** *Centrophorus acus*   mature ♀154–161cm ♂100–105cm

DN Western-Indo Pacific. **HT** Outer continental shelves and upper slopes; 150–950m, possibly 1786m. **ID** Rough skin. Fairly long flat snout. First dorsal fin low and long, second dorsal fin similar; pectoral fin free rear tip long and angular. **CR** Brown above, slightly lighter below. Darker edges to posterior fin margins. **Status:** NT.

2 **Gulper Shark** *Centrophorus granulosus*   105–110cm

DN Atlantic, West Indian Ocean and West Pacific. **HT** On or the near bottom; 50–1440m. **ID** Smooth skin. Short thick snout. Second dorsal fin shorter but nearly as high as first dorsal; pectoral fin free rear tip long and acute. **CR** Dark grey or grey-brown above, lighter below. Fin webs dusky, dark tips only in juveniles. **Status:** CE.

3 **Longnose Gulper Shark** *Centrophorus harrissoni*   ♀114cm ♂101cm

DN Eastern Australia and New Zealand. **HT** Continental slope; 220–1050m. **ID** Smooth skin. Long flat narrow snout. Second dorsal fin shorter and lower than first dorsal; pectoral fin free rear tip very long and narrowly angular; notch in terminal margin. **CR** Light greyish, paler below. Dorsal fins with dark oblique bar. **Status:** CE.

4 **Lowfin Gulper Shark** *Centrophorus lusitanicus*   ♀67cm ♂54cm

DN Eastern Atlantic, West Indian Ocean and Western Pacific. **HT** Outer continental shelves and upper slopes; 300–1400m. **ID** Smooth skin. Long flat snout. First dorsal fin very long, second dorsal third as long but as high or higher; pectoral fin free rear tips long and narrowly angular; notch in terminal margin. **CR** Dusky fin webs. **Status:** V.

5 **Smallfin Gulper Shark** *Centrophorus moluccensis*   100cm

DN Scattered Indo-Western Pacific. **HT** Outer continental and insular shelves and upper slpoes; 125–820m. **ID** Smooth skin. Short thick snout. Second dorsal fin less than half height of first dorsal; pectoral fin free rear tips long and narrowly angular; caudal fin deep ventral lobe. **CR** Greyish-brown above, much paler below. First dorsal fin dark blotch near apex in juvenile; caudal fin and sometimes pectoral and pelvic fins with narrow pale posterior margins. **Status:** DD.

6 **Taiwan Gulper Shark** *Centrophorus niaukang*   170cm

DN Patchy Atlantic and Indo-Pacific. **HT** Outer continental shelves and upper slopes; 98 to about 1000m. **ID** Fairly rough skin. Short broad snout. First dorsal fin long, second dorsal fin nearly as large; pectoral fin free rear tips short and angular; caudal fin posterior margin straight with weak ventral lobe. **CR** Dark grey or grey-brown above, slightly lighter below; dusky fin webs but no prominent markings. **Status:** NT.

7 **Leafscale Gulper Shark** *Centrophorus squamosus*   164cm

DN Atlantic, Western Indian Ocean and southeastern Pacific. **HT** Continental slopes; 230–2400m. **ID** Rough skin. Short thick slightly flattened snout. First dorsal fin long and low second dorsal shorter, higher, pectoral fin free rear tip short; caudal fin posterior margin weakly concave. **CR** Uniform grey, grey-brown or reddish-brown, dusky fins, no prominent markings. **Status:** V.

8 **Mosaic Gulper Shark** *Centrophorus tessellatus*   89cm (♂ holotype)

DN West and central Pacific, Atlantic and Indian Ocean? **HT** Insular slopes, on or near the bottom; 260–730m. **ID** Smooth skin; fairly long thick snout; second dorsal fin about the same as first dorsal, pectoral fin free rear tips long and narrowly angular. **CR** Light brownish above, white below, light margins to fins. **Status:** DD.

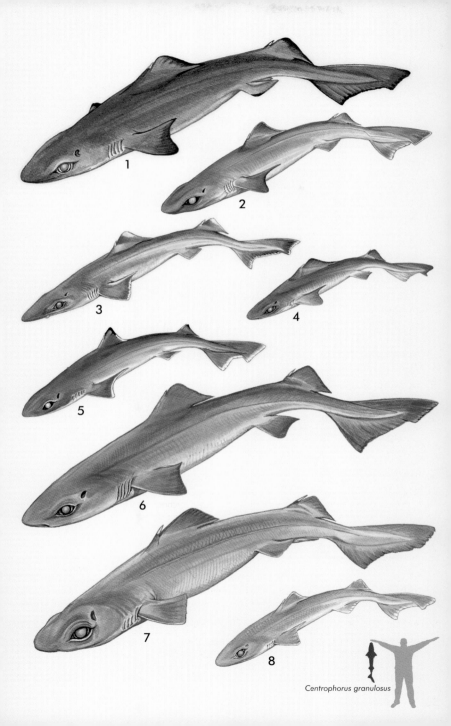

Centrophorus granulosus

Plate 7: GULPER SHARKS II

1 Dwarf Gulper Shark *Centrophorus atromarginatus* at least 94cm

DN Northwest Indian Ocean and West Pacific. **HT** Outer continental and insular shelves and upper slopes; 150–450m. **ID** Smooth skin. Fairly long flat snout. First dorsal fin low, second dorsal nearly as large; pectoral fin free rear tips long and narrowly angular. **CR** Grey or grey-brown above, lighter below. Dusky fin webs, dark fin tips only in juvenile. **Status:** DD.

2 Blackfin Gulper Shark *Centrophorus isodon* at least 108cm

DN Western Pacific and possibly Indian Ocean. **HT** Upper continental slopes ; 760–770m. **ID** Smooth skin. Long flat snout. First dorsal fin short, second dorsal lower but as long; pectoral fin free rear tips long and narrowly angular. **CR** Blackish-grey above, lighter below. Blackish fin webs especially second dorsal fin and caudal fin. **Status:** DD.

3 Seychelles Gulper Shark *Centrophorus seychellorum* 80cm

DN Indian Ocean, Seychelle Islands. **HT** Insular slopes; 1000m. **ID** Relatively long snout. High first dorsal fin, second dorsal base long; pectoral fin angular, rounded at apex, with free rear tip reaching midbase of first dorsal. **CR** Uniform grey, with blackish margins on dorsal fin apices. **Status:** DD.

4 Western Gulper Shark *Centrophorus westraliensis* ♀91cm

DN Western Australia. **HT** Upper slopes on or near bottom; 600–750m. **ID** Skin smooth. Snout elongate, bluntly pointed at tip. Pectoral fins extended at tips into angular lobe; first dorsal fin originates well behind pectoral fin axil, second dorsal fin smaller than first. **CR** Grey above with dorsal fins having a narrow blotch on upper anterior margin. **Status:** LC.

5 Southern Dogfish *Centrophorus zeehaani* ♀about 96cm ♂about 80cm

DN Southern Australia. **HT** Insular slopes, on or near bottom; 210–700m. **ID** Skin smooth. Snout short, bluntly pointed. First dorsal fin originates behind pectoral insertion and is slightly larger than second dorsal fin. **CR** Uniform grey-brown above, lighter below. **Status:** NE.

6 Birdbeak Dogfish *Deania calcea* 122cm

DN East Atlantic and Pacific. **HT** Continental and insular shelves and slopes; 70–1470m. **ID** Rough skin. Extremely long flat snout. No subcaudal keel. First dorsal fin low and long, second dorsal shorter and higher with longer spine. **CR** Grey to dark brown with darker fins. Juvenile with blackish markings on fins, dusky on head. **Status:** LC.

7 Rough Longnose Dogfish *Deania hystricosa* 111cm

DN East Atlantic and Northwest Pacific. **HT** Insular slopes; 470–1300m. **ID** Very rough skin. Extremely long flat snout. No subcaudal keel. First dorsal fin low, second dorsal shorter and higher. **CR** Blackish-brown to grey-brown, no obvious markings. **Status:** DD.

8 Arrowhead Dogfish *Deania profundorum* 97cm

DN East Atlantic, West Atlantic and Indo West Pacific. **HT** Upper continental and insular slopes, on or near bottom; 275–1785m. **ID** Smooth skin. Extremely long flat snout. Subcaudal keel. First dorsal fin relatively short and high, second dorsal similar but taller with much longer spine. **CR** Dark grey or brown. **Status:** LC.

9 Longsnout Dogfish *Deania quadrispinosa* about 114cm

DN South Africa, Australia and New Zealand. **HT** Outer continental shelf and slope; 150–1360m. **ID** Rough skin. Extremely long flat snout. No subcaudal keel, First dorsal fin relatively high, angular and short, second dorsal higher with longer spine. **CR** Grey or grey-brown to blackish, sometimes white-edged fins. **Status:** NT.

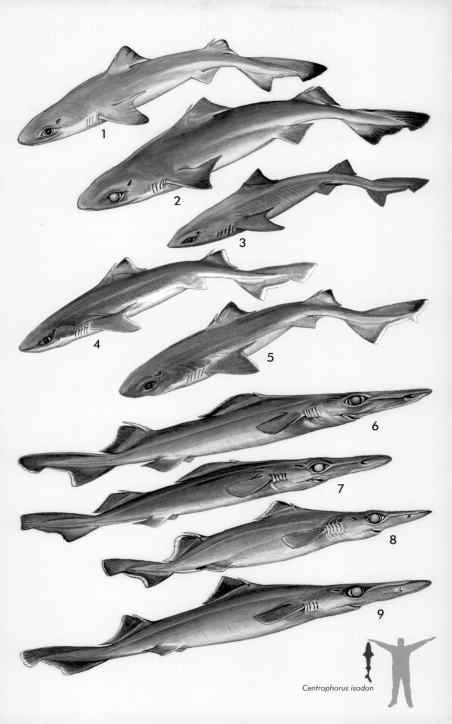

Centrophorus isodon

LANTERNSHARKS: Etmopteridae – pages 62–72

The largest family of squaloid sharks, with more than 50 species in four genera (*Aculeola, Centroscyllium, Etmopterus, Trigonognathus*) occurring almost worldwide in deepwater, some wide-ranging, many endemic. New species are continually being discovered. The family includes what may be the smallest known species of sharks (*Etmopterus carteri* and *E. perryi*) whose females mature and give birth to litters of live young at a length of just 10–20cm.

Identification Dwarf to moderate-sized sharks (adults 10–107cm long) with photophores, inconspicuous or forming distinct black marks on abdomen, flanks or tail (confined to or denser on ventral surface). Two dorsal fins with strong grooved spines (second fin and spine usually larger). No anal fin. No precaudal pits or lateral keels on caudal peduncle. *Centroscyllium* species (comb-tooth dogfishes) have short to moderately long snouts, comb-like teeth with cusps and cusplets in both jaws, and strong grooved dorsal fin spines (second strikingly larger than first). Lanternsharks, *Etmopterus* species, often have dark markings (light organs to photophores) on underside. Second dorsal fin and fin spine are much larger than the first. Some species have lines of denticles along their flanks and dorsal surfaces that give them an engraved appearance. These deepwater sharks tend to be in poor condition when collected due to damage by fishing gear. It is also hard to confirm identifications without examining details of denticle and tooth structure, coloration and photophore patterns, and taking precise body measurements.

Biology Most species are bottom-dwelling in deep water, 200–1500m, (range 50–4500m); some semi-oceanic. Several etmopterid dogfishes are social, and form small to huge schools or aggregations. Reproduction, where known, is viviparous with a yolk sac, with 3 to 20 pups/litter.

Status Most species are common, but poorly known. Few are large enough to be of any commercial value and most are discarded if caught as bycatch.

SLEEPER SHARKS: Somniosidae – pages 74–78

Seventeen deepwater benthic and oceanic species in seven genera (*Centroscymnus, Centroselachus, Proscymnodon, Scymnodalatias, Scymnodon, Somniosus,* and *Zameus*). Occur circumglobally in most seas, ranging from the tropics to Arctic and Antarctic oceans. Size ranges from small (40 to 69cm) to gigantic (6m or more).

Identification Fairly broad head and flat snout. Short, thin-lipped, almost transverse mouth. Small needle-like upper teeth, large compressed blade-like lower teeth. Spiracles large, close behind eyes. Lateral ridges on abdomen, not usually on caudal peduncle (except most *Somniosus*). Pectoral fins low, angular or rounded, not falcate, rear tips rounded and short. Pelvic fins subequal or larger than first dorsal and pectoral fins, and subequal to or smaller than second dorsal fin. Two small broad dorsal fins, origin of first in front of pelvic fin origins, space between greater than fin base length, second usually smaller or same size as first. Spines on both fins (may be covered by skin), or neither (*Scymnodalatias* and *Somniosus*). No anal fin. Caudal fin heterocercal with strong subterminal notch. No photophores.

Biology Poorly known. Viviparous with yolk sac (four to at least 59 pups/litter). Mostly occur near the seabed on continental and insular slopes from 200m to at least 3675m; a few species are oceanic or semi-oceanic. In high northern latitudes, *Somniosus microcephalus* and *S. pacificus* occur on continental shelves, penetrate the intertidal, and occur at the surface.

Status Moderately common and an important component of commercial targeted and bycatch deepwater shark fisheries. Caught by line gear, demersal trawls, gillnets, traps, and even by spear or gaff. Their flesh is used for food or fishmeal. In Australia, many species have high mercury levels in their flesh and are discarded from deepwater fisheries. Their large, very oily livers are processed for their high squalene content. Conservation status poorly known, but of considerable concern because expanding deepwater fisheries are now taking large numbers of deepwater sharks, including somniosids. Although the life history of these sharks is sketchily known, it is suspected that reproduction is limited and growth slow. If so, these species are highly vulnerable to overfishing.

ROUGHSHARKS: Oxynotidae – page 80

Identification Five unmistakable species of small sharks. Compressed body, triangular in cross-section with lateral ridges on abdomen and rough skin from large, prickly and close-set denticles. Two high sail-like spined dorsal fins. Rather broad flattened head with flat blunt snout, small thick-lipped mouth encircled by elongated labial furrows, close-set large nostrils, and large to enormous spiracles close behind eyes. Small, spear-like upper teeth form a triangular pad; lower teeth highly compressed to form a saw-like cutting edge, in only 9 to 18 rows. No anal fin.

Biology Poorly known deepwater sharks. Scattered distribution, mainly on temperate to tropical continental and island shelves. May be weak swimmers, relying on large oily livers for buoyancy. Diet mainly small bottom-living invertebrates (worms, crustaceans and molluscs) and fishes. Females bear litters of 7 to 23 pups.

Status Uncommon bycatch in deepwater bottom fisheries. May be processed for fish meal, liver oil or occasionally human food.

KITEFIN SHARKS: Dalatiidae – pages 80–82

Ten species in seven genera of dwarf to medium-sized deepwater sharks (*Dalatias*, *Euprotomicroides*, *Euprotomicrus*, *Heteroscymnoides*, *Isistius*, *Squaliolus*, *Mollisquama*) distributed almost worldwide in open ocean or on bottom in mostly temperate to tropical seas. Some species are wide-ranging, others restricted to single ocean basins or ridges, (but may prove to be more widespread once more research has been undertaken).

Identification Head narrow and conical, snout short. Strong jaws with small spear-like upper teeth, large blade-like interlocked lower teeth with smooth or serrated (*Dalatias* only) edges. Pectoral fins with short, broadly rounded free rear tips. Two dorsal fins without fin spines or with first dorsal fin spine only (*Squaliolus* species). Second dorsal varies from slightly smaller to much larger than first. No anal fin. Caudal fin with long upper lobe, long to very short or absent lower lobe, and well-developed subterminal notch.

Biology Poorly known deepwater and deep midwater species. The sharks of this family are all viviparous (with yolk sac); the larger species may produce litters containing as many as six to 16 pups.

Status One species (*Dalatias licha*) is important in target and bycatch fisheries for meat (which is used for human consumption and/or fishmeal) and squalene oil from the large livers. Others are too small to be of value and are assessed either as Least Concern or Data Deficient – some are known from just one or a very few specimens.

Plate 8: LANTERNSHARKS I

Dwarf to medium-sized sharks with photophores either inconspicuous or forming distinct black marks. Two dorsal fins with strong, grooved spines; second dorsal fin and spine much larger than first dorsal; no anal fin and no keel. Many species difficult to distinguish.

1 Hooktooth Dogfish *Aculeola nigra* ♀67cm ♂54cm

DN Eastern Pacific. **HT** Benthic and epibenthic; 110–735m. **ID** Stocky. Broad, blunt snout with broad, long arched mouth; gills quite large. Short dorsal fin spines, much lower than dorsal fins; pectoral fins with rounded tips. **CR** Blackish-brown. **Status:** DD.

2 Highfin Dogfish *Centroscyllium excelsum* 64cm

DN Northwestern Pacific. **HT** Deep seamounts; 800–1000m. **ID** First dorsal fin high and rounded with short spine; second dorsal spine very long reaching higher than fin apex; short caudal peduncle. Dorsal denticles sparse and irregular, ventrally none. **CR** Light brown above, darker below; lighter fin margins, intense black marks around mouth and beneath pectoral fins. **Status:** DD.

3 Black Dogfish *Centroscyllium fabricii* 84–107cm

DN Widespread temperate Atlantic. **HT** Outer continental shelves and slopes;180–2250m. **ID** Fairly stout, compressed long abdomen. Arched mouth. First dorsal fin low; short caudal peduncle. Numerous close-set denticles. **CR** Uniformly blackish-brown. **Status:** LC; except Northeast Atlantic **NT**.

4 Granular Dogfish *Centroscyllium granulatum* at least 28cm

DN South America. **HT** Deepwater, upper continental slope; 400–448m. **ID** Small, slender and cylindrical long abdomen. Mouth narrowly arched. First dorsal fin small, much smaller than second dorsal; second dorsal spine very large, higher than apex; long caudal peduncle. Numerous close-set sharp denticles. **CR** Uniformly brownish-black. **Status:** DD.

5 Bareskin Dogfish *Centroscyllium kamoharai* 63cm

DN Western Pacific. **HT** On or near bottom, deep continental shelf; 500–1200m. **ID** Stout and compressed. Very short, broadly arched mouth. First dorsal fin very low and rounded, second dorsal fin slightly higher; second dorsal fin spine about the same height as fin apex; short caudal peduncle. Skin smooth, almost naked. **CR** Uniformly blackish. **Status:** DD.

6 Combtooth Dogfish *Centroscyllium nigrum* 52cm

DN Central and Eastern Pacific. **HT** On or near bottom; 400–1143m. **ID** Fairly stout. Short, broadly arched mouth. Dorsal fins about the same size; first dorsal fin spine short; second dorsal fin spine about the same height as its fin apex. **CR** Blackish-brown body; fins with prominent white tips and margins. **Status:** DD.

7 Ornate Dogfish *Centroscyllium ornatum* at least 30cm

DN Northern Indian Ocean. **HT** Near the bottom; 521–1262m. **ID** Narrowly arched mouth. First dorsal fin low and rounded with very long spine nearly as high as second dorsal fin spine. Numerous close-set denticles. **CR** Uniformly blackish. **Status:** DD.

8 Whitefin Dogfish *Centroscyllium ritteri* mature ♀42–43cm

DN Northwestern Pacific. **HT** Deepwater; continental slopes and sea mounts; 320–1100m. **ID** Mouth broadly arched First dorsal fin low and rounded with very short fin spine; first dorsal fin about the same as second; second dorsal fin spine higher than its fin apex. Numerous close-set denticles. **CR** Only *Centroscyllium* with obvious black markings on underside of head, abdomen, pectoral fins with stripe below caudal peduncle; white posterior fin margins. **Status:** DD.

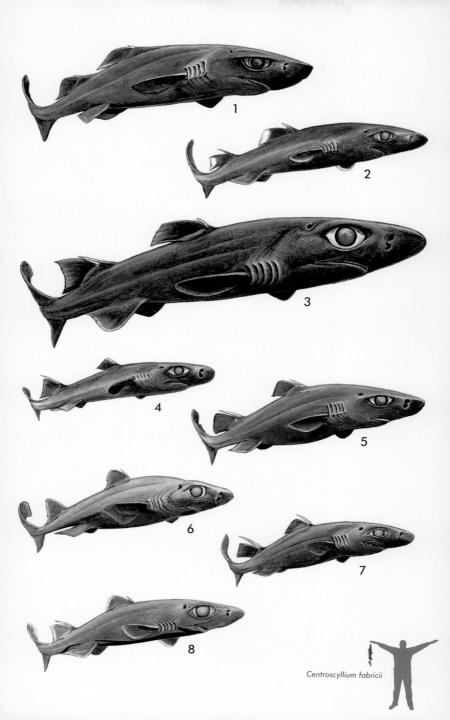

Centroscyllium fabricii

1 **Lined Lanternshark** *Etmopterus bullisi* 27cm (immature)

DN Northwest Atlantic. **HT** Continental slopes, on or near bottom; 275–824m. **ID** Slender. Gills very short. Long tail. Conspicuous longitudinal row of denticles on sides and back. **CR** Dark sooty-grey above, black below; light band midline eye to first dorsal fin; black ventral and tail markings. **Status:** DD.

2 **Caribbean Lanternshark** *Etmopterus hillianus* ♀28cm ♂26cm

DN Northwest Atlantic. **HT** Upper continental and insular slopes, on or near bottom; 311–695m. **ID** Moderately stout. Gills very short. Moderately long tail. Second dorsal fin much higher than first dorsal but less than twice area of first dorsal. No regular rows of denticles but largely cover snout. **CR** Grey or dark brown above, black below; black ventral and tail markings. **Status:** LC.

3 **African Lanternshark** *Etmopterus polli* about 24cm

DN Eastern Atlantic, Venezualan record may be different species. **HT** Upper continental slopes, on or near bottom; 300–1000m. **ID** Fairly stout. Gills short. Fairly long tail. Second dorsal fin same height or higher than first dorsal. Denticles widely spaced, no regular rows, largely cover snout. **CR** Dark grey body, blackish below; black ventral and tail markings. **Status:** DD.

4 **Great Lanternshark** *Etmopterus princeps* 89cm

DN North Atlantic, some South Atlantic islands. **HT** Continental slopes, on or near bottom; 350–4,500m. **ID** Stout. Gills very long. Tail moderately long and broad. Second dorsal fin much higher than first dorsal but less than twice area of first dorsal. Denticles largely cover snout. **CR** Blackish body with no conspicuous markings. **Status:** DD.

5 **Smooth Lanternshark** *Etmopterus pusillus* 50cm

DN Widespread Atlantic, Indo–West Pacific. **HT** Continental slopes, on or near bottom; 274–1000m. **ID** Fairly slender. Gills rather long. Fairly short broad tail. Second dorsal fin less than twice area first dorsal. Denticles widely spaced, not in rows, cover snout. **CR** Blackish-brown body with obscure black ventral markings. **Status:** LC.

6 **Fringefin Lanternshark** *Etmopterus schultzi* 30cm

DN Western Atlantic. **HT** Upper continental slopes, on or near bottom; 220–915m. **ID** Slender. Gills very short. Moderately long tail. Second dorsal fin about twice area first dorsal. Denticles widely spaced, no rows, largely cover snout. Fin margins naked. **CR** Light brown above, dusky-grey below; dark ventral and tail markings. **Status:** LC.

7 **Velvet Belly** *Etmopterus spinax* 41cm

DN Eastern Atlantic and Western Mediterranean. **HT** Outer continental shelves and upper slopes, near or well above bottom; 70–2000m. **ID** Long, fairly stout. Gills very short. Long tail. Second dorsal fin about twice area first dorsal. Denticles largely cover snout. **CR** Brown above, abruptly black below; black marks pelvic fin area to tail. **Status:** NT.

8 **Green Lanternshark** *Etmopterus virens* 26cm

DN Northwest Atlantic. **HT** Upper continental slopes, 196–915m. **ID** Moderately slender. Gills very short. Long narrow tail. Second dorsal fin area greater than twice the first dorsal. Denticles widely spaced, no rows, largely cover snout. **CR** Dark brown or grey-black above, black below; black ventral and tail markings. **Status:** LC.

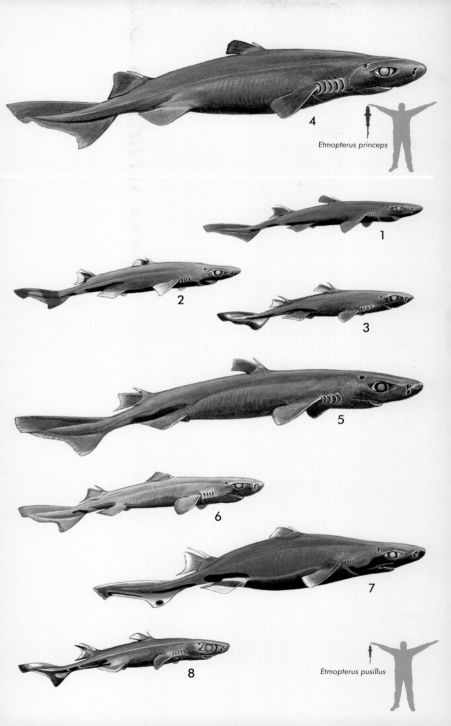

4

Etmopterus princeps

1

2

3

5

6

7

8

Etmopterus pusillus

1 **Blurred Smooth Lanternshark** *Etmopterus bigelowi*   at least 72cm

DN Central to southern Atlantic, Western Indian Ocean and western Pacific. **HT** Continental and insular shelves and slopes and submarine ridges; 163 to deeper than 1000m. **ID** Slender. Broad head with long thick flat snout. Long tail. First dorsal fin less than second dorsal. Smooth skin. **CR** Dark brown or blackish underside slightly darker; white spot on head. Light edges to fins but no conspicuous markings. **Status:** LC.

2 **Cylindrical Lanternshark** *Etmopterus carteri*   21cm

DN Northwest Atlantic. **HT** Upper continental slopes, 283–356m. **ID** Head semi-cylindrical, about deep as wide at eyes, snout very short and rounded. Gills broad. **CR** Uniformly dark without concentrations of photophores. Fins with pale webs. **Status:** DD.

3 **Brown Lanternshark** *Etmopterus compagnoi*   67.4cm

DN Southeastern Atlantic. **HT** On or near bottom; 473–923m. **ID** Moderately stout body. Short caudal fin. **CR** Brown above, becoming black below with inconspicuous elongated black flank markings above and behind pelvic fins. **Status:** NE.

4 **Broadband Lanternshark** *Etmopterus gracilispinis*   about 33cm

DN Western Atlantic; Western Indian Ocean records maybe different species. **HT** Outer continental shelves and upper-middle slopes, on or near bottom; 70–1000m, 2240m off Argentina. **ID** Stout. Gills very short. Slender short tail. Second dorsal fin about twice area first dorsal. No regular rows of denticles. **CR** Blackish-brown body underside grading black, inconspicuous black ventral and tail markings. **Status:** LC.

5 **Dwarf Lanternshark** *Etmopterus perryi*   about 21cm

DN Western central Atlantic. **HT** Upper continental slope, 283–375m. **ID** One of smallest living sharks. Long broad flat head. Second dorsal fin height than first dorsal. **CR** Brownish above, black below; conspicuous black ventral and tail markings. **Status:** DD.

6 **West Indian Lanternshark** *Etmopterus robinsi*   ♀34cm ♂31cm

DN Western central Atlantic. **HT** Continental and insular slopes, 412–787m. **ID** Moderately stout. Gills very short. Second dorsal fin much higher than first dorsal but less than twice area of first dorsal. Denticles widely spaced, no rows, largely cover snout. **CR** Grey or dark brown above, abruptly black below; black ventral and tail markings. **Status:** LC.

7 **Sculptured Lanternshark** *Etmopterus sculptus*   about 53cm

DN Southern Africa. **HT** Near bottom; 240–1023m. **ID** Moderately large, stout. Denticles give body a sculpted textured appearance. **CR** Dark grey brown above, black below with well-defined narrow, elongated flank markings extending to anterior and posterior of pelvic fins. **Status:** NE.

8 **Brown Lanternshark** *Etmopterus unicolor*   ♀79cm

DN Western Pacific. **HT** Continental slope and seamounts; 465–1500m. **ID** Robust. Fairly large gills. Moderately long tail. Long low first dorsal fin with very short spine, second dorsal fin about twice height first dorsal with strong spine. Denticles not in rows but cover snout. **CR** Dark brown to brownish-black with darker underside. **Status:** DD.

Etmopterus gracilispinis

colour variants

Etmopterus unicolor

Plate 11: LANTERNSHARKS IV

1 **Combtooth Lanternshark** *Etmopterus decacuspidatus*   ♂29cm (holotype)

DN Northwestern Pacific. **HT** On or near bottom; 512–692m. **ID** Moderately slender. Gills very short. Fairly long broad tail. Second dorsal fin about twice area first dorsal. No regular rows of denticles. **CR** Brown above, black below; black ventral and tail markings. **Status:** DD.

2 **Blackmouth Lanternshark** *Etmopterus evansi*   at least 32cm

DN Western Indo-Pacific. **HT** Shoals and reefs on continental shelf, 430–550m. **ID** Slender. Weakly defined rows of denticles on dorsal midline and caudal peduncle but not head. **CR** Light brown above, darker below; dark borders around mouth, above eyes and sometimes gills, also black tail markings. **Status:** LC.

3 **Pygmy Lanternshark** *Etmopterus fusus*   at least 30cm

DN Eastern Indian Ocean. **HT** Continental slope, 430–550m. **ID** Cylindrical with long caudal peduncle. Second dorsal fin more than twice height first dorsal fin. Regular rows of denticles on flanks and caudal peduncle but not head. **CR** Dark greyish or black; faint dark marks on flanks and tail. Fins pale with dark markings. **Status:** LC.

4 **Thorny Lanternshark** *Etmopterus sentosus*   about 27cm

DN Western Indian Ocean. **HT** Near bottom; perhaps 200–500m. **ID** Slender. Gills quite long. Moderately long broad tail. Second dorsal fin area greater than twice the first dorsal. Two rows of denticles on flanks. Fin margins largely naked. **CR** Greyish-black above, inconspicuously black below; black ventral and tail markings. **Status:** LC.

5 **Rasptooth Dogfish** *Etmopterus sheikoi*   at least 43cm

DN Western North Pacific. **HT** Upper slope of submarine ridge; 340–370m. **ID** Unmistakable long flat snout with short mouth. Grooved dorsal fin spines, second dorsal fin spine higher than first dorsal. **CR** Dark brown above, black below; black tail markings. **Status:** DD.

6 **Splendid Lanternshark** *Etmopterus splendidus*   ♀26cm (immature)

DN Northwest Pacific. **HT** Continental slope; 200–300m. **ID** Spindle-shaped similar to *E. fusus*. **CR** Above purplish-black, bluish-black below; precaudal fins pale red-brown webs and lighter patch on caudal fin. **Status:** DD.

7 **Hawaiian Lanternshark** *Etmopterus villosus*   17cm (holotype)

DN Hawaiian Islands. **HT** Insular slopes, on or near bottom; 406–911m. **ID** Stout. Gills moderately long. Short broad tail. Second dorsal fin much higher than first dorsal but less than twice area of first dorsal. Denticles widely spaced, rows on trunk and tail, cover snout. **CR** Dark brown or blackish above, slightly darker below; indistinct black ventral markings. **Status:** LC.

8 **Viper Dogfish** *Trigonognathus kabeyai*   at least 54cm

DN North and central Pacific. **HT** Upper continental slopes, on bottom; 250–1000m. **ID** Very long snake-like mouth with huge curved fang-like teeth, deep pockets on head in front of very large elongated spiracles. Grooved spines on both dorsal fins. **CR** Dark brown above, black below; black tail markings. **Status:** DD.

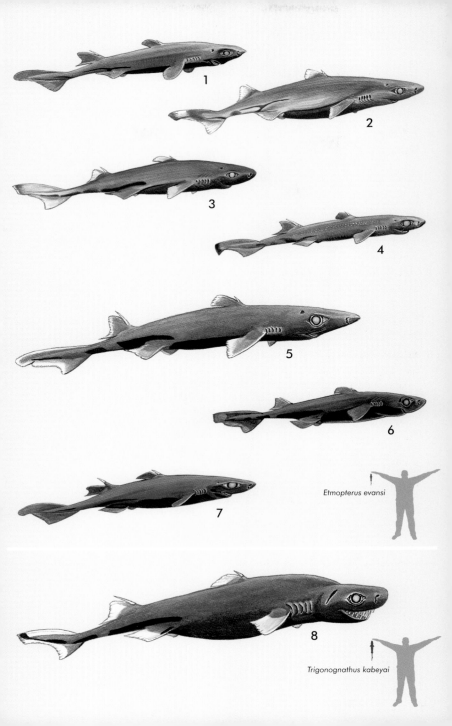

Etmopterus evansi

Trigonognathus kabeyai

Plate 12: LANTERNSHARKS V

1 Shorttail Lanternshark *Etmopterus brachyurus*   at least 42cm

DN Western Pacific. **HT** Near bottom; 481m. **ID** Heavy-bodied. Broad head with short thick flat snout. Short tail. Second dorsal fin higher than first dorsal; second dorsal spine strongly curved. Conspicuous line of denticles. **CR** Light brown above graduating to black below; black ventral and tail markings. **Status:** DD.

2 Broadsnout Lanternshark *Etmopterus burgessi*   41cm

DN Northwestern Pacific, Taiwan. **HT** Upper continental slopes; deeper than 300m. **ID** Moderate-size, with broad snout. **CR** Uniformly grey above, darker grey to black below; flank markings elongated, posterior branch marking about as long as anterior or slightly shorter. **Status:** DD.

3 Pink Lanternshark *Etmopterus dianthus*   at least 41cm

DN Southwest Pacific. **HT** Upper continental shelf, bottom; 708–800m. **ID** Stout. First dorsal fin small and low with short spine, second dorsal fin less than twice first dorsal with second dorsal spine about the same as fin. Bristle-like denticles not in rows. **CR** Pinkish fresh (brownish-grey preserved) above, dusky to black below. **Status:** LC.

4 Shortfin Smooth Lanternshark *Etmopterus joungi*   ♀46cm (immature)

DN Northwest Pacific, Taiwan. **HT** Upper continental and insular slopes; about 300m. **ID** Moderately elongated body. Subconical snout. Moderately long tail. **CR** Dark grey above, darker below with inconspicuous flank anterior marking, and no posterior flank marking. **Status:** NE.

5 Smalleye Lanternshark *Etmopterus litvinovi*   ♀61cm ♂55cm

DN Southeastern Pacific. **HT** Upper slopes, on or near bottom; 630–1100m. **ID** Stout. Large flat head. Gills long. Moderately long tail. First dorsal fin origin behind pectoral fin rear tip, second dorsal fin slightly higher than first dorsal fin; interdorsal space short. No rows of denticles. **CR** Plain-coloured with no distinct markings. **Status:** DD.

6 Blackbelly Lanternshark *Etmopterus lucifer*   about 47cm

DN Western Pacific. **HT** Outer continental and insular shelves and upper slopes, on or near bottom; 158–1357m. **ID** Stocky. Gills moderately long, Moderately long tail. Second dorsal fin very large. Longitudinal rows of denticles snout to tail. **CR** Brown above, black below; black ventral and tail markings. **Status:** LC.

7 Slendertail Lanternshark *Etmopterus molleri*   about 46cm

DN Western Pacific. **HT** Outer continental and insular shelves and upper slopes, on or near bottom; 238–655m. **ID** Slender. Second dorsal fin much higher than first dorsal. Regular longitudinal rows of denticles snout to tail, except above pectoral fins. **CR** Light brown above, dark brown with black stripes on sides, abruptly black below. **Status:** LC.

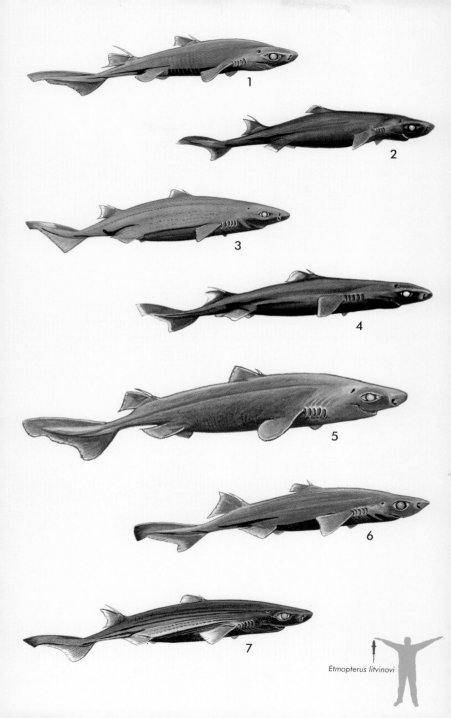

Etmopterus litvinovi

1 Giant Lanternshark *Etmopterus baxteri* — 86cm

DN South Australia, New Zealand. **HT** Upper insular slopes, on or near bottom; 250–1500m. **ID** Stout. Short thick snout. Short broad tail. Dorsal fins widely spaced, second dorsal fin twice area first dorsal, second dorsal spine strongly curved. Rough-textured. **CR** Uniformly dark brown to blackish above with inconspicuous white blotch on head, black below; black tail markings. **Status:** LC.

2 Tailspot Lanternshark *Etmopterus caudistigmus* — ♀34cm

DN New Caledonia. **HT** Insular slope; 638–793m. **ID** Slender. Narrow head with long thick narrow snout. Long tail. Second dorsal fin higher than first dorsal. Longitudinal row of small close-set denticles on body and tail. **CR** Dark above, black below with obvious photophores on tail. **Status:** LC.

3 Lined Lanternshark *Etmopterus dislineatus* — at least 45cm

DN Northeast Australia. **HT** Upper continental slope, on or near bottom; 590–800m. **ID** Elongate attractive lanternshark. First dorsal fin small and low about half size second dorsal fin. Bristle-like denticles not in rows. **CR** Light silvery-brown above, much darker below; dark broken lines on flanks with black tail markings. **Status:** LC.

4 Southern Lanternshark *Etmopterus granulosus* — 85.5cm

DN Southern Oceans. **HT** Outermost continental shelves and upper slopes; 220–1430m. **ID** Heavy-bodied. Big head. Very short gills. Tail short and broad. Second dorsal fin much higher than first dorsal. Conspicuous lines of large rough denticles on body not head. **CR** Grey-brown above, abruptly black below; black marks above pelvic fin and caudal fin base. **Status:** LC.

5 False Lanternshark *Etmopterus pseudosqualiolus* — 45cm

DN Western Pacific. **HT** Oceanic ridges; 870–1170m. **ID** Fusiform similar shape to *E. carteri*. Very short deep snout with short round eyes. **CR** Dark brown to black, paler tail with inconspicuous dark marks. Distal fin webs pale; terminal caudal lobe dark. **Status:** LC.

6 Densescale Lanternshark *Etmopterus pycnolepis* — 41–45cm

DN Southeast Pacific. **HT** Upper slopes, on or near bottom; 33–763m. **ID** Slender. Narrow head. Gills long. Moderately long tail. First dorsal fin origin ahead pectoral fin rear tip, second dorsal fin higher than first dorsal. Very small denticles in dense rows head to tail. **CR** Black body and tail markings. **Status:** DD.

7 Traveller Lanternshark *Etmopterus viator* — at least 58cm

DN Southern Oceans. **HT** Little known; 830–1610m. **ID** Body stout. Snout short. Lateral denticles partially form short broken linear rows, giving it a rough texture. **CR** Dark brown to blackish above, darker below; base of black flank markings indistinct in adults, very distinct in subadults; anterior flank marking elongated, posterior branch much shorter. **Status:** LC.

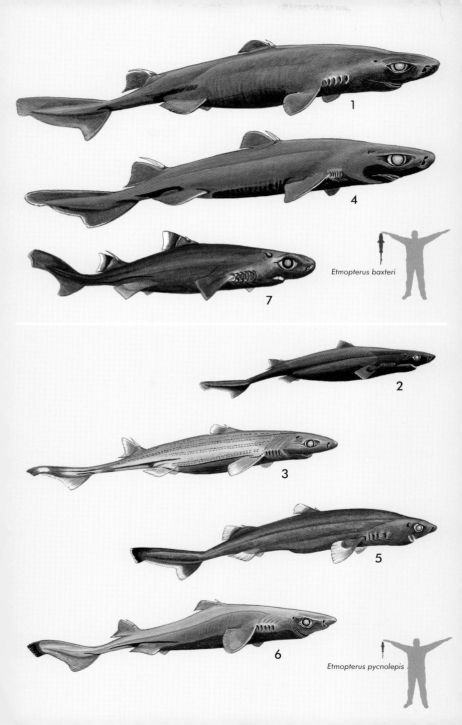

Etmopterus baxteri

Etmopterus pycnolepis

Plate 14: SLEEPER SHARKS I

Small to gigantic (40cm to 6m or more); fairly broad head and flat snout, spiracles large and close behind eyes; lateral ridges on abdomen; pectoral fins low with short rounded free rear tips, two small dorsal fins with spines which may be covered with skin, no anal fin, caudal fin heterocercal with strong posterior notch.

1 **Portuguese Dogfish** *Centroscymnus coelolepis*   about 122cm

DN Atlantic and Indo-Pacific. **HT** Continental slopes, upper and middle abyssal plain rises, on or near bottom; 128–3675m. **ID** Stocky. Short snout, short labial furrows. Dorsal fin spines usually just visible. Small dorsal fins of equal size, second dorsal fin close to asymmetrical caudal fin. **CR** Uniform golden-brown to blackish. **Status:** NT.

2 **Roughskin Dogfish** *Centroscymnus owstonii*   120cm

DN Atlantic, Indian and Pacific Oceans. **HT** Upper continental slopes and submarine ridges, on or near bottom; 150–1459m. **ID** Similar to *C. coelolepis* but longer snout, longer lower first dorsal fin, taller triangular second dorsal fin. Dorsal fin spines barely exposed. **CR** Uniformly dark brownish or black. **Status:** LC.

3 **Longnose Velvet Dogfish** *Centroselachus crepidater*   possibly105cm

DN Eastern Atlantic and Indo-Pacific but not Northeast Pacific. **HT** Upper continental and insular slopes, on or near bottom; 200–2080m. **ID** Slender. Very long snout, small mouth with encircling very long upper labial furrows. Dorsal fin spines very small, dorsal fins about the same as sized, first dorsal fin extends forward in prominent ridge origin over pectoral bases, second dorsal free rear tip nearly reaches upper caudal origin. **CR** Black to dark brown. Narrow light posterior fin margins. **Status:** LC.

4 **Largespine Velvet Dogfish** *Proscymnodon macracanthus*   ♀68cm (holotype)

DN Southwest Atlantic and West Pacific. **HT** Not recorded. **ID** Stocky, tapering strongly behind pectoral fins. Fairly long snout, thick fleshy lips and short upper labial furrows. Pectoral fins large; prominent stout dorsal fin spines, second dorsal fin larger than first dorsal. **CR** Uniform dark brown to blackish. **Status:** DD.

5 **Plunket's Shark** *Proscymnodon plunketi*   170cm

DN Indo-Pacific. **HT** Continental and insular slopes, near bottom; 219–1550m. **ID** Stocky, tapering strongly behind pectoral fins. Very short snout. Dorsal fin spines just visible; dorsal fins of equal size, first dorsal fin extends forward in prominent ridge, length second dorsal fin to upper caudal fin origin opposite dorsal bases, second dorsal free rear tip well in front of upper caudal fin. **CR** Uniform dark brown to blackish. **Status:** NT.

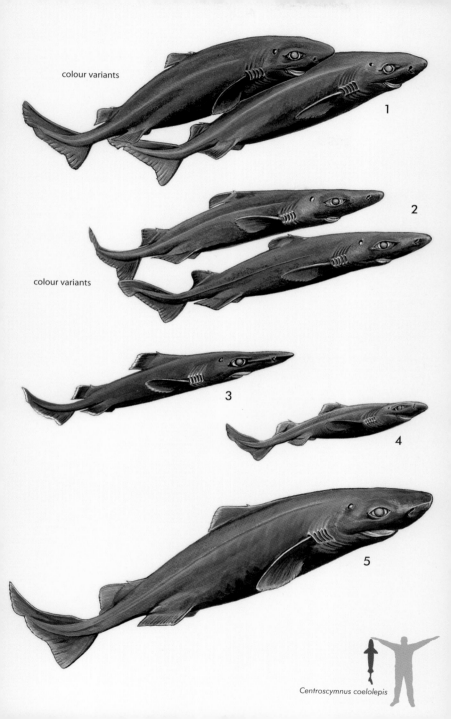

colour variants

1

2

colour variants

3

4

5

Centroscymnus coelolepis

1 Whitetail Dogfish *Scymnodalatias albicauda* 110cm

DN Southern Ocean. **HT** Oceanic in epipelagic zone, near bottom on submarine ridge; 0–200m and deeper. **ID** Short broad round snout, long broad arched mouth, horizontal elongate eyes. Pectoral fins elongate; no dorsal fin spines; second dorsal fin slightly larger than first and very close to caudal fin. **CR** Dark brown or mottled grey. Whitish-grey fin margins; caudal fin white blotches on dark terminal lobe. **Status:** DD.

2 Azores Dogfish *Scymnodalatias garricki* ♂40.6cm

DN North Atlantic Ridge. **HT** Oceanic or deep benthic; caught 300–580m. **ID** Small. Long broad rounded snout, long broad arched mouth, horizontal elongate eyes. No dorsal fin spines; first dorsal fin mid back. **CR** Uniform dark brown. **Status:** DD.

3 Sparsetooth Dogfish *Scymnodalatias oligodon* ♂26cm (immature)

DN Southeast Pacific. **HT** Oceanic; caught 0–200m. **ID** Small. Long broad pointed snout, long broad arched mouth, horizontal elongate eyes. No dorsal fin spines; first dorsal fin mid back; caudal fin ventral lobe weak. **CR** Uniform dark brown. **Status:** DD.

4 Sherwood Dogfish *Scymnodalatias sherwoodi* 85cm

DN Southwest Pacific. **HT** Deepwater; 400–500m. **ID** Moderately long flat pointed snout, long broad arched mouth, horizontally elongate eyes. Pectoral fins leaf-shaped; no dorsal fin spines; first dorsal fin mid back, second dorsal fin origin above rear third of pelvic fin bases; caudal fin ventral lobe short, strong. **CR** Dark brown above, lighter below. Light margins on gills and pectoral fins. **Status:** DD.

5 Knifetooth Dogfish *Scymnodon ringens* 110cm

DN East Atlantic and West Pacific. **HT** Continental slope, on or near bottom; 200–1600m. **ID** Thick high head, short broad snout, very large broad arched mouth. Long gills more or equal to eye length. Dorsal fin spines small; second dorsal fin slightly larger than first dorsal fin; caudal fin asymmetric with weak subterminal notch and no ventral lobe. **CR** Uniform black. **Status:** DD.

6 Japanese Velvet Dogfish *Zameus ichiharai* at least ♀146cm ♂101cm

DN Japan. **HT** Slope, on or near bottom 450–1500m. **ID** Low flat head, moderately long snout, short narrow mouth. Short gills less or equal to eye length. Caudal peduncle long. Pectoral fins narrow leaf-shaped; dorsal fin spines small; pelvic fins small about the same as second dorsal fin; caudal fin with strong subterminal notch and short ventral lobe. **CR** Uniform black. **Status:** DD.

7 Velvet Dogfish *Zameus squamulosus* 84cm

DN Patchy worldwide. **HT** Continental and insular slopes, on or near bottom; 550–1450m. **ID** Slender. Low flat head, fairly long narrow snout, short narrow mouth, nasoral grooves much longer than upper labial furrows. Long tail. Dorsal fin spines small; second dorsal fin larger than first dorsal fin and about the same as pelvic fins; caudal fin with strong terminal notch and short ventral lobe. **CR** Uniform black. **Status:** DD.

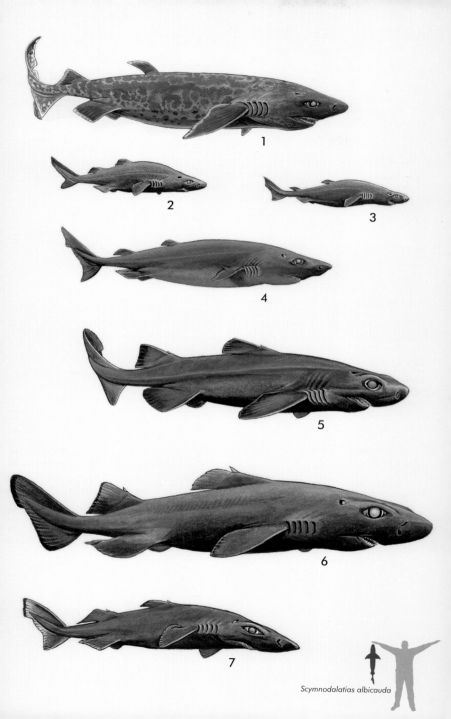

Scymnodalatias albicauda

Plate 16: SLEEPER SHARKS III

1 Southern Sleeper Shark *Somniosus antarcticus*   600cm

DN Southern Ocean. **HT** Continental and insular shelves and upper slope; 245m and deeper. **ID** Gigantic, heavy cylindrical body. Short rounded snout. Short caudal peduncle, keels on base of caudal fin. Very small precaudal fins; no dorsal fin spines; very low dorsal fins equal sized, first dorsal fin closer to pelvic fins than pectoral fins, distance between dorsal fin bases about 80% snout to first gill slit; caudal fin long ventral lobe, short dorsal lobe. Skin rough. **CR** Uniform grey to blackish. **Status:** DD.

2 Frog Shark *Somniosus longus*   about 140cm

DN West and Southeast Pacific. **HT** Outer continental shelves and upper slopes, on or near bottom; 200–1160m. **ID** Slender cylindrical body. Short head with short rounded snout. Short caudal peduncle, keels on base of caudal fin. No dorsal fin spines; first dorsal fin about long as second dorsal fin and closer to pectoral fins than pelvic fins; caudal fin long ventral lobe, short dorsal. Smooth skin. **CR** Uniformly blackish. **Status:** DD.

3 Greenland Shark *Somniosus microcephalus*   at least 640cm

DN North Atlantic and Arctic Oceans. **HT** Continental and insular shelves and upper slopes; 180m and deeper, inshore in winter. **ID** Gigantic, heavy body. Short rounded snout. Short caudal peduncle, keels on base of caudal fin. Small precaudal fins; no dorsal fin spines; low dorsal fins equal-sized, first dorsal fin closer to pectoral fins than pelvic fins, distance between dorsal fin bases about the same as snout to first gill slit; caudal fin long ventral lobe, short dorsal. Skin rough. **CR** Mid grey or brown, occasionally transverse bands, small spots/blotches or light spots. **Status:** NT.

4 Pacific Sleeper Shark *Somniosus pacificus*   ♀700cm ♂456cm

DN North Pacific. **HT** Continental shelves and slopes; 200m and deeper, shallower at high latitiudes. **ID** Gigantic, heavy (when mature) cylindrical body. Short rounded snout. Short caudal peduncle, keels absent or present on base of caudal fin. Small precaudal fins; no dorsal fin spines; low dorsal fins equal sized, first dorsal fin closer to pelvic fins than pectoral fins, distance between dorsal fin bases about 70% snout to first gill slit; caudal fin long ventral lobe, short dorsal lobe. Skin rough and bristly. **CR** Uniform greyish. **Status:** DD.

5 Little Sleeper Shark *Somniosus rostratus*   143cm

DN Northeast and Northwest Atlantic and West Mediterranean. **HT** Outer continental shelves, upper and lower slopes, on or near bottom; 180–2200m. **ID** Similar to *S. longus* but smaller eyes, shorter second dorsal fin and shorter gills, about eye length (*S. longus* more than twice eye length). **CR** Uniform blackish. **Status:** DD.

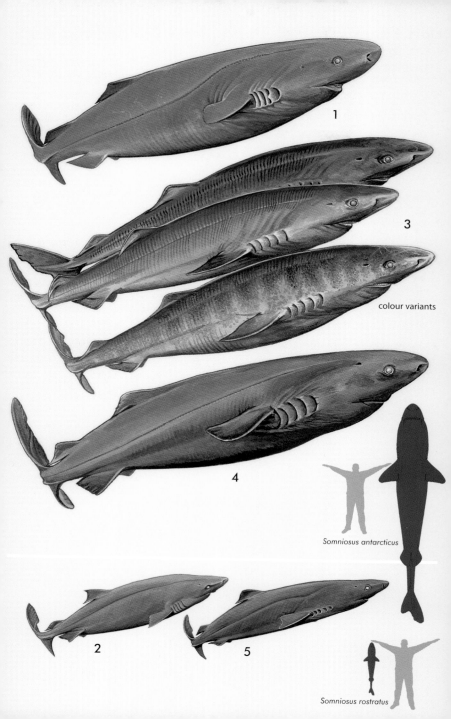

colour variants

Somniosus antarcticus

Somniosus rostratus

Plate 17: ROUGHSHARKS AND KITEFIN SHARKS

Unmistakable small sharks. Compressed, triangular in cross-section, lateral ridges on abdomen; flat blunt snout, small thick-lipped mouth, close-set large nostrils; two high-spined dorsal fins; rough skin.

1 Prickly Dogfish *Oxynotus bruniensis*   72–91cm

DN Temperate southwest Pacific. **HT** Deepwater on outer continental and insular shelves and upper slopes: 46–1067m. **ID** Small circular spiracles. Dorsal fins with triangular tips, trailing edges straight to slightly concave; first dorsal fin spine leans forward. **CR** Uniformly light grey-brown. **Status:** DD.

2 Caribbean Roughshark *Oxynotus caribbaeus*   at least 49cm

DN Northwest Atlantic. **HT** Upper continental slopes, bottom; 402–457m. **ID** Small circular spiracles. Dorsal fins with narrow triangular tips, trailing edges concave; first dorsal fin spine leans forward. **CR** Grey or brownish with dark bands, blotches and small spots separated by prominent light areas over pectoral and pelvic fins. **Status:** DD.

3 Angular Roughshark *Oxynotus centrina*   about 150cm

DN East Atlantic and Mediterranean. **HT** Coralline algal and muddy bottom on continental shelves and upper slopes, bottom; 50–660m. **ID** Large expanded ridges over eyes covered with large denticles; very large vertical elongate spiracles. First dorsal fin spine leans forward. **CR** Grey or grey-brown with dark blotches on head and sides (less prominent in adults) and light horizontal line over cheeks below eye. **Status:** V.

4 Japanese Roughshark *Oxynotus japonicus*   ♂54cm

DN Known only from southern Japan. **HT** 150–350m. **ID** Large vertical oval spiracles. Dorsal fins with narrow triangular tips, trailing edges shallowly concave; first dorsal fin spine leans back. **CR** Uniformly dark brown except white lips, nasal flap margins, fin axils and inner clasper margins. **Status:** DD.

5 Sailfin Roughshark *Oxynotus paradoxus*   about 118cm

DN Eastern Atlantic. **HT** Continental slope; 265–720m. **ID** Small almost circular spiracles. Dorsal fins very tall with narrow pointed tips, trailing edges very concave; first dorsal fin spine leans back. **CR** Uniformly dark brown or blackish. **Status:** DD.

Kitefin sharks

Narrow conical head with short snout; pectoral fins with short broad and round free rear tips, two dorsal fins without spines, no anal fin, caudal fin with long dorsal lobe and well-developed terminal notch.

6 Kitefin Shark *Dalatias licha*   159–182cm

DN Atlantic, Indian and Pacific Oceans. **HT** Warm-temperate and tropical outer continental and insular shelves and slopes, usually on or near bottom; 37–1800m. **ID** Medium-sized cylindrical body. Short blunt snout, thick fringed lips. Dorsal fins equal sized, first dorsal fin base closer to pectoral fins than pelvic fins; weak caudal fin ventral lobe. **CR** Uniform brown to blackish. **Status:** NT.

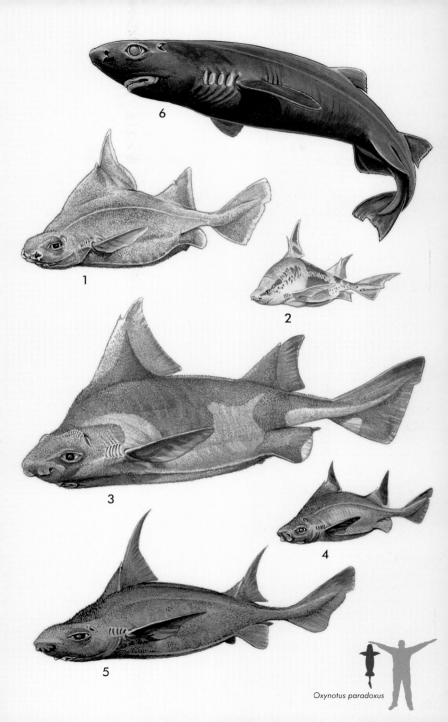

Oxynotus paradoxus

1 **Taillight Shark** *Euprotomicroides zantedeschia* ♀17.6cm (immature) ♂41.6cm

DN South Atlantic. **HT** Possibly epipelagic; surface to 641m. **ID** Tiny, cylindrical. Short blunt snout, thick fringed lips. Very long fifth gill slit. Luminous gland. First dorsal fin base closer to pelvic than pectoral fins, second dorsal fin origin in front of pelvic fins; caudal fin paddle-shaped. **CR** Blackish-brown; all fins with prominent white margins. **Status:** DD.

2 **Pygmy Shark** *Euprotomicrus bispinatus* 27cm

DN South Atlantic, Indian and Pacific Oceans. **HT** Epipelagic, mesopelagic, perhaps bathypelagic in mid-ocean, surface to 1800m or more. **ID** Tiny, cylindrical. Bulbous snout, large eyes. Gills tiny. Luminous gland. Low lateral keels on caudal peduncle. First dorsal fin tiny flag-like, second dorsal fin origin well behind pelvic fin; caudal fin paddle-shaped nearly symmetrical. **CR** Uniformly black. **Status:** LC.

3 **Longnose Pygmy Shark** *Heteroscymnoides marleyi* about ♂37cm

DN Southern Ocean. **HT** Oceanic, epipelagic in cold, sub-antarctic oceanic waters and cold current systems; possibly surface to 502m. **ID** Dwarf, cylindrical. Very long bulbous snout; thin unpleated lips. Small gills. First dorsal fin origin over pectoral fins, second dorsal fin slightly larger than first dorsal; caudal fin paddle-shaped nearly symmetrical with strong ventral lobe. **CR** Uniformly dark brown. **Status:** LC.

4 **Cookiecutter Shark** *Isistius brasiliensis* at least ♀50cm ♂39cm

DN Atlantic, southern Indian Ocean and Pacific. **HT** Tropical, oceanic; epipelagic to bathypelagic; 0–3500m. **ID** Small, cigar-shaped. Very short bulbous snout. Ventral luminous organs except on prominent dark collar and light-edged fins. First dorsal fin base over pelvic fin origins; pectoral fins larger than dorsal fins; nearly symmetrical paddle-shaped caudal fin. **CR** Mid grey to grey-brown with prominent dark collar. **Status:** LC.

5 **South China Cookiecutter Shark** *Isistius labialis* 44.2cm (one specimen)

DN West Pacific. **HT** Continental slope; 520m. **ID** Similar to *I. brasiliensis* but eyes further forward, caudal fin less symmetrical with shorter ventral lobe. **CR** Grey-brown; dark collar breaks up on ventral surfaces and dark markings on dorsal surface. **Status:** DD.

6 **Largetooth Cookiecutter Shark** *Isistius plutodus* at least ♀42cm ♂34cm

DN West and Northeast Atlantic and West Pacific. **HT** Epipelagic, possibly bathypelagic; 100–200m. **ID** Similar to *I. brasiliensis* and *I. labialis*, but larger jaws and teeth; caudal fin smaller. **CR** Mid grey to grey-brown with no or faint collar markings. **Status:** LC.

7 **Pocket Shark** *Mollisquama parini* ♀40cm (adolescent)

DN Southeast Pacific. **HT** Submarine ridge; 330m. **ID** Dwarf spindle-shaped. Long bulbous conical snout, lateral papillae on upper lips. Gland opening above pectoral fin. Only first dorsal fin with spine, second dorsal fin base more than twice first dorsal; caudal fin paddle-shaped. **CR** Dark brown. Prominent white fin margins. **Status:** DD.

8 **Smalleye Pygmy Shark** *Squaliolus aliae* about 22cm

DN Southeast Indian Ocean and West Pacific. **HT** Epipelagic or mesopelagic near land; 200–2000m. **ID** Dwarf spindle-shaped. Long bulbous conical snout, lateral papillae on upper lips, eyes smaller than *S. laticaudus*. Photophores on ventral surface. Only first dorsal fin with spine, second dorsal fin base more than twice first; caudal fin paddle-shaped. **CR** Blackish. Prominent light fin margins. **Status:** LC.

9 **Spined Pygmy Shark** *Squaliolus laticaudus* ♀about 28cm ♂about 22cm

DN Atlantic and Indo-Pacific. **HT** Tropical epipelagic; 60–750m. **ID** Very similar to *S. aliae* but has larger eye with broad arched upper eyelid; lateral papillae absent or weak on upper lip. **CR** Blackish. Prominent light fin margins. **Status:** LC.

Heteroscymnoides marleyi

SAWSHARKS Pristiophoriformess – pages 86–88

This order contains one family of little-known small sharks, distributed worldwide in the fossil record, but now found only on the continental and insular shelves and upper slopes of the northwest and southeast Atlantic, west Indian and west Pacific Oceans, in shallow water in temperate regions, deeper in the tropics. Sometimes found in large schools or feeding aggregations. At least one species segregates by depth (adults in deeper water than young). Some have a very restricted distribution. Eight species.

Identification Small slender sharks (maximum about 150cm total length, most less than 70cm) with cylindrical bodies, flattened heads and a long, flat saw-like snout with a pair of long string-like ventral barbels in front of the nostrils and close-set rows of lateral and ventral sawteeth. Eyes on the side of the head, large spiracles. Two spineless dorsal fins, no anal fin. Thick lateral ridges on the caudal peduncle, a long dorsal caudal lobe and no ventral lobe. May be confused with the sawfishes, which are batoids (rays) with flattened bodies, pectoral fins fused to the head, and gill slits underneath the head.

Biology Viviparous; foetuses gain all food from their yolk sac, which is reabsorbed just before the litters of 7 to 17 pups are born. The large lateral rostral teeth erupt before birth but lie flat against the rostrum until after birth. The tooth-studded rostrum has sensors to detect vibrations and electrical fields and is probably used to capture and kill prey in the same manner to that used by the very similar batoid sawfishes, which use their saws to slash and stun small fishes. It may also be used for defence, or when competing or courting with other sawsharks (parallel cuts and scratches occasionally seen on adults are presumably from interactions with other sawsharks). The long rostral barbels may have taste, touch or other sensors and be trailed along the bottom to locate prey, including small fishes, crustaceans and squid.

Status Harmless to man, despite very sharp (non-toxic) teeth; handle with care. Some species are or were common where they occur. Very vulnerable to bycatch if a restricted range coincides with fisheries; their saws may easily be entangled in fishing gear including nets. Taken as a bycatch in demersal gillnet and bottom trawl fisheries and marketed for food or discarded. Saws may be sold as curios.

SAWSHARKS: Pristiophoridae – pages 86–88

Eight species in two genera. All are described in the following pages. *Pristiophorus* have five lateral pairs of gill slits, *Pliotrema* have six, but these unusual small sharks are all otherwise rather similar in appearance (see above). The morphologically similar batoid sawfishes are all assessed as Critically Endangered, because the majority of their range overlaps with intensive human use of coastal areas and their saws make them extremely vulnerable to net bycatch. The deeper water sawsharks, however, appear not to have been so seriously affected by target or bycatch fisheries mortality.

ANGELSHARKS Squatiniformes – pages 90–94

The angelsharks were originally known as monkfish (this name was first reported by Guillame Rondelet in 1555) because, when viewed from above, they have the outline of a man dressed in the flowing robes of a monk. These bottom-living sharks are found mainly on mud and sand on cool temperate continental shelves, from intertidal to continental slopes, deeper in tropical water. Absent from most of the northern Indian Ocean and central Pacific.

Identification Medium-sized (mostly smaller than 1.6m) bizarrely shaped sharks. May be heavily patterned on dorsal surface, most are uniformly pale below. Similar to rays, with a broad flattened body, short snout and large fins, but with gill openings on the sides of the head, not beneath, and very large pectoral fins not attached to the head opposite the gills (hindmost gill opening is in front of pectoral fin origins, but covered by triangular anterior fin lobes). Eyes on top of head, close to and level with large spiracles. Large mouth and nostrils (barbels on anterior nasal flaps) at front of snout are separate, mouth extends at sides to opposite or slightly behind the eyes. Very large labial furrows. Two spineless dorsal fins set back on precaudal tail, first over or behind the free rear tips of the very large pelvic fins. No anal fin. Short very thick keels at the base of the caudal peduncle, caudal fin with long dorsal lobe and even longer expanded ventral lobe. Some species are very hard to distinguish.

Biology Poorly known, outside Europe and northeast Pacific. Reproduction viviparous; litters of 1–25 pups obtain all nourishment from a yolk sac before birth. Some species have a three-year reproductive cycle. Often lie buried by day in mud and sand (except for eyes and spiracles). Ambush feeders, using their unusually flexible 'necks' to raise their heads and protruding trap-like jaws to snap up prey at high speed. Food includes small bony fishes, crustaceans, squids, gastropods and clams. At least some species are nocturnally active and move off the seabed. Do not swim far; populations may easily be isolated by deepwater or areas of unsuitable habitat.

Status Harmless, unless disturbed or provoked. Many species are intensively fished for food (they have valuable flesh), also oil, fishmeal and leather. Very vulnerable as target and bycatch species in bottom trawl, line gear and fixed bottom nets. Significant population reductions reported for many heavily fished species. Recolonisation of depleted populations from adjacent areas may be very slow. Some tropical species are very poorly known. Divers have photographed an apparently undescribed species (not included in this book) on a coral reef in the Andaman Sea.

ANGELSHARKS: Squatinidae – pages 90–94

The order Squatiniformes contains just one family (Squatinidae), which in turn contains only one genus, *Squatina*. Although 20 species are featured in this book, there are others, which have not yet been described and named by scientists.

The angelsharks have the most unfortunate distinction of facing a higher relative threat of extinction than any other order or family of sharks. More than half of all angelshark species are currently listed by IUCN as threatened with extinction in the IUCN Red List of Threatened Species, but as many as 80% could turn out to be threatened once we know more about them. Only two species have been assessed as Least Concern – both of these are Australian endemics, most of whose geographic range is either unfished or only very lightly exploited.

Plate 19: SAWSHARKS I

Slender distinctive sharks; flat heads, long flat saw-like snout with long ventral barbels and close-set rows of lateral and ventral saw teeth, large spiracles; thick lateral ridges on caudal peduncle; long caudal fin dorsal lobe.

1 Sixgill Sawshark *Pliotrema warreni* at least ♀136cm, ♂112cm

DN Southeast Atlantic and Southwest Indian Ocean. **HT** Offshore continental shelf and upper slope, on or near bottom; 37–500m. **ID** Only sawshark with six pairs of gills. Barbs on posterior edges of larger rostral sawteeth; barbels closer to mouth than other species. **CR** Pale brown above, white below. **Status:** NT.

2 Longnose Sawshark *Pristiophorus cirratus* 149cm

DN South Australia. **HT** Continental shelf and upper slope, on or near sandy or gravel-sand bottom; to 630m. **ID** Stocky sawshark. Lateral teeth: 9–11 in front of barbels, 9–10 behind. Barbels much closer to rostral tip than mouth. **CR** Pale yellow to greyish-brown, sometimes with faint blotches spots and bars; dark brown rostral midline stripes and edges, tooth margins blackish. **Status:** LC.

3 Japanese Sawshark *Pristiophorus japonicus* 136–153cm

DN Northwest Pacific. **HT** Temperate continental shelves and upper slopes, on or near sand or mud bottom; 50–800 m. **ID** Stocky sawshark. Lateral teeth: 15–26 in front of barbels, 8–17 or more behind: ventral teeth: 9–14 in front of barbels, 8–9 behind. Barbels closer to mouth than rostral tip. **CR** Brown or reddish-brown; dark brown rostral midline stripes and edges. **Status:** DD.

4 Shortnose Sawshark *Pristiophorus nudipinnis* about ♀124cm

DN South Australia. **HT** Temperate-subtropical continental shelf, on or near bottom; to deeper than 110m. Stocky sawshark. Lateral teeth: 12–14 in front of barbels, 6–8 behind, ventral teeth 13–14 in front of barbels, four behind. Barbels closer to mouth than rostral tip. **CR** Uniformly slate grey above, indistinct dusky rostral midline stripes and edges. **Status:** LC.

Pristiophorus cirratus

colour variants

1

2

3

4

Plate 20: SAWSHARKS II

1 Tropical Sawshark *Pristiophorus delicatus* — at least 85cm

DN East Australia. **HT** Continental slope; 245–405m. **ID** Slender sawshark. Juveniles usually have two or three smaller teeth between larger teeth. Barbels slightly closer to mouth than rostral tip or equidistant. **CR** Uniformly pale yellow-brown above, white below; no spots or bars. **Status:** LC.

2 Lana's Sawshark *Pristiophorus lanae* — at least 73cm

DN Philippine islands. **HT** Upper tropical continental slopes, on bottom; 229–593m. **ID** Slender sawshark. Lateral teeth: 13–14 in front of barbels, 7–8 behind, juveniles have two or three smaller teeth between larger teeth. Barbels slightly closer to mouth than rostral tip. **CR** Uniformly dark brown above, white below; no spots or bars. **Status:** NE.

3 African Dwarf Sawshark *Pristiophorus nancyae* — at least 62cm

DN West Indian Ocean. **HT** Upper continental slope; 286–500m. **ID** Small sawshark. Two rows of four to five pits beneath rostrum; prominent ridges on large teeth bases. Barbels much closer to mouth than rostral tip. Broad triangular first dorsal fin. **CR** Brown above with pale rostrum, dark brown rostral midline and edges. Dark anterior edges to pectoral and dorsal fins (conspicuous in juveniles). **Status:** NE.

4 Bahamas Sawshark *Pristiophorus schroederi* — at least 81cm

DN Northwest Atlantic. **HT** Continental and insular slopes, on or near bottom; 438–952m. **ID** Slender sawshark. Lateral teeth: 13 in front of barbels, 10 behind, juveniles with 1 smaller tooth between larger teeth. Barbels midway between mouth and rostral tip. **CR** Uniformly light grey above, whitish below; dark brown rostral midline stripes and edges. Juveniles with dark anterior edges to dorsal fins. **Status:** DD.

Pristiophorus lanae

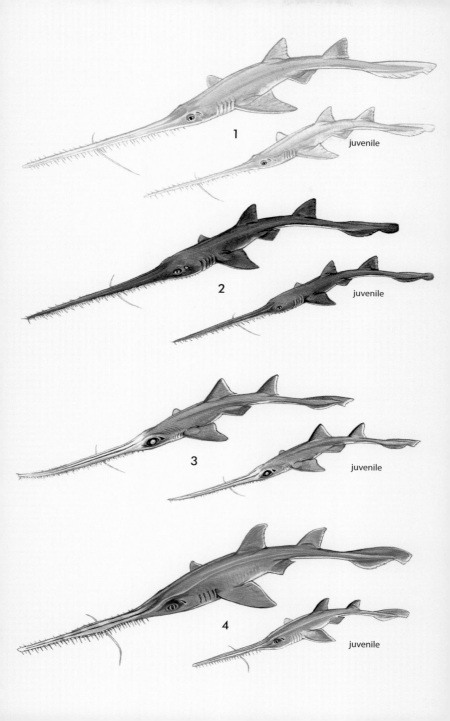

1

juvenile

2

juvenile

3

juvenile

4

juvenile

Plate 21: ANGELSHARKS I

Distinct broad flattened body; short snout with large mouth and nostrils, eyes on top of head close to and level with large spiracles, gills on side of head; short thick keel at base of caudal peduncle; very large pectoral fins, two spineless dorsal fins set back on caudal peduncle, first dorsal fin over or behind very large pelvic fins free rear tip, no anal fin, caudal fin with long dorsal lobe and larger ventral lobe; dorsal surface usually patterned, pale below. Some species are hard to distinguish.

1 Sawback Angelshark *Squatina aculeata* 188cm

DN Atlantic. **HT** Offshore, outer continental shelf and upper slope, mud bottom; 30–500m. **ID** Concave between eyes; heavily fringed nasal barbels and anterior nasal flaps. Large thorns on head and one row on along back. **CR** Dull grey or light brown; sparsely scattered with small irregular white spots and regular small dark brownish spots; large dark blotches on dorsal surface and tail. No ocelli. **Status:** CE.

2 African Angelshark *Squatina africana* about 122cm

DN East and South Africa. **HT** Continental shelf and upper slope, sand and mud; surf–494m. **ID** Concave between eyes; simple flat nasal barbels with tapering or spatulate tips, anterior nasal flaps smooth or weakly fringed. Large thorns on head not back. **CR** Grey- or red-brown; many light and dark spots with larger symmetrical dark bands or saddles; blotches on pectoral fins. Dark tail base with white margins. Juveniles often with large ocelli. **Status:** DD.

3 Argentine Angelshark *Squatina argentina* 138cm (unconfirmed 170cm)

DN Southwest Atlantic. **HT** Continental shelf and upper slope; 51–320m. **ID** Concave between eyes; simple spatulate nasal barbels, weakly fringed or smooth anterior nasal flaps. Large thorns on snout, not back. Convex anterior margin to pectoral fins forming distinct 'shoulder'. **CR** Purplish-brown with many scattered dark brown spots, mostly in circular groups around darker spot. Paler dorsal fins. No ocelli. **Status:** E.

4 Sand Devil *Squatina dumeril* 152cm

DN Northwest Atlantic. **HT** Continental shelf and slope, on or near the bottom; inshore to 1290m. **ID** Strongly concave between eyes; simple tapering nasal barbels, weakly fringed or smooth anterior nasal flaps. Discrete thorns on snout and between eyes and spiracles in young, more numerous and in patches in adult. Fairly broad, posterior angular pectoral fins. **CR** Uniform bluish to ash grey; irregular dusky or blackish spots may be present, young with white spots. Dorsal and caudal fins darker with light bases; dorsal fins with light tips. Underside white with red spots and reddish fin margins. **Status:** DD.

5 Angular Angelshark *Squatina guggenheim* 95cm

DN Southwest Atlantic. **HT** Continental shelf; 10–80m. **ID** Broadly concave between eyes; lateral head folds without triangular lobes, expanded slightly spatulate unfringed nasal barbels, anterior nasal flaps weakly fringed. Short stout symmetrical thorns on snout and between eyes and a pair between spiracles, also row on midline of back. Pectoral fins relatively small, high and angular with nearly straight anterior margin. **CR** Dark tan above with regular pattern of several small to large blackish spots; small irregular dark spots sometimes present. No ocelli. **Status:** E.

6 Angelshark *Squatina squatina* possibly ♀244cm, ♂183cm

DN Northeast Atlantic. **HT** Continental shelf, mud or sand; 5–150m or more. **ID** Large, stocky. Lateral head folds with single triangular lobe each side; simple nasal barbels with straight or spatulate tips, smooth or weakly fringed anterior nasal flaps. Small thorns on mid back in young; adult just very rough, patches small thorns on snout and between eyes. Very high broad pectoral fins. **CR** Grey to red- or green-brown with scattered small white spots and blackish dots and spots; nuchal spot maybe present. Young often with white reticulations and large dark blotches. No ocelli. **Status:** CE.

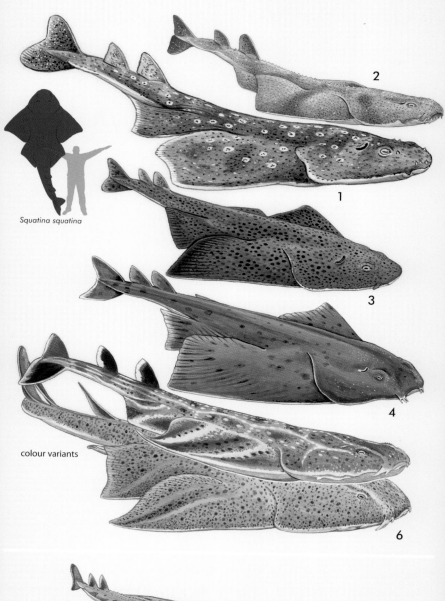

Squatina squatina

colour variants

Squatina guggenheim

1

2

3

4

5

6

1 Chilean Angelshark *Squatina armata*

♂103cm (holotype)

DN Southeast Pacific. **HT** Continental shelf, depth not known. **ID** Narrow head. Large thorns on snout, between eyes and large spiracles; double row on midline of back, between and behind dorsal fins also row on anterior margin of pectoral fins. **CR** Grey to reddish-brown above, paler below; no described markings. **Status:** DD.

2 Australian Angelshark *Squatina australis*

♀152cm ♂122cm

DN South Australia. **HT** Sand, mud, sea grass; surf–130m. **ID** Flat or convex between eyes; heavily fringed nasal barbels and anterior nasal flaps; small spiracles. No large thorns in adults; young enlarged denticles on snout; head and predorsal rows on back. **CR** Dull grey to brown with dense white spots and smaller dark brown spots. No large ocelli. **Status:** LC.

3 Philippines Angelshark *Squatina caillieti*

33cm (immature)

DN Western North Pacific. **HT** Outer continental shelf and upper slope; 363–385m. **ID** Upper lip arch semi-oval in shape, height less than one-half arch width; slightly concave between eyes with smooth patch; simple unfringed nasal barbels. No thorns in young, unknown in adults. Pelvic fin tips reach first dorsal fin origins. Inter-dorsal space greater than dorsal-caudal distance. **CR** Greenish brown with numerous darker brown spots outlined in white margins; black subdorsal saddles present along dorsal fins. **Status:** NE.

4 Pacific Angelshark *Squatina californica*

♀152–175cm ♂120cm

DN Northeast Pacific. **HT** Continental shelf, rocks and near kelp; 1–200m. **ID** Concave between large eyes; simple conical nasal barbels with spatulate tips, anterior nasal flaps weakly fringed. Thorns in young; small or absent in adults. Fairly broad long high pectoral fins. **CR** Red-brown to blackish; scattered light spots around dark blotches in adults. White-edged pectoral and pelvic fins; pale dorsal fins with dark blotches on base; dark spot at base of pale caudal fin. Ocelli in young. **Status:** NT.

5 Taiwan Angelshark *Squatina formosa*

about 150cm

DN Northwest Pacific. **HT** Outer continental shelf and upper slope; 100–400m. **ID** Concave between large eyes; simple very flat nasal barbels with round tips, anterior nasal flaps smooth or weakly fringed. Patches of large denticles on snout and between eyes (rows on back in young). **CR** Yellow-grey or brown; numerous small dark brown spots and large irregular blotches; small light spots between head and first dorsal fin. Saddle/band alongside dorsal fins. Small paired dark ocelli. **Status:** E.

6 Japanese Angelshark *Squatina japonica*

up to 200cm

DN Northwest Pacific. **HT** Habitat and depth poorly known. **ID** Concave between large eyes; cylindrical nasal barbels with slightly expanded tips, anterior nasal flaps smooth or weakly fringed. Small thorns on snout, between eyes and spiracles; one row on midline of back; skin rough. Fairly broad, high, rounded pectoral fins. **CR** Rusty or blackish-brown with dense dark and small irregular white spots; large paired red-brown blotches from base of head to dorsal fins. No ocelli. **Status:** V.

7 Indonesian Angelshark *Squatina legnota*

♀unknown, at least ♂134cm

DN Southern Indonesia. **HT** Habitat and depth unknown. **ID** Interdorsal space weakly concave. Snout very short; anterior nasal barbel flap with unfringed barbells. No median row of denticles on back. First dorsal fin base longer than second dorsal fin base. **CR** Above uniformly greyish-brown with two dark saddles below dorsal fins; anterior ventral surface of pectoral fins blackish. **Status:** DD.

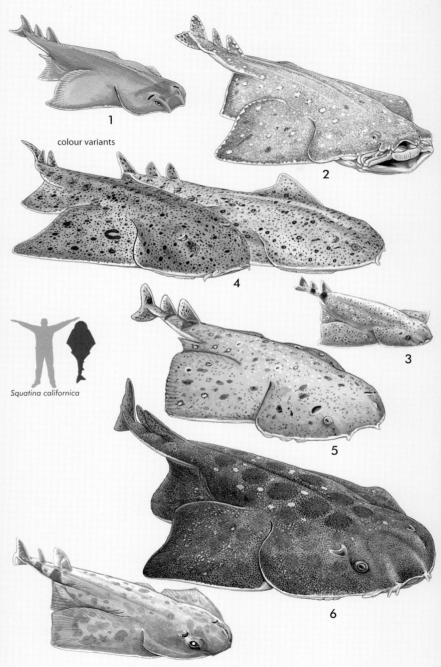

colour variants

Squatina californica

Plate 23: ANGELSHARKS III

1 Eastern Angelshark *Squatina albipunctata* ♀130cm ♂110cm

DN East Australia. **HT** Outer continental shelf and upper slope; 35–415m. **ID** Low lateral head folds; very short snout; concave between eyes; nasal barbels with expanded tips and lobate fringes. Strong thorns above eyes; no thorns on back. **CR** Yellow-brown to chocolate brown with dense pattern of symmetrical small white dark-edged spots; many large brownish blotches and white nuchal spot. Light, unspotted dorsal and caudal fins. **Status:** V.

2 Clouded Angelshark *Squatina nebulosa* at least 200cm

DN Northwest Pacific. **HT** Continental shelves and upper slopes; surf–330m. **ID** Lateral head folds with two triangular lobes each side; simple tapering nasal barbels, anterior nasal flaps smooth or weakly fringed. No thorns. Very broad, low, obtuse, rounded pectoral fins. **CR** Brown to blue-brown with scattered light spots and numerous small back dots; dark spot at base of pectoral fin. Dark blotches below dorsal fins. Ocelli absent or small. **Status:** V.

3 Hidden Angelshark *Squatina occulta* 130cm

DN Southwest Atlantic. **HT** Continental shelf, 35–320m. **ID** Concave between eyes; cylindrical bases to nasal barbels with expanded unfringed tips, anterior nasal flaps very weakly fringed. Short stout symmetrical grouped thorns on snout and between eyes; pair between spiracles. Pectoral fins quite large, high and angular. **CR** Dark tan with numerous yellow spots and larger blackish marks. A few ocelli on pectoral fins. **Status:** CE.

4 Smoothback Angelshark *Squatina oculata* ♀160cm ♂145cm

DN East Atlantic and Mediterranean. **HT** Continental shelves and upper slopes; 20–500m. **ID** Strongly concave between eyes; weakly bifurcate or lobed nasal barbels, anterior nasal flaps weakly fringed. Large thorns on snout and above eyes. **CR** Grey-brown with small white and blackish spots. Large dark blotches on base and rear tips of pectoral fins, tail base and under dorsal fins. Dorsal and caudal fin margins white; pectoral and pelvic fin margins dusky. White nuchal spot; sometimes symmetrical dark ocelli. **Status:** CE.

5 Western Angelshark *Squatina pseudocellata* at least 114cm

DN West Australia. **HT** Tropical outer continental shelf and uppermost slope; 150–310m. **ID** Very short snout, concave between eyes; nasal barbels with expanded tips and lobate fringes. Strong thorns above eyes; single row of thorns on back. **CR** Medium to pale brownish or greyish with widely spaced blue spots and brown blotches. Light unspotted dorsal and caudal fins. Single white nuchal spot; no ocelli. **Status:** DD.

6 Ornate Angelshark *Squatina tergocellata* 140cm

DN Southwest Australia. **HT** Continental shelf and upper slope, on or near bottom; 130–400m. **ID** Strongly concave between large eyes; strongly fringed nasal barbels and anterior nasal flaps. No dorsal thorns. **CR** Pale yellow-brown with grey-blue or white spots. Three pairs of large ocelli with dark rings surrounding thread-like patterned centres. **Status:** LC.

7 Ocellated Angelshark *Squatina tergocellatoides* at least 100cm

DN Northwest Pacific. **HT** Continental shelf; 100–300m. **ID** Concave between eyes; strongly finely fringed nasal barbels, anterior nasal flaps strongly fringed. No large predorsal thorns on back. **CR** Light yellowish-brown with dense scattering of small round white spots. Dorsal fins with black base and anterior margins. Six pairs of large ocelli of dark rings around light centres on pectoral and pelvic fins and tail base. **Status:** V.

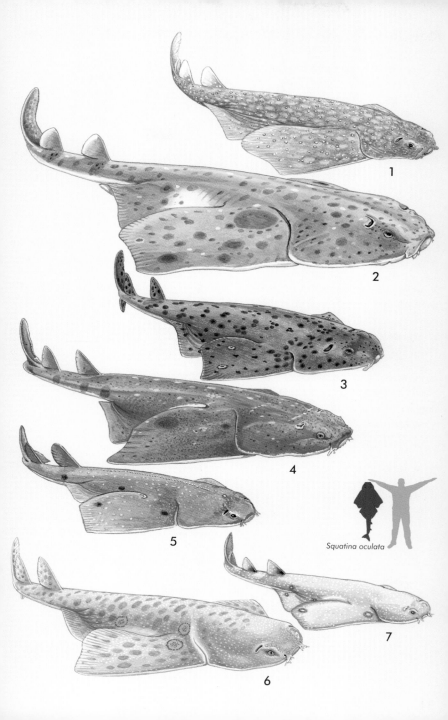

Squatina oculata

This is an ancient order with a long fossil record (almost to the beginning of the Mezozoic Era), now represented by one living family, but with many fossil species. The taxonomic genus name *Heterodontus*, 'different-teeth', refers to the remarkably dissimilar small pointed holding front teeth, compared with the large blunt rear teeth that are used for crushing invertebrates.

Identification Bullhead sharks are small to medium-sized (maximum total length 165cm, mostly smaller than 100cm) stout-bodied sharks, whose bodies taper posteriorly from the large head down to their tails. They have two dorsal fins (each preceded by a spine) and an anal fin. The caudal fin has a conspicuous sub-terminal lobe. All species have blunt, 'pig-like' snouts, small mouths in front of the eyes, enlarged first gill slits, prominent eye crests, rough skin and paddle-like paired fins. The teeth are sharp and pointed in the front, but flattened and crushing (molariform) at the back of the jaw.

Biology These are sluggish benthic sharks, which swim slowly or crawl over rocky, kelp-covered and sandy bottom hunting for prey. They are more active by night than during the day, when some species rest in rocky crevices and caves or with their heads tucked under a ledge. They may return at dawn to the same daily resting place. Bullhead sharks are oviparous, laying unique large screw- or auger-shaped leathery egg cases. Large young (bigger than 4cm) hatch more than five months later (incubation may take up to 12 months in some species, possibly being influenced by water temperature). Where known, the appearance of the egg cases is quite characteristic for each species, although it has not been described for all of them. Most bullhead sharks exhibit strong segregation by sex, size, and life history stage. At least two species lay eggs in particular 'nesting' sites. At least one species is migratory when adult, returning each year after long migrations to its breeding sites, but most have a restricted distribution. They mainly feed on benthic invertebrates (sea urchins, crabs, shrimp, marine gastropods, oysters and worms), rarely on small fish.

Status Rare to uncommon, not important in commercial fisheries but often taken as a bycatch. They are also caught by sports fishers and divers, but no species are currently known to be depleted and under threat. Some do well in aquaria and can be bred successfully under good conditions.

BULLHEAD OR HORN SHARKS Heterodontidae – pages 100–102

Order Heterodontiformes contains just one family, Heterodontidae, which is a small taxonomic group with a single genus, *Heterodontus*, containing nine similar-looking stout-bodied species. Both of the widely used common English names for this family are derived from the broad crest over the eyes. These are mostly warm-temperate to tropical sharks, typically nocturnal, usually found where the water temperature is above 21°C in the eastern and western Pacific and the Indian Ocean. They are absent from the Atlantic Ocean. These are the only living sharks that have a fin spine in front of each dorsal fin and an anal fin. They are unique among sharks in that they may pick up their newly laid eggs and wedge them (while the casing is still soft) into a suitable location for them to develop. Otherwise, not much is known about the life histories of these rather curious-looking sharks, whose morphological characters are rather similar to those of the prehistoric hybodont sharks.

1

young

2

young

3

young

4

young

Plate 25: BULLHEAD SHARKS II

1 Mexican Hornshark *Heterodontus mexicanus* ♀70cm ♂55cm

DN East Pacific. **HT** Rock, coral reefs and sand; intertidal–50m. **ID** Stocky. Blunt head. Prominent eye ridges are low and finish behind eyes. First dorsal fin origin over pectoral fin bases. **CR** Light grey-brown brown with large (same size or larger than eye diameter) black spots. One or two indistinct blotches under eye; light bar between eye ridges; no harness pattern. Young with more obvious dark blotches. **Status:** DD.

2 Oman Bullhead Shark *Heterodontus omanensis* mature: ♀61cm ♂52cm

DN North Indian Ocean. **HT** Soft bottom? 80m. **ID** Stocky. Large, blunt head. Prominent eye ridges are low and finish behind eyes. First dorsal fin origin over pectoral fin inner margins. **CR** Tan to brown; no spots. Dark blotch under eye; dark bar between eye ridges; no harness pattern; four to five broad dark brown saddles. Dark-tipped fins with white spot on dorsal fin tips. No information on young. **Status:** DD.

3 Galapagos Bullhead Shark *Heterodontus quoyi* 105cm

DN East Pacific. **HT** Rock and coral reefs; 3–30m. **ID** Stocky. Blunt head. Prominent eye ridges are low and finish gradually behind eyes. First dorsal fin origin over pectoral fin inner margins. **CR** Light grey or brown; usually with large (less than half eye diameter) black spots. Mottled dark spots or blotches under eye; no light bar between eye ridges; no harness pattern. Young with less distinct markings and small spots. **Status:** DD.

4 Whitespotted Bullhead Shark *Heterodontus ramalheira* at least 83cm

DN North and western Indian Ocean. **HT** Outer continental shelf and uppermost slope in deepish water; 40–275m. **ID** Stocky. Blunt head. Prominent eye ridges are low and finish abruptly behind eyes. First dorsal fin origin over pectoral fin inner margins. **CR** Dark red-brown; usually with small white spots. No dusky patch under eye in adults; no light bar between eye ridges; no harness pattern. Young with unique striking whorl pattern lost with age; parallel dark lines between and under eyes change to dusky patch in large juvenile and lost in adult. **Status:** DD.

5 Zebra Bullhead Shark *Heterodontus zebra* 122cm

DN West Pacific. **HT** Rock, kelp and sand; intertidal–200m. **ID** Stocky. Large blunt head. Prominent eye ridges are low and finish gradually behind eyes. **CR** White or cream; no spots. No light bar between eye ridges; no harness pattern but striking black to dark brown zebra-like narrow vertical saddles and bands. Young similar but bands are red-brown. **Status:** LC.

Heterodontus quoyi

1

young

3

young

2

4

young

young

5

1 Crocodile Shark *Pseudocarcharias kamoharai* — 122cm

DN Tropical oceans worldwide. **HT** Usually well offshore; surface to at least 590m. **ID** Very distinctive, cylindrical, slender body. Conical head; no barbels or grooves; nostrils free from mouth; huge eyes; large mouth with prominent long slender teeth and highly protrusible jaws; very small spiracles. Five broad gills. Small fins; two spineless dorsal fins; anal fin; long dorsal caudal fin lobe. **CR** Colour grey or grey-brown above, light below. Light-edged fins. **Status:** NT.

2 Goblin Shark *Mitsukurina owstoni* — at least 550cm

DN Patchy Atlantic, West Indian Ocean and Pacific distribution. **HT** Deepwater, outer continental shelves, upper slopes and off seamounts; 95–1300m or more. **ID** Unmistakable soft, flabby body. Flat elongated snout; no barbels or grooves; nostrils free from large mouth with long-cusped slender teeth and protrusible jaws; very small spiracles. Five broad gills. Two spineless dorsal fins; anal fin; long caudal fin without a ventral lobe. **CR** Colour pinkish-white. **Status:** LC.

Sandtiger sharks

3 Sandtiger Shark *Carcharias taurus* — 320cm (unconfirmed 430cm)

DN Warm temperate and tropical Atlantic, Mediterranean and Indo-West Pacific. **HT** Coastal waters; to at least 191m. **ID** Flattened conical snout; large slender pointed teeth. Large dorsal fins and anal fin of similar size; first dorsal fin closer to pelvic fin than pectoral fin; caudal fin with a short ventral lobe. **CR** Light brown above, white below; often with scattered dark spots. **Status:** V.

4 Smalltooth Sandtiger *Odontaspis ferox* — about 450cm

DN Worldwide warm temperate and tropical deep water. **HT** Continental and insular shelves and upper slopes, on or near bottom, possibly epipelagic; 10–883m. **ID** Differs from *C. taurus* with: long conical snout, fairly large eyes; first dorsal fin closer to pectoral fin than pelvic fin; first dorsal fin larger than second dorsal and anal fins. **CR** Grey or grey-brown above, light below; often with dark spots. **Status:** V.

5 Bigeye Sandtiger *Odontaspis noronhai* — at least 427cm

DN Atlantic and central Pacific, possibly worldwide. **HT** Midwater in open ocean, near bottom on continental and island slopes; 600–1000m or more. **ID** First dorsal fin larger than second dorsal and anal fins. Differs from other sandtigers with large eyes and unspotted. **CR** Colour a uniform dark red-brown to black above and below. Often a white blotch on first dorsal fin. **Status:** DD.

Odontaspis noronhai

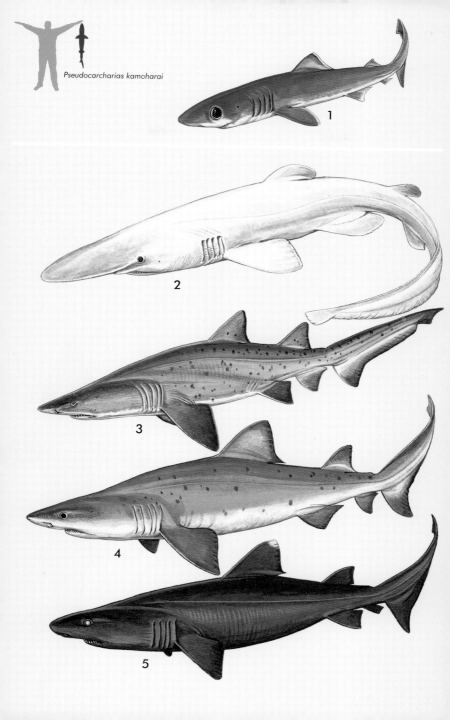

Pseudocarcharias kamoharai

1

2

3

4

5

Plate 27: PLANKTON-FEEDING SHARKS

1 Basking Shark *Cetorhinus maximus* more than 1000cm

DN Worldwide, cold to warm temperate. **HT** Usually recorded from the coast to the continental shelf edge and slope, often associated with coastal and oceanic fronts. **ID** Unmistakable, very large cylindrical body. Conical head; pointed snout; huge mouth with tiny teeth; nostrils free from mouth; no barbels or grooves, very small spiracles well behind eyes. Huge gills almost encircle head. Two spineless dorsal fins; anal fin; lunate caudal fin. Strong lateral keels on caudal peduncle. **CR** Variable colour, darker above often, with mottled pattern on back and sides, white blotches under head. **Status: V.**

2 Megamouth Shark *Megachasma pelagios* more than 550cm

DN Probably worldwide in tropics. **HT** Oceanic, coastal and offshore; 5–40m on continental shelf, 8–166m over very deep water. **ID** Unmistakable, large cylindrical body. Large long head; short round snout; huge terminal mouth with numerous small hooked teeth; nostrils free from mouth; no barbels or grooves; very small spiracles behind eyes. Large gills. Two spineless dorsal fins; anal fin. **CR** Grey above, white below. Light margins to blackish pectoral and pelvic fins. Dark spotting on lower jaw. **Status: DD.**

3 Whale Shark *Rhincodon typus* possibly 1700–2100cm

DN Worldwide all tropical and warm temperate seas except Mediterranean. **HT** Pelagic; to 700m or more. **ID** Unmistakable, huge body. Broad flat head; very short snout; huge transverse mouth in front of eyes; comparatively small barbels; long nasoral grooves; spiracles close to and larger than eyes. Huge gills. Prominent ridges on body, lowest terminating in a keel on caudal peduncle. Two spineless dorsal fins; anal fin; caudal fin lunate and unnotched. **CR** Chequerboard pattern of yellow or white spots and blotches on a grey, blue-grey to green-brown background, white or yellow underside. **Status: V.**

Cetorhinus maximus

1

colour variants

2

3

Plate 28: THRESHER SHARKS

1 Pelagic Thresher *Alopias pelagicus*
365cm

DN Indo-Pacific. **HT** Oceanic usually offshore, sometimes nearshore on narrow continental shelf; 0–152m. **ID** Very narrow head with straight forehead and arched profile; no labial furrows; fairly large eyes. Long, straight broad-tipped pectoral fins; caudal fin dorsal lobe nearly as long as the rest of the body. **CR** Deep blue above, white below. No white above pectoral fin bases. **Status:** V.

2 Bigeye Thresher *Alopias superciliosus*
at least 480cm

DN Worldwide tropical and temperate seas. **HT** Close inshore to open ocean; surface to 500m. **ID** Distinctive huge eyes extend onto flat-topped head; deep horizontal groove above gills. Large, very long, narrow pectoral fins. **CR** Purplish-grey or grey-brown above, light grey to white below which does not extend above pectoral fin bases. **Status:** V.

3 Thresher Shark *Alopias vulpinus*
at least 575cm (possibly 635cm)

DN Worldwide tropical to cold temperate seas. **HT** Nearshore to far offshore; surface to at least 400m. **ID** Fairly large eyes; labial furrows. Long, curved, narrow, pointed pectoral fins; caudal fin dorsal lobe nearly as long as the rest of the body. **CR** Blue-grey to dark grey above, silvery or coppery sides, white below extending in a patch above pectoral fins. White dot on pectoral fin tips. **Status:** V.

Alopias superciliosus

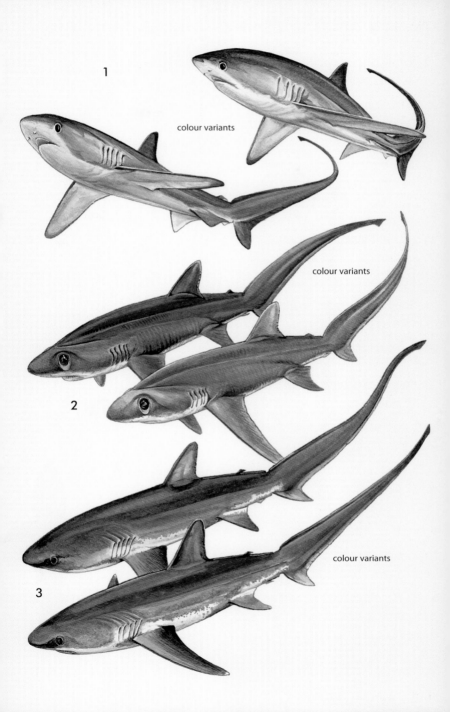

1   colour variants

colour variants

2

3   colour variants

Plate 29: MACKEREL SHARKS

1 White Shark *Carcharodon carcharias* — about 600c

DN Worldwide except polar seas. **HT** From very shallow water inshore, to the continental shelf and remo‖ oceanic islands, with long periods spent in pelagic habitat while travelling across the mid ocea‖ 0–1300m. **ID** Heavy body. Relatively long snout; very black eyes. Very long gills. Large first dorsal fin. Stro‖ keels on caudal peduncle. **CR** Grey above with sharp demarcation to white below. First dorsal fin with da‖ free rear tip; black tip to underside of pectoral fins; usually black spot at pectoral fin insertion. Old adu‖ often become paler above and off-white below giving rise to a great 'white' shark. **Status: V**.

2 Shortfin Mako *Isurus oxyrinchus* — about 400c‖

DN Worldwide in temperate and tropical seas. **HT** Coastal and oceanic; 0–600m. **ID** U-shaped mout‖ black eyes. Very long gills. Strong keels on caudal peduncle. **CR** Brilliant blue or purple above, paler a‖ more silvery on sides, white below. Underside of snout and mouth white in adult (dusky in Azores speci‖ 'marrajo-criolloí'). Anterior half pelvic fins dark, rear and underside white. **Status: V**.

3 Longfin Mako *Isurus paucus* — about 430c‖

DN Probably worldwide. **HT** Poorly known, possibly epipelagic in deepwater. **ID** Differs from *I. oxyrinch‖* by a less pointed snout; pectoral fins as long as head and relatively broad-tipped. **CR** Dusky underside ‖ snout and mouth in adults. **Status: V**.

4 Salmon Shark *Lamna ditropis* — about 305c‖

DN North Pacific. **HT** Cool coastal and oceanic; surface to 375m or more. **ID** Heavy body. Short snou‖ Long gills. Strong keels on caudal peduncle with short secondary keels on caudal fin base. **CR** Dark gre‖ or blackish above, white below with dusky blotches and dark underside to snout in adults. White patc‖ over pectoral fin bases. First dorsal fin with dark free rear tip. **Status: LC**.

5 Porbeagle Shark *Lamna nasus* — 355c‖

DN North Atlantic and cool southern hemisphere waters. **HT** Inshore to offshore; surface to 1360‖ **ID** Very similar to *L. ditropis* except for more pointed snout. **CR** No white patch above pectoral fins; ve‖ distinctive white free tip to first dorsal fin. Northern species have no dusky blotches; southern speci‖ have distinctive dusky hood and dusky blotches similar to *L. ditropis*. **Status: V** globally, **CE** in NE Atlant‖ and Mediterranean.

Carcharodon carcharias

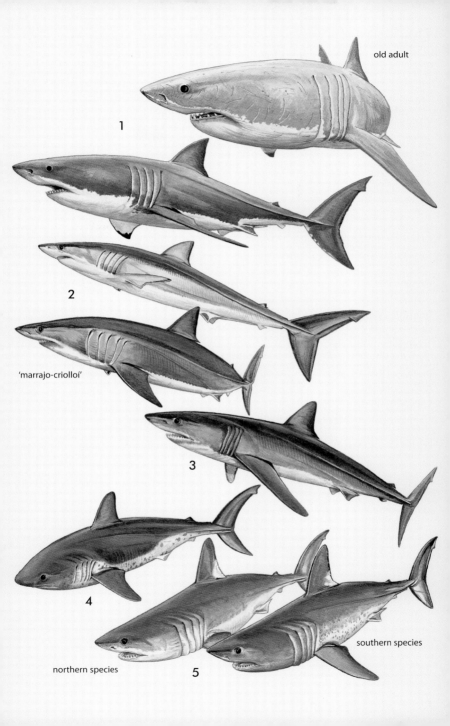

old adult

1

2

'marrajo-criolloi'

3

4

5

northern species

southern species

CARPETSHARKS Orectolobiformes – pages 114–130

This order contains about 42 species in seven families: Parascyllidae (collared carpetsharks), Brachaeluridae (blind sharks), Orectolobidae (wobbegongs), Hemiscyllidae (longtailed carpetsharks), Ginglymostomatidae (nurse sharks), Stegostomatidae (Zebra Shark) and Rhincodontidae (Whale Shark). Recent genetic investigation suggests that the Zebra Shark, Whale Shark and the Shorttail Nurse Shark are more closely related to each other than they are to other species of nurse sharks.

Identification Two spineless dorsal fins and an anal fin. Nostrils have barbels (rudimentary in whale shark) and are connected via nasoral grooves to short mouths that end in front of the eyes (no nictitating eyelids).

Biology Varied reproductive strategies, including oviparity (egg-laying) or yolk-sac viviparity (foetuses retained inside the female and nourished by their yolk sac until birth).

COLLARED CARPETSHARKS: Parascylliidae – pages 114–116

Two genera occur in the western Pacific, from inshore to deepish continental shelf. All five *Parascyllium* species are Australian endemics. Genus *Cirrhoscyllium* (three species) occurs from Vietnam to Taiwan Island and Japan. Most of these species are known from very few specimens, and appear to have very restricted deepwater ranges.

Identification Small slender sharks (less than 1m). First dorsal fin originates behind pelvic fin bases, second well behind anal fin origin. Mouth entirely in front of eyes; tiny spiracles. *Cirrhoscyllium* have unique cartilage-cored paired barbels on throat, dark saddles and no spots or collar markings. *Parascyllium* have no barbels on throat and a pattern of saddles and spots.

Biology Little-known benthic species which can apparently change colour to match the seabed. Some (possibly all) are oviparous, laying elongated flattened egg cases.

Status Some are hardy in captivity. May be taken in bycatch (particularly in trawl nets) and although usually discarded may be threatened in heavily fished areas.

BLIND SHARKS: Brachaeluridae – page 116

So named because they close eyelids out of water. Endemic to eastern Australian coast, from the intertidal and rock pools, or just a few centimeters deep to 140m, on rocky or coral reefs or seaweed. Two species in one genus, *Brachaelurus*.

Identification Small stout sharks (most smaller than 80cm) with two spineless dorsal fins set far back. Anal fin origin well behind origin of second dorsal fin, gap between anal and lower caudal fin shorter than length of anal fin. Large spiracles below and behind eyes, nasoral and circumnarial grooves, long barbels, small transverse mouth in front of eye, no lateral skin flaps on head.

Biology Viviparous (litters of six to eight finish absorbing their large yolk sacs just before birth). Feed on small fishes, crustaceans, squid and sea anemones. *Brachaelurus waddi* can survive long periods out of water.

Status Very restricted geographic range. *B. colcloughi* is known from only about 50 specimens, despite its range being well-surveyed and heavily fished, and seems to be very rare; it is assessed as Vulnerable. *B. waddi* is relatively common and Least Concern. Survive well in captivity.

WOBBEGONGS: Orectolobidae – pages 118–122

Three genera, 12 species, but additional undescribed species probably present within west Pacific range of the family, Australia to Japan. Live on the bottom in warm-temperate to tropical continental waters, intertidal to deeper than 110m, often on rocky and coral reefs or on sandy bottom.

Identification Distinctive, flattened, highly patterned, well-camouflaged sharks. Dermal flaps along sides of broad, flat head; long barbels; short mouth in front of eyes and almost at the very front of the short snout. Heavy jaws, two rows of enlarged, sharp, fang-like teeth in upper jaw, three in lower. Nasoral grooves, circumnarial grooves and flaps, symphysial grooves. Spiracles larger than upward-facing eyes. Two spineless dorsal fins and an anal fin. First dorsal fin origin over pelvic fin bases.

Biology Viviparous with yolk sac, large litters of 20 or more young. Powerful seabed predators on bottom-dwelling animals (fishes, crabs, lobsters and octopi), lurking camouflaged by colour patterns and dermal lobes around head, sucking in and impaling prey on large teeth. Use paired fins to clamber around the bottom, even out of the water.

Status Potentially dangerous bite if provoked. Some species kept and bred in aquaria. Some are important in fisheries. Some species appear to have an extremely limited distribution and are known from only a few specimens; their conservation status is unknown.

LONGTAILED CARPETSHARKS Hemiscylliidae – pages 124–126

Two Indo-west Pacific genera, *Chiloscyllium* (seven wide-ranging species) and *Hemiscyllium* (eight species, mainly in the western Pacific, also Seychelles). Occur in intertidal pools, very shallow water, rocky and coral reefs close inshore and on sediments, inshore and offshore in bays.

Identification Small (mostly less than 1m) and slender with very long tails, two equal-sized unspined dorsal fins, origin of second well ahead of origin of long, low rounded anal fin, which is separated by a notch from lower caudal fin. Small transverse mouth well in front of dorsolateral eyes, large spiracles below eyes, nasoral and circumnarial grooves, short barbels. Colour patterns of young often different and bolder than adults. *Chiloscyllium* species without a black hood on head or large dark spots on sides of body, mouth closer to eyes than snout tip. *Hemiscyllium* species with spots or hood, nostrils at end of snout, and obvious ridges above eyes.

Biology Poorly known. Some (presumably all) are oviparous, laying oval eggcases. Distinct colour patterns of young suggest different habitat preferences from adults. Strong, muscular, leg-like paired fins used to clamber on reefs and in crevices. Large epaulette spots on *Hemiscyllium* species may be eyespots to intimidate predators. Food includes small seabed fishes, cephalopods, shelled molluscs and crustaceans.

Status Taken in multispecies fisheries and as bycatch, sometimes in large numbers. Hardy, attractive and bred in captivity. Often common to abundant, but some species are extremely rare, known from only a few specimens, with a very limited distribution in threatened habitats. More of these colourful species may be discovered as divers explore new areas within this family's Indo-Pacific distribution.

Plate 30: COLLARED CARPETSHARKS I

1 Collared Carpetshark *Parascyllium collare*   mature: ♀85–87cm ♂80–85cm

DN East Australia. **HT** Continental shelf, rocky reefs and hard-bottomed trawl grounds; 20–175m, possibly to 230m. **ID** Body elongate. Nasoral and circumnarial grooves; nasal barbels, small eyes. **CR** Light yellow to red-brown with dark unspotted sharp edged collar. Five dusky saddles; large dark spots except pectoral fins; less than six spots on sides of tail between dorsal fins. **Status:** LC.

2 Elongate Carpetshark *Parascyllium elongatum*   ♀42cm (holotype)

DN West Australia. **HT** On or near bottom; to at least 50m. **ID** Body extremely elongate. Short head; nasoral and circumnarial grooves; nasal barbels short; very small eyes. **CR** Pale brown with white spots in vertical rows separated by darker brown bands over abdomen. No dark collar or black spot. **Status:** DD.

3 Rusty Carpetshark *Parascyllium ferrugineum*   80cm

DN South Australia. **HT** Rocks, river mouths, algae and seagrass beds, on or near bottom; 5–150m. **ID** Body elongate. Nasoral and circumnarial grooves; nasal barbels, small eyes. **CR** Grey-brown with indistinct collar. Six to seven dusky saddles. Dark spots, more than six spots on sides of tail between dorsal fins, more heavily spotted in Tasmanian specimens. **Status:** LC.

4 Ginger Carpetshark *Parascyllium sparsimaculatum*   at least 79cm

DN West Australia. **HT** Upper continental slope, deepwater; 205–245m. **ID** Body elongate. Nasoral and circumnarial grooves; nasal barbels, small eyes. **CR** Pale brown or grey with indistinct unspotted collar. Five indistinct dark saddles; sparse large spots and blotches; less than six spots on sides of tail between dorsal fins. **Status:** DD.

5 Necklace Carpetshark *Parascyllium variolatum*   about 90cm

DN South Australia. **HT** Continental shelf, variety of habitats, bottom; to 180m. **ID** Body elongate. Nasoral and circumnarial grooves; nasal barbels, small eyes. **CR** Dark grey to chocolate brown with dark white spotted collar. Unmistakable highly variable pattern of dark blotches and dense white spots; obvious black spots on fins. **Status:** LC.

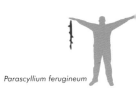

Parascyllium ferugineum

1

2

3

Tasmania

4

colour variants

colour variants

5

Plate 31: COLLARED CARPETSHARKS II AND BLIND SHARKS

1 Barbelthroat Carpetshark *Cirrhoscyllium expolitum*
known ♀33.5cm

DN South China Sea. **HT** Outer continental shelf, bottom; 183–190m. **ID** Very small, slender shark. Short mouth ahead of eyes; nasoral grooves; cartilage-cored paired barbels on throat; small spiracles. Head 3 times length of first dorsal fin base. Origin of first dorsal fin over pelvic free rear tips. **CR** Six to ten diffuse saddles not 'C'-shaped; one saddle long and round between pectoral and pelvic fins extending over pelvic fin bases. **Status:** DD.

2 Taiwan Saddled Carpetshark *Cirrhoscyllium formosanum*
known 39cm

DN Northwest Pacific, most common off southwest Taiwan. **HT** Outer shelf; about 110m. **ID** Very small, slender shark. Short mouth ahead of eyes; nasoral grooves; cartilage-cored paired barbels on throat; small spiracles. Head 2.3–2.6 times length first dorsal fin base. Origin of first dorsal fin over pelvic free rear tips. **CR** Six diffuse saddles not 'C'-shaped; one saddle long and round between pectoral and pelvic fins extending over pelvic fin bases. **Status:** DD.

3 Saddled Carpetshark *Cirrhoscyllium japonicum*
49cm

DN Northwest Pacific. **HT** 250–290m. **ID** Small, slender shark. Short mouth ahead of eyes; long snout; nasoral grooves; cartilage-cored paired barbels on throat; small spiracles. Origin of first dorsal fin behind pelvic free rear tips. **CR** Nine bold saddles, one 'C'-shaped between pectoral and pelvic fin bases. **Status:** DD.

Blind sharks

4 Bluegrey Carpetshark *Brachaelurus colcloughi*
at least 75cm

DN East Australia. **HT** Shallow inshore, prefers sand and reefs with caves and crevices, bottom; less than 4m to 217m. **ID** Stout. Short mouth ahead of eyes; nasoral and circumnarial grooves; long barbels with posterior hooked flap; large spiracle well behind eyes. First dorsal fin larger than second; short precaudal tail. **CR** Grey above with no spots, white below. Young with distinct black markings that fade with age. **Status:** V.

5 Blind Shark *Brachaelurus waddi*
120cm

DN East Australia. **HT** Rocky shores, reefs and seagrass; 0–140m. **ID** Stout. Short mouth ahead of eyes; nasoral and circumnarial grooves; long tapering barbels; large spiracle close to eyes. First dorsal fin about the same size as second, anal and lower caudal fins almost touch. **CR** Brown with small, sparsely scattered white spots. Dark saddles in young disappear or indistinct in adults. **Status:** LC.

1

2

3

Cirrhoscyllium formosanum

4

young

5

colour variants

Brachaelurus waddi

Plate 32: WOBBEGONGS I

1 Tasselled Wobbegong *Eucrossorhinus dasypogon*   at least 125cm

DN Southwest Pacific. **HT** Inshore coral reefs. **ID** Medium-sized, wide-bodied, moderately depressed body; tapering abruptly behind pelvic fins. Broad head with numerous highly branched dermal lobes 'beard' on chin. Very broad paired fins. **CR** Indistinct saddles. Variable reticulated pattern of narrow dark lines on light background; scattered enlarged dark blotches at line junctions (**1a**). **Status:** NT.

2 Japanese Wobbegong *Orectolobus japonicus*   at least 118cm

DN Northwest Pacific. **HT** Inshore rocky and coral reefs; intertidal to 200m. **ID** Medium-sized, moderately depressed body; tapering behind pelvic fins. Long branched nasal barbels, five dermal lobes below and in front of eye. **CR** Obvious dark dorsal saddles with spots and blotches and dark (not black), corrugated edges separated by lighter areas with dark broad reticular lines (**2a**). **Status:** DD.

3 Northern Wobbegong *Orectolobus wardi*   63cm possibly 100cm

DN Australia. **HT** Shallow reefs, often turbid water; less than 3m. **ID** Small, moderately depressed body, tapering behind pelvic fins. Unbranched nasal barbels; two dermal lobes below and in front of eye; dermal lobes behind spiracle unbranched and broad. **CR** Simple colour pattern; three large dark light edged rounded saddles; light background with indistinct darker mottling and a few dark spot (**3a**). **Status:** LC.

4 Cobbler Wobbegong *Sutorectus tentaculatus*   recorded 92cm

DN South and west Australia. **HT** Rocky and coral reefs; to at least 35m. **ID** Small, rather slender body, tapering behind pelvic fins; with rows of warty dermal tubercules on back and bases of very low long dorsal fins. Simple unbranched nasal barbels; chin smooth; few slender short unbranched dermal lobes form isolated groups in four to six pairs. **CR** Striking pattern of broad dark dorsal saddles with jagged corrugated edges; lighter background with irregular dark spots (**4a**). **Status:** LC.

Eucrossorhinus dasypogon

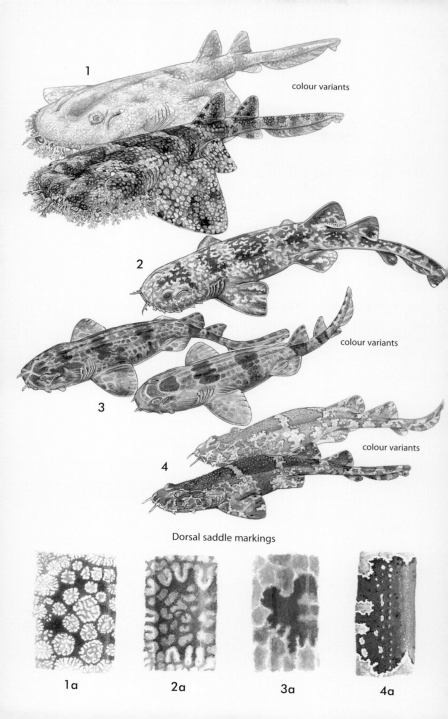

colour variants

colour variants

colour variants

Dorsal saddle markings

1a   2a   3a   4a

Plate 33: WOBBEGONGS II

1 Western Wobbegong *Orectolobus hutchinsi* 149cm

DN West Australia. **HT** Intertidal to about 105m. **ID** Medium-sized, relatively slender body; tapering behind pelvic fins. Long nasal barbels with one small branch; four dermal lobes below and in front of eye; behind spiracles weakly or unbranched and slender lobes. **CR** Strongly contrasting, broad, dark, rectangular, deeply corrugated, dorsal saddles with light spots; background lighter with numerous broad dark blotches; without numerous light O-shaped rings (**1a**). **Status:** DD.

2 False Cobbler Wobbegong *Orectolobus leptolineatus* ♀120cm ♂112cm

DN Indonesia. **HT** Little known, may prefer cooler water below 20m. **ID** Medium-sized, moderately depressed body; tapering behind pelvic fins. Nasal barbels branching, dermal lobes complex with five to eight branches; branching at extremities. **CR** Dark brown saddles with lighter-coloured blotches irregularly spaced (**2a**). **Status:** NE.

3 Spotted Wobbegong *Orectolobus maculatus* 170cm (320cm unconfirmed)

DN Australia. **HT** Intertidal areas; to about 218m or more. **ID** Large, robust body; tapering behind pelvic fins. Long branched nasal barbels, six to ten dermal lobes below and in front of eye. **CR** Dark back; broad darker dorsal saddles with white O-shaped spots and blotches and corrugated edges; light background with dark broad reticular lines (**3a**). **Status:** NT.

4 Ornate Wobbegong *Orectolobus ornatus* 110cm

DN Australia. **HT** Intertidal areas; to about 100m. **ID** Relatively small, moderately depressed body; tapering behind pelvic fins. Nasal barbels with a few branches, five dermal lobes below and in front of eye, behind spiracles weakly or unbranched broad lobes. **CR** Obvious broad dark dorsal saddles with light spots and conspicuous black corrugated borders; light background with conspicuous dark light-centred spots (**4a**). **Status:** NT.

Orectolobus leptolineatus

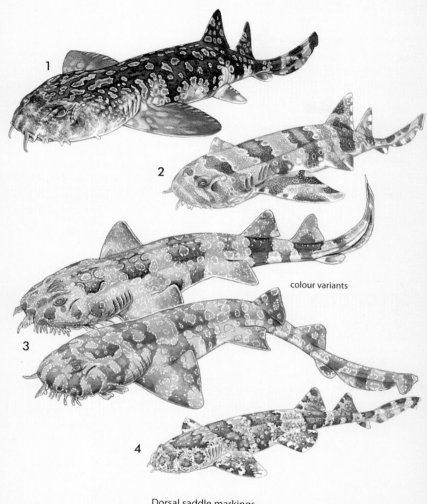

colour variants

Dorsal saddle markings

1a 2a 3a 4a

Plate 34: WOBBEGONGS III

1 Floral Banded Wobbegong *Orectolobus floridus* at least 75cm

DN Southwest Australia. **HT** Reefs and seagrass beds; 40–85m. **ID** Small, depressed, slender body, tapering behind pelvic fins. Nasal barbels with a single branch; dermal lobes on sides of head few and unbranched; no warty tubercules. **CR** Yellowish-brown above with dark brown bands separated by conspicuous clusters of lighter spots on dorsal surface (**1a**); head with small black spots; midback with dark brown band. **Status:** DD.

2 Gulf Wobbegong *Orectolobus halei* at least 206cm

DN Southern Australia. **HT** Reefs; shallows to 100m. **ID** Large, robust body; tapering behind pelvic fins. Dermal lobes with multiple branches along head margin; warty tubercles along back with two above the eyes; slender nasal barbels with two branches; nasal and circumnarial grooves present. **CR** Strikingly ornate, variegated shark with yellow to grey-brown saddles each with paler bluish to white patches with small black spots bordering them (**2a**). **Status:** NT.

3 Dwarf Spotted Wobbegong *Orectolobus parvimaculatus* at least 94cm

DN Southwestern Australia. **HT** 10–135m deep, but little else known. **ID** Relatively small, depressed, elongate body. Dermal lobes with six to ten coarse branches; nasal barbels with one to two branches; nasal and circumnarial grooves present. **CR** Upper surface brownish-yellow with dark brown saddles and blotches; white to bluish rings, spots, and reticulations (**3a**). **Status:** DD.

4 Network Wobbegong *Orectolobus reticulatus* at least 52cm

DN Northern Territories, Australia. **HT** Coastal. **ID** Small, moderately depressed body; tapering behind pelvic fins. Paired dermal lobes in front of eyes and behind spiracles, absent from chin; nasal barbels simple, flattened and unbranched; nasal and circumnarial grooves present. **CR** Upper surface greyish-brown with three conspicuous dark saddles, but not lighter margins surrounding saddles (**4a**). **Status:** DD.

Orectolobus floridus

Dorsal saddle markings

1a

2a

3a

4a

1 Arabian Carpetshark *Chiloscyllium arabicum* 70cm

DN Northwest Indian Ocean. **HT** Coral reefs, lagoons, rocky shores and mangrove estuaries, bottom 3–100m. **ID** Slender with long, thick tail. Mouth well in front of eyes, nasoral and circumnarial grooves short barbels; large spiracle below eyes. Prominent ridges on back. Dorsal fins with straight posterior margins; first dorsal fin origin opposite or just behind pelvic fin insertion; second dorsal base longer than first. **CR** Adult unpatterned. Juveniles with light spots on fins. **Status:** NT.

2 Burmese Bambooshark *Chiloscyllium burmensis* ♂57cm (holotype

DN Northeast Indian Ocean. **HT** Habitat and depth unknown. **ID** Slender with long, thick tail. Mouth well in front of eyes, nasoral and circumnarial grooves, short barbels; spiracle below eye. No body ridges Dorsal fins straight to convex posterior margins; first dorsal fin origin opposite pelvic fin insertion; long low anal fin. **CR** Adult with dark fin webs. Juvenile colour unknown. **Status:** DD.

3 Grey Bambooshark *Chiloscyllium griseum* 77cm

DN Indo-west Pacific. **HT** Inshore, rocks and lagoons; 5–80m. **ID** Slender with long, thick tail. Mouth well in front of eyes, nasoral and circumnarial grooves, barbels; very large spiracle below eye. No body ridges Dorsal fins straight to convex posterior margins; first dorsal fin origin over rear; pelvic fin bases; long low anal fin. **CR** Adult unpatterned. Juveniles with dark saddles and transverse bands. **Status:** NT.

4 Indonesian Bambooshark *Chiloscyllium hasselti* 61cm

DN Indo-west Pacific. **HT** Probably close inshore; to 12m. **ID** Slender with long, slender tail. Mouth well in front of eyes, nasoral and circumnarial grooves, short barbels; large spiracle just below and behind eye No body ridges. Dorsal fins straight to convex posterior margins; first dorsal fin origin over rear of pelvic fin base. **CR** Adult with dusky fins. Juveniles with prominent saddles and blotches on fins. **Status:** NT.

5 Slender Bambooshark *Chiloscyllium indicum* 65cm

DN Indo-west Pacific. **HT** Inshore. **ID** Very slender with long, slender tail. Mouth well in front of eyes nasoral and circumnarial grooves, short barbels; spiracle just behind and below eye. Lateral ridges. Dorsal fins straight/convex posterior margin, first dorsal fin origin opposite or just behind pelvic fin insertion. **CR** Adult with small dark spots, bars and dashes on light brown background. Juveniles with no dark posterior margins to fins. **Status:** NT.

6 Whitespotted Bambooshark *Chiloscyllium plagiosum* 95cm

DN Indo-west Pacific. **HT** Inshore, bottom, reefs in tropics; 0–18m. **ID** Slender with long, thick tail. Mouth well in front of eyes, nasoral and circumnarial grooves, short barbels; large spiracle below eye. Lateral ridges on trunk. Dorsal fins straight to convex posterior margins; first dorsal fin origin opposite or just behind pelvic fin insertion. **CR** Dark bands, not conspicuously edged, with numerous light and dark spots. Juveniles are usually dark with white or bluish spots; as they mature their base colour lightens, becoming dark to light brown. **Status:** NT.

7 Brownbanded Bambooshark *Chiloscyllium punctatum* 132cm

DN Indo-west Pacific. **HT** Coral reefs possibly soft bottom; to 85m or more. **ID** Slender with long, thick tail. Mouth well in front of eyes, nasoral and circumnarial grooves, short barbels; very large spiracle below and behind eye. No body ridges. Dorsal fins have concave posterior margins and long free tips; first dorsal fin origin over front of pelvic fin base. **CR** Adult unpatterned. Juveniles with dark bands with scattered small dark spots. **Status:** NT.

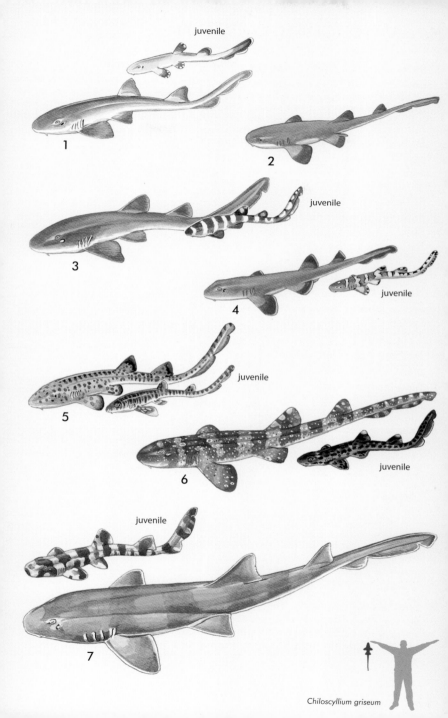

juvenile

1

2

juvenile

3

4

juvenile

juvenile

5

juvenile

6

juvenile

7

juvenile

Chiloscyllium griseum

1 **Indonesian Speckled Carpetshark** *Hemiscyllium freycineti* ♀72cm

DN New Guinea. **HT** Coral reefs and seagrass. **ID** Slender with long, thick tail. Mouth well in front of eyes nasoral and circumnarial grooves, very short barbels; spiracle below eye. **CR** Moderately large dark epaulette spot without white ring or dark blotches; small dark spots on snout, large and small spots on body. Juvenile with dark paired fins and broad dark bands under head and on tail. **Status:** NT.

2 **Gale's Epaulette Shark** *Hemiscyllium galei* at least 57cm

DN Indonesia. **HT** Reefs, shallow water; 3–4m. **ID** Slender with long tail. Mouth well in front of eyes nasoral and circumnarial grooves, short barbels; spiracle below and behind eye. **CR** Prominent white spots along margin of darker saddles along back with scattered white and dark spots along sides; 7 to 8 dark oval spots on sides between abdomen and caudal fin. **Status:** DD

3 **Papuan Epaulette Carpetshark** *Hemiscyllium hallstromi* 77cm

DN South Papua New Guinea. **HT** Bottom; inshore. **ID** Slender with long, thick tail. Mouth well in front of eyes, nasoral and circumnarial grooves, short barbels; spiracle below and behind eye. **CR** No dark spots on snout; large sparse dark spots on body. Moderately large black epaulette spot with white ring and black blotches. Juvenile with black webbed paired fins (dusky in adult) and dark bands on tail. **Status:** V

4 **Henry's Epaulette Shark** *Hemiscyllium henryi* at least 70cm

DN Indonesia. **HT** Fringing reefs; 30m or deeper. **ID** Slender with long tail. Mouth well in front of eyes, nasoral and circumnarial grooves, short barbels; spiracle below eye. **CR** Numerous scattered spots over body, including head and fins. Distinct double ocellus on sides behind head. **Status:** DD.

5 **Michael's Epaulette Shark** *Hemiscyllium michaeli* at least 82cm

DN Papua New Guinea. **HT** Fringing and patch reef; 2–20m. **ID** Slender with long tail. Mouth well in front of eyes, nasoral and circumnarial grooves, short barbels; spiracle below eye. **CR** Brilliant leopard pattern of spots covering body. Large prominent spot on side and just behind head. Dark blotches on anterior dorsal fin margins. Faint saddles on sides of body between pectoral and caudal fins. **Status:** NT.

6 **Epaulette Shark** *Hemiscyllium ocellatum* 107cm

DN Southwest Pacific. **HT** Coral in shallow water; very shallow water to 50m. **ID** Slender with long, thick tail. Mouth well in front of eyes, nasoral and circumnarial grooves, short barbels; spiracle below eye. **CR** No dark spots on snout; small dark spots on body and unpaired fins. Large black epaulette spot with white ring and black blotches. Juvenile with black webbed paired fins (dusky in adult) and dark bands on tail. **Status:** LC.

7 **Hooded Carpetshark** *Hemiscyllium strahani* 80cm

DN East Papua New Guinea. **HT** Coral; 3–18m. **ID** Slender with extremely long, thick tail. Mouth well in front of eyes, nasoral and circumnarial grooves, very short barbels; spiracle below eye. **CR** Black mask on snout and head; white spots on body and fins over dark saddles and blotches. Black epaulette spot partially merged with shoulder saddle. Margins of paired fins white spots on black; dark rings round tail. Juveniles no white spots with less bold markings. **Status:** V.

8 **Speckled Carpetshark** *Hemiscyllium trispeculare* 79cm

DN North Australia. **HT** Coral reefs in shallow water; 0–50m. **ID** Slender with long, thick tail. Mouth well in front of eyes, nasoral and circumnarial grooves, short barbels; spiracle below eye. **CR** Small dark spots on snout; body and fins have numerous large and small dark spots separated by a reticular network; no white spots. Large black epaulette spot with white ring and two curved black blotches. Juvenile coloration unknown. **Status:** LC.

Hemiscyllium michaeli

ZEBRA SHARKS: Stegostomatidae – page 130

One genus, one species *Stegostoma fasciatum*.

Identification Only juveniles have 'zebra' stripes; the ridged bodies of the adults are strongly spotted. See description on page 130.

Biology Oviparous, lays large dark brown or purplish-black eggcases, anchored to bottom with fine tufts of fibres. Females of this species exhibit parthenogenesis: they can produce viable eggs that hatch into female pups without needing to be fertilised by a male. Feeds on molluscs, crustaceans, small bony fishes, and possibly sea snakes.

Status Relatively common, but this species' inshore habitat is heavily fished throughout its range except in Australian waters. It is taken in demersal trawls, floating and fixed bottom gillnets and on baited hooks, and seen in fish markets in Indonesia, Thailand, Malaysia, Philippines, Pakistan, India, Taiwan and elsewhere. Depleted populations are unlikely to recover rapidly through recolonisation from other areas because of its limited potential for dispersal. Its coral reef habitat is also threatened.

NURSE SHARKS: Ginglymostomatidae – page 130

Three mono-specific genera of subtropical and tropical continental and insular waters, including coral and rocky reefs, sandy areas, reef lagoons and mangrove keys. Depth range from the intertidal and surf zone (sometimes barely covered) to at least 70m. There is at least one more undescribed species, and genus *Pseudoginglymostoma* may prove to be more closely related to *Rhincodon* and *Stegostoma* than to the other nurse sharks.

Identification Head broad and flattened, no lateral skin flaps. Snout rounded or truncated. Transverse, subterminal mouth in front of eyes, long nasoral grooves. Nostrils with barbels. Small spiracles behind eyes. Small gill slits, fifth almost overlaps fourth. Two spineless dorsal fins, second level with and about same size as anal fin; latter close to lower caudal fin. Precaudal tail much shorter than head and body. Caudal fin elongated with a strong terminal lobe and subterminal notch but no or very short ventral lobe. Unpatterned or a few dark spots in young.

Biology Viviparous (or possibly so in *Pseudoginglymostoma*). Nocturnal. Social, rest on the bottom in small groups. Cruise and clamber on bottom, mouths and barbels close to bottom, searching for food. Short small mouths with large buccal cavities suck in a variety of bottom invertebrates and fishes, including active reef fish.

Status Larger species are or were formerly common and often caught in local inshore fisheries for food, liver oil and tough leather. Some local extirpations reported. *Ginglymostoma* and *Nebrius* are hardy and can survive well in large aquaria. Not usually aggressive, but can bite hard and will hang on if provoked. Popular for dive tourism.

WHALE SHARKS: Rhincodontidae – page 106

One genus, one species *Rhincodon typus*.

Identification Unmistakable huge spotted filter-feeder. See description on page 106.

Biology Viviparous. The only recorded pregnant female, from Taiwan, had about 300 pups in her uterus. Feeds on planktonic crustaceans, fish eggs, and small shoaling fishes.

Status Has been fished, apparently unsustainably, for meat in many areas. The fins are reportedly not of good quality for soup, but are valued for their great size. Steep declines in yields from harpoon fisheries were reported from the Philippines, Taiwan, Maldives and India. Whale Sharks are legally protected in many states, and quota management is in place for the Taiwanese fishery. A few Whale Sharks are on display in very large public aquaria. The species is listed on Appendix II of CITES (to ensure that international trade is sustainable) and on Appendix II and the Migratory Sharks Memorandum of Understanding of the Convention on Migratory Species, to encourage collaborative international management of the species and its migratory pathways and habitats.

FILTER-FEEDING SHARKS

The three gigantic plankton-feeding sharks, Basking Shark, Whale Shark and Megamouth Shark (page 106), are all from different families and not particularly closely related. In taking up a filter-feeding lifestyle, they have undergone a process of convergent evolution; each species has developed, independently, a slightly different strategy for consuming their planktonic prey.

The Basking Shark is a ram-feeder: it swims steadily through the dense blooms of planktonic crustaceans that form in highly productive cool temperate waters, with its enormous mouth held wide open. Vast numbers of its minute prey pass in through the great mouth and, as the water leaves through the large gill slits, become trapped on this species' numerous long slender gill filaments, which play the same role as baleen plates in the great whales. From time to time the mouth and gills close, and huge mouthfuls of plankton are gulped down. Although the numerous tiny teeth of these giant sharks are not needed for feeding, the teeth of mature male Basking Sharks are worn down, presumably from holding onto the rough skin of females during mating.

Ram-feeding would be a costly and unsuccessful feeding strategy in unproductive tropical waters. Instead, Whale Sharks use their powerful throat and gill muscles to suck in the isolated patches of zooplankton and associated small fishes and squid characteristic of tropical oceans, sometimes hanging vertically near the surface and pumping water containing concentrations of prey over their gills. They also travel long distances to locate the brief (but predictable) blooms of food produced during coral, crustacean and fish spawning events.

The mysterious deepwater Megamouth Shark, the smallest of the three filter-feeders, has not been observed feeding, but one animal tracked using an electronic tag followed the daily vertical migrations of a dense layer of deepwater zooplankton. The Megamouth probably also uses suction feeding, but a former theory that it has luminescent tissue inside its mouth to attract prey now seems unlikely.

Plate 37: NURSE AND ZEBRA SHARKS

1 Nurse Shark *Ginglymostoma cirratum* about 300cm (possibly 430cm)

DN East Pacific, west and east Atlantic. **HT** Reefs, channels between mangrove keys and sand flats; shallows usually to 12m (40–130m off Brazil). **ID** Large. Transverse, subterminal mouth in front of eyes; long nasoral grooves; long barbels; tiny spiracle behind eye. Dorsal fins broadly rounded; first dorsal fin larger than second dorsal and anal fins; caudal fin longer than a quarter of total length. **CR** Uniform yellow- to grey-brown above, paler below. Young with small dark light-ringed ocellar spots and obscure saddles. **Status:** DD.

2 Tawny Nurse Shark *Nebrius ferrugineus* 314–320cm

DN Tropical Indo-Pacific. **HT** On or near bottom in sheltered areas; intertidal to 70m or more. **ID** Large. Transverse, subterminal mouth in front of eyes; long nasoral grooves; fairly long barbels, tiny spiracle behind eye. Fins angular; first dorsal fin larger than second and anal fins; first dorsal fin base over pelvic fin bases; caudal fin longer than a quarter of total length. **CR** Uniform shades of brown (depending on habitat) above, paler below. **Status:** V.

3 Shorttail Nurse Shark *Pseudoginglyostoma brevicaudatum* 75cm

DN West Indian Ocean. **HT** Coral reefs; depth unknown. **ID** Small. Transverse, subterminal mouth in front of eyes; long nasoral grooves; short barbels; tiny spiracle just below and behind eye. All fins rounded; first dorsal fin about same size as second dorsal and anal fin; caudal fin less than 20% of total length. **CR** Uniform dark brown. **Status:** V.

Zebra sharks

4 Zebra Shark *Stegostoma fasciatum* 235cm

DN Indo-west Pacific. **HT** Coral reefs, sands between reefs and offshore sediment; intertidal to 62m. **ID** Large, slender, ridged body with very long tail. Small transverse mouth in front of eyes; small barbels; large spiracle behind eye. First dorsal fin set well forward on back, first dorsal fin larger than second; anal fin close to lower fin; broad caudal fin about same length as rest of body. **CR** Yellowish to darker brown above, white below with distinct dark brown spotting. Juveniles with unique banding of dark brown above and yellowish below with vertical yellow stripes and spots separating dark saddles. Intermediately aged sharks (50–90cm) with saddles breaking up into spotted adult patterning. **Status:** V.

Ginglymostoma cirratum

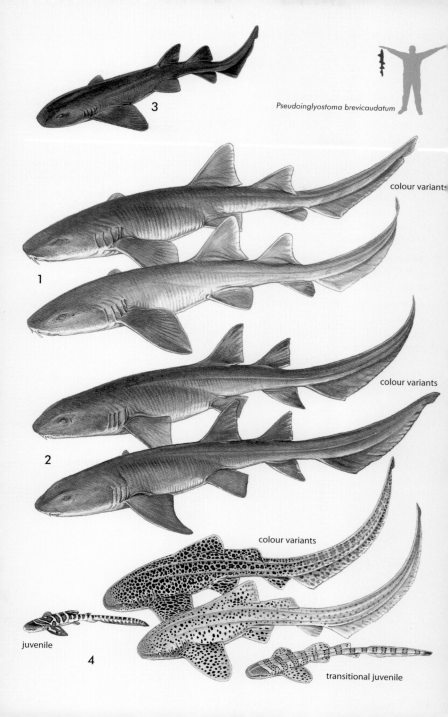

3

Pseudoinglyostoma brevicaudatum

colour variants

1

colour variants

2

colour variants

juvenile

4

transitional juvenile

This order is the largest, most diverse and widespread group of sharks. It contains at least 291 species in eight families: Scyliorhinidae (catsharks), Proscylliidae (finback catsharks), Pseudotriakidae (false catsharks), Leptochariidae (barbeled houndsharks), Triakidae (houndsharks), Hemigaleidae (weasel sharks), Carcharhinidae (requiem sharks), and Sphyrnidae (hammerhead sharks). Most are small and harmless to people, but this order also includes some of the largest predatory sharks.

Identification A very wide range of appearances, from strange bottom-living deepwater sharks, to typical large sharks. All have two spineless dorsal fins and an anal fin. A long mouth extends to or behind the eyes, which are protected by nictitating lower eyelids. Nasoral grooves are usually absent (broad and shallow when present in a few catsharks). If barbels are present, these are developed from anterior nasal flaps of nostrils. Largest teeth are well lateral on dental band, not on either side of symphysis, with no gap or intermediate teeth separating the large anterior teeth from still larger teeth in upper jaw. Intestine usually has a spiral or scroll valve.

Distribution Worldwide, from cold to tropical seas, intertidal to deep ocean (to depths of 2000m), to pelagic in the open ocean. Some are poor swimmers and restricted to small areas of seabed, others are strong long-distance swimmers and highly migratory.

Biology Very varied reproductive strategies, also very poorly known in some groups. Many species are oviparous (egg-laying), some depositing eggs on the seabed with embryos developing for up to a year before hatching, others retaining the eggs until close to hatching. More evolutionarily advanced families retain foetuses inside the female, nourished by the yolk sac or by a placenta, until live young are born. Age at maturity, number of pups, gestation times and reproductive periodicity are also very variable; some species breed rapidly and are resilient to fishing pressure, others do not reproduce every year. Longevity is also highly variable, with maximum ages from six to more than 60 years.

Status This order supports larger targeted fisheries than any other taxonomic group of sharks (although ray fisheries are even more important). It also contains most of the shark species that have been implicated in biting humans. The most important commercially fished families are the Carcharhinidae (*Carcharhinus* species), followed by the Triakidae (particularly the smoothhounds, *Mustelus* species). Some of these species are also very important for sports angling and, to a lesser extent, for dive tourism.

CATSHARKS: Scyliorhinidae – pages 134–170

By far the largest shark family; at least 160 species in 17 genera (146 species described here), with considerable taxonomic research still needed. More species are continually being discovered and described as commercial fisheries and research efforts move into deeper water – we unfortunately cannot include all recently discovered species here. Catsharks are found worldwide, from tropical to arctic waters, usually on or near the seabed, from the intertidal to the deep sea (below 2000m), but often restricted to relatively small ranges. Many are rarely seen deepwater species, known from very few specimens (over a third of *Apristurus* spp. are known from only one scientifically described specimen and in several cases the original and only specimen has been lost).

Identification Usually small (less than 80cm long; some may mature at about 30cm, a few reach about 160cm). Elongated body, two small spineless dorsal fins (first dorsal base over or behind pelvic bases) and an anal fin. Long arched mouth reaches past the front end of the cat-like eyes. Members of some genera (e.g. *Apristurus* demon catsharks) are very difficult to tell apart.

Biology Mostly poorly known (particularly deepwater species). Many are oviparous (egg laying). The most primitive species lay many pairs of large eggs (one from each oviduct), protected by tough eggcases with corner tendrils, onto the seabed. Hatching may take nearly a year. More advanced species retain their eggs until the embryos' development is almost complete, laying larger numbers of eggs about a month before hatching. A few retain the eggs until the embryos are fully developed and give birth to live young (ovoviviparity). There are poor swimmers that do not undertake long distance migrations. Some inshore species are nocturnal. They may sleep in groups in crevices by day, moving out to feed at night. They eat benthic invertebrates and small fishes.

Status None are dangerous to people. A few are important in fisheries; many are taken as a bycatch. Some are regularly kept and breed in aquariums.

Plate 38: CATSHARKS I

1 White Ghost Catshark *Apristurus aphyodes* ♀53cm ♂54cm

DN Northeast Atlantic. **HT** Deep slope, possibly soft bottom; 1014–1800m. **ID** First dorsal fin about the same size as second; large short, moderately deep anal fin. **CR** Pale grey, slightly darker grey edges to some fins. **Status:** DD.

2 Hoary Catshark *Apristurus canutus* about 46cm

DN Caribbean. **HT** Insular slopes; 521–915m. **ID** First dorsal fin much smaller than second; very large, long anal fin separated from caudal fin by small notch. **CR** Dark grey with blackish fin margins. **Status:** DD.

3 Iceland Catshark *Apristurus laurussonii* about 72cm

DN North Atlantic. **HT** Continental slopes, deepwater on or near bottom, continental slopes; 560–2060m. **ID** Small eyes. First dorsal fin slightly larger than second; very large, moderately long, angular anal fin separated from caudal fin by small notch. **CR** Uniform dark brown. **Status:** DD.

4 Ghost Catshark *Apristurus manis* 88cm

DN North Atlantic, and possibly off South Africa. **HT** Continental slopes; 600–1900m. **ID** Distinctively stout body. Very large, long mouth. First dorsal fin same size as second dorsal; large, broadly rounded anal fin; caudal fin with enlarged crest of dermal denticles. **CR** Dark grey or blackish, fin tips sometimes whitish (particularly in juveniles). **Status:** LC.

5 Smalleye Catshark *Apristurus microps* 61cm

DN North and southeast Atlantic and southwest Indian Ocean. **HT** Continental slopes; 700–2200m. **ID** First dorsal fin about the same size as second; very large, long, rounded-angular anal fin separated from caudal fin by small notch; caudal fin with enlarged crest of dermal denticles. **CR** Uniform dark brown or grey-brown to purplish-black. **Status:** LC.

6 Smallfin Catshark *Apristurus parvipinnis* 52cm

DN Gulf of Mexico and Caribbean. **HT** Continental slope, on or near bottom; 600–1200m. **ID** First dorsal fin extremely small; large, long anal fin separated from caudal fin by small notch; caudal fin with moderately enlarged crest of dermal denticles. **CR** Grey-brown to blackish. **Status:** DD.

7 Deepwater Catshark *Apristurus profundorum* 76cm

DN North Atlantic. **HT** Continental slope; about 1100–1830m. **ID** Erect dermal denticles gives the shark a fuzzy texture. First dorsal fin same size as second; large, long rounded-angular anal fin separated from caudal fin by small notch; caudal fin with enlarged crest of dermal denticles. **CR** Uniform brownish. **Status:** DD.

8 Broadgill Catshark *Apristurus riveri* 48cm

DN Gulf of Mexico and Caribbean. **HT** Continental slopes, on or near bottom ; 700–1500m. **ID** Slender. Very long mouth with very long labial furrows. First dorsal fin much smaller than second; deep, angular anal fin separated from caudal fin by small notch. **CR** Uniform dark. **Status:** DD.

9 Saldanha Catshark *Apristurus saldanha* reported 89cm

DN South Africa. **HT** Continental slope; 344–1009m. **ID** First dorsal fin slightly smaller than or equal to second; long, angular anal fin separated from caudal fin by small notch. **CR** Uniform dark slate-grey or grey-brown. **Status:** DD.

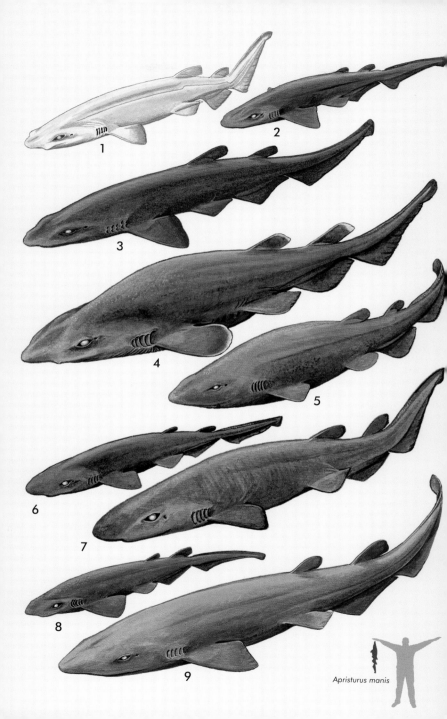

Apristurus manis

Plate 39: CATSHARKS II

1 Smallbelly Catshark *Apristurus indicus* immature to 34cm

DN Western Indian Ocean. **HT** Continental slopes, deep water on bottom; 1289–1840m. **ID** First dorsal fin lower than second and extends as long low ridge; paired, anal and caudal fins very close together. **CR** Uniform brownish or blackish. **Status:** DD.

2 Shortnose Demon Catshark *Apristurus internatus* probably immature to 42cm

DN East China Sea. **HT** Continental slope; 670m. **ID** First dorsal fin slightly smaller than second; very large moderately long, deep, angular anal fin separated from caudal fin by small notch. **CR** Uniform dark colour. **Status:** DD.

3 Longhead Catshark *Apristurus longicephalus* at least 59cm

DN West Pacific and western Indian Ocean. **HT** Deepwater, probably near bottom; 500–1140m. **ID** Very long snout (about 12% of total length). First dorsal fin slightly smaller than second; paired and anal fins close together; large, long angular anal fin separated from caudal fin by small notch. **CR** Uniform grey-black or dark brown. **Status:** DD.

4 Flathead Catshark *Apristurus macrorhynchus* ♀66cm

DN East China Sea and South Sea of Japan. **HT** Island and continental slopes, deepwater, bottom; 220–1140m. **ID** First dorsal fin two thirds size of second dorsal; very large, long, angular anal fin separated from caudal fin by small notch. Light grey-brown above, whitish below and on fins. **CR** Light grey-brown above, whitish below and on fins. **Status:** DD.

5 Largenose Catshark *Apristurus nasutus* ♂59cm

DN Eastern Pacific. **HT** Upper continental slopes, on or near bottom; 400–925m. **ID** First dorsal fin slightly smaller than second dorsal, large angular anal fin separated from caudal fin by small notch. **CR** Medium brown, grey or grey-blackish body, posterior fin margins pale. **Status:** DD.

6 Pale Catshark *Apristurus sibogae* juvenile 21cm

DN Indonesia, Makassar straits. **HT** Insular slope; 655m. **ID** Very large pectoral fins; first dorsal fin much smaller than less than second dorsal; small low pelvic fins; long, angular anal fin separated from caudal fin by small notch. **CR** White or reddish-white. **Status:** DD.

7 South China Catshark *Apristurus sinensis* at least 75cm

DN South China Sea, Australia and possibly New Zealand. **HT** Continental slope; 537–1290m. **ID** Pointed snout. First dorsal fin about half the size of second; large, angular anal fin separated from caudal fin by small notch. **CR** Uniformly dark coloration. **Status:** DD.

8 Spongehead Catshark *Apristurus spongiceps* gravid ♀51cm

DN West Pacific and Hawaii. **HT** Insular slopes, on or near bottom; 572m. **ID** Stout with grooved and pleated throat area. First dorsal fin about the same size as second; very large anal fin separated from caudal fin by small notch. **CR** Uniform dark brown. **Status:** DD.

9 Panama Ghost Catshark *Apristurus stenseni* ♂ possibly 46cm

DN Eastern Central Pacific. **HT** Continental slope; 915–975m. **ID** Slender. Extremely large mouth with very long labial furrows. First dorsal fin about same size as second; moderately high rounded angular anal fin separated from caudal fin by small notch. **CR** Uniformly blackish. **Status:** DD.

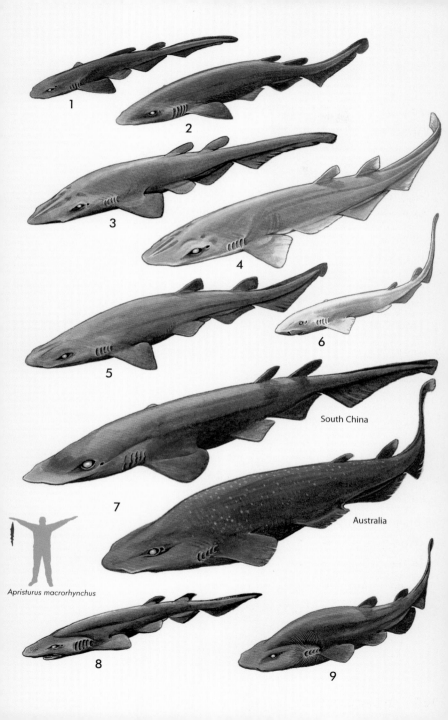

South China

Australia

Apristurus macrorhynchus

1

2

3

4

5

6

7

8

9

Plate 40: CATSHARKS III

1 **Roughskin Catshark** *Apristurus ampliceps* at least 87cm

DN Southern Australia and New Zealand. **HT** Continental shelf; 840–1500m. **ID** First dorsal fin slightly smaller than second; fairly long, rounded anal fin. **CR** Dark brownish to black with scattered paler spots and squiggles and pale tip to outer caudal fin. **Status:** DD.

2 **Pinocchio Catshark** *Apristurus australis* 62cm

DN Eastern Australia. **HT** Continental slope and seamounts; 485–1035m. **ID** Slender. Very long narrow pointed snout. First dorsal fin smaller than second; large pectoral fins; long, very shallow, angular anal fin separated from caudal fin by small notch. **CR** Pale greyish-brown to brown. **Status:** DD.

3 **Bighead Catshark** *Apristurus bucephalus* at least 68cm

DN Western Australia. **HT** Continental slope; 920–1140m. **ID** Pleats on throat. Fins rather broad and rounded; first dorsal fin lower than second; short, very deep anal fin. **CR** Uniform greyish-brown with black rear margins to anal and caudal fins. **Status:** DD.

4 **Flaccid Catshark** *Apristurus exsanguis* 91cm

DN New Zealand. **HT** Insular slopes; 573–1200m. **ID** Flaccid body. Dorsal fins about the same size; very long, low anal fin separated from caudal fin by small notch. **CR** Uniform pale grey to pale brown. **Status:** LC.

5 **Stout Catshark** *Apristurus fedorovi* at least 68cm

DN Northern Japan. **HT** 810–1430m. **ID** Elongated snout. Very small eyes. First dorsal fin smaller to slightly smaller than second; very large, deep, rounded anal fin. **CR** Uniform dark brown. **Status:** DD.

6 **Fleshynose Catshark** *Apristurus melanoasper* at least 79cm

DN North Atlantic, Southern Australia and New Zealand. **HT** Continental shelf; 512–1520m. **ID** Slender body with slender fleshy snout. Dorsal fins same size; long deep angular anal fin. **CR** Dark brown body with irregular scattering of pale flecks on most individuals and black naked fin tips. **Status:** DD.

7 **Bulldog Catshark** *Apristurus pinguis* ♂ up to 65cm

DN East China Sea, Australia and New Zealand. **HT** Continental slope; captured 996–2057m. **ID** Dorsal fins fairly equal-sized; large, elongated, deep, rounded-angular anal fin separated from caudal fin by small notch. **CR** Brown to blackish-brown, slightly lighter above and on fins, often with indistinct blotches; head with irregular lighter blotches. **Status:** DD.

8 **Bigfin Catshark** *Apristurus platyrhynchus* 71cm

DN Western Pacific: Japan, southward to the East China Sea, Taiwan, Philippines, South China Sea, Sabah, Borneo, Malaysia, and Australia. **HT** Continental slope; 400–1080m. **ID** First dorsal fin much smaller than second; pectoral fins large; very long, deep, angular anal fin; deep notch near top of caudal fin. **CR** Uniform light brown, or grey, to dark brown with blackish fin margins. **Status:** DD.

Apristurus platyrhynchus

Plate 41: CATSHARKS IV

1 White-bodied Catshark *Apristurus albisoma* ♀60cm ♂57cm

DN New Caledonia. **HT** Deep slope, possibly soft bottom; 935–1564m. **ID** Very small eyes. First dorsal fin slightly smaller than second; large, short, deep anal fin separated from caudal fin by small notch. **CR** Uniform whitish. **Status:** NT.

2 Brown Catshark *Apristurus brunneus* 69cm

DN East Pacific. **HT** Outer continental shelf and upper slope, on or well above bottom; 33–1298m. **ID** Dorsal fins same size; very large, long anal fin. **CR** Uniform dark brown with obvious light posterior margins on fins and upper tail edge. **Status:** DD.

3 Humpback Catshark *Apristurus gibbosus* 51cm

DN South and East China Sea. **HT** Continental slope; 600–913m. **ID** Prominent humped back. Broad, spatulate snout. First dorsal fin slightly smaller than second; very large, moderately long, deep angular anal fin separated from caudal fin by small notch. **CR** Uniform dark to dusky. **Status:** DD.

4 Longfin Catshark *Apristurus herklotsi* about 49cm

DN South and East China Seas. **HT** Deepwater, bottom; 520–910m. **ID** Small with very short abdomen. First dorsal fin about a third the size of second; pectoral and anal fins very close together; very long shallow angular anal fin. **CR** Uniform brownish to blackish-brown. **Status:** DD.

5 Broadnose Catshark *Apristurus investigatoris* ♀type specimen 26cm

DN Indian Ocean: Andaman Sea. **HT** Continental slope, deepwater, bottom; 1040m. **ID** Elongated, broad snout. First dorsal fin two thirds the area of second; very large low rounded–angular anal fin separated from caudal fin by small notch; well-developed caudal crest. **CR** Uniform medium brown. **Status:** DD.

6 Japanese Catshark *Apristurus japonicus* 71cm

DN East China Sea and Sea of Japan. **HT** Slope, near bottom; 820–915m. **ID** Extremely long abdomen. Short snout for an *Apristurus* catshark. Dorsal fins about the same size; very large, moderately long, angular anal fin. **CR** Uniform blackish-brown. **Status:** DD.

7 Longnose Catshark *Apristurus kampae* at least 65cm

DN Northeast Pacific. **HT** Continental shelf and upper slope; 180–1888m. **ID** Very long gill slits. First dorsal fin about the same size as second, very deep rounded anal fin. **CR** Uniform blackish or dark brown to grey, precaudal fins with light or lighter edges. **Status:** DD.

8 Broadmouth Catshark *Apristurus macrostomus* holotype ♂38cm

DN South China Sea. **HT** Captured 913m. **ID** First dorsal fin less than half the size of second; pectoral fins very large; very large, long, angular anal fin separated from caudal fin by small notch. **CR** Possibly dark brown or grey-brown above and below, rear fin margins blackish. **Status:** DD.

9 Smalldorsal Catshark *Apristurus micropterygeus* holotype adolescent ♂37cm

DN South China Sea. **HT** Captured 913m. **ID** First dorsal fin very small, about a ninth the size of second; very large, long, angular anal fin separated from caudal fin by small notch. **CR** Possibly grey-brown body, fins not conspicuously marked. **Status:** DD.

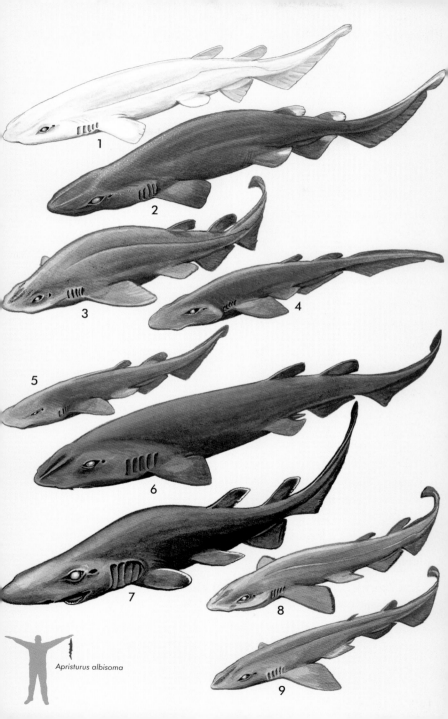

Apristurus albisoma

Plate 42: CATSHARKS V

1 Grey Spotted Catshark *Asymbolus analis*
61cm

DN East to southeast Australia. **HT** Continental shelf, bottom; 25–200m. **ID** Short head with short thick snout; narrow ridges below eyes. Two small dorsal fins behind pelvic bases. **CR** Greyish with obscure dark saddle-like blotches; equal sized, widely-spaced, dark brown spots; some whitish specks. **Status:** DD.

2 Blotched Catshark *Asymbolus funebris*
holotype ♀44cm

DN Western Australia. **HT** Outer continental shelf; 145m. **ID** Small. Short head with short thick snout; narrow ridges below eyes. Two small dorsal fins behind pelvic bases. **CR** Brown with dark brown blotches; three predorsal saddles with bars beneath each dorsal fin and one between; ventral surfaces slightly paler; no spots. **Status:** DD.

3 Starry Catshark *Asymbolus galacticus*
48cm

DN Western South Pacific off New Caledonia. **HT** Continental slope; 235–550m. **ID** Small, slender. Shortish head; narrow ridges below eyes. First dorsal fin origin over pelvic inserts. **CR** A very striking catshark with numerous spots and rusty blotches and spots; about 10 faint dusky saddles. **Status:** LC.

4 Western Spotted Catshark *Asymbolus occiduus*
at least 60cm

DN South and western Australia. **HT** Outer continental shelf, bottom; 98–400m. **ID** Short head with short thick snout; narrow ridges below eyes. Two dorsal fins behind pelvic bases. **CR** Yellow-green with eight to nine distinct saddles; similar sized dark brown spots, one dark spot in front of dorsal fins. **Status:** LC.

5 Pale Spotted Catshark *Asymbolus pallidus*
47cm

DN Northeast Australia. **HT** Continental shelf, bottom; 225–400m. **ID** Small. Short head with short thick snout; narrow ridge below eyes. Two dorsal fins behind pelvic bases. **CR** Pale yellowish with no distinct saddles; obvious even-sized dark brown spots, none under eye. **Status:** LC.

6 Dwarf Catshark *Asymbolus parvus*
about 40cm

DN Tropical northwestern Australia. **HT** Continental shelf, bottom; 59–360m. **ID** Very small. Short head with short thick snout; narrow ridges below eyes. Two small dorsal fins behind pelvic bases. **CR** Pale brown with faint dark saddles or bands; many white spots and lines. **Status:** LC.

7 Orange Spotted Catshark *Asymbolus rubiginosus*
at least 53cm

DN Eastern Australia. **HT** Continental shelf and upper slope, bottom; 25–290, possibly to 540m. **ID** Short head with short thick snout; narrow ridges below eye. Two dorsal fins behind pelvic bases. **CR** Pale brown with obscure dark saddles separated by clusters of spots along spine; many dark brown spots with orange-brown borders. **Status:** LC.

8 Variegated Catshark *Asymbolus submaculatus*
44cm

DN Southwestern Australia. **HT** Continental shelf in caves and on ledges; 30–200m. **ID** Small. Short head with short thick snout; narrow ridge below eyes. Two dorsal fins behind pelvic bases and close together. **CR** Greyish–brown with irregular rusty-brown saddle-like blotches; many small black spots. **Status:** LC.

9 Gulf Catshark *Asymbolus vincenti*
at least 61cm

DN Southern Australia. **HT** Often in sea grass down to 100m; 27–220m in Great Australian Bight. **ID** Short head with short thick snout; narrow ridge below eye. Two small dorsal fins behind pelvic bases. **CR** Mottled grey-brown or chocolate with seven or eight saddles; many small, faint, white spots. **Status:** LC.

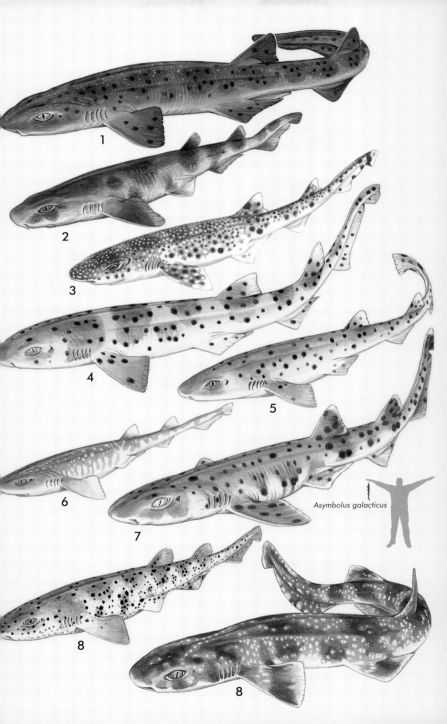

Asymbolus galacticus

1 Bali Catshark *Atelomycterus baliensis*   47cm

DN Indonesia, Bali. **HT** Crevices and coral and rocky reefs. **ID** Small, slender. Relatively short snout; large nasal flaps extending nearly to mouth. Tall dorsal fins, first dorsal origin over pelvic bases. **CR** A variegated pattern of four well-defined dark brown saddles and scattered blotches and small black spots. **Status: V**

2 Banded Sand Catshark *Atelomycterus fasciatus*   45cm

DN Northwestern Australia. **HT** Continental shelf, bottom on sand and shelly sand; 25–125m. **ID** Small slender. Narrow head; very large nasal flaps extending to mouth. Triangular dorsal fins, first dorsal origin over last third of pelvic bases. **CR** Light background with brown saddles; few scattered small black spots; sometimes small white spots. **Status: LC.**

3 Australian Marbled Catshark *Atelomycterus macleayi*   60cm

DN Northern Australia. **HT** Sand and rock in very shallow water; 0.5–3.5m. **ID** Slender. Narrow head; very large nasal flaps extending nearly mouth. Tall dorsal fins, first dorsal origin over pelvic fin insertions. **CR** Light grey to grey-brown with darker grey or brown saddles outlined and partly covered by small black spots; no white spots. **Status: LC.**

4 Coral Catshark *Atelomycterus marmoratus*   70cm

DN Indo-west Pacific. **HT** Inshore; crevices or holes on coral reefs. **ID** Slender. Narrow head; very large nasal flaps extending to mouth. Tall dorsal fins, first dorsal origin over or slightly in front of pelvic fin insertions. **CR** Dark with no clear saddles; scattered white spots over large black spots and bars; white fin margins. **Status: NT.**

5 Whitespotted Sand Catshark *Atelomycterus marnkalha*   49cm

DN Northern Australia and southern Papua New Guinea. **HT** Sandy to coarse rubble; 10–75m. **ID** Small slender. Short rounded snout; very large nasal flaps extending to mouth. First dorsal fin origin over pelvic fin bases. **CR** Light grey to brown with three to four darker predorsal saddles and seven poorly defined saddles behind first dorsal fin; vertical rows of small white spots; sparse scatered black spots. **Status: DD**

6 New Caledonia Catshark *Aulohalaelurus kanakorum*   adult ♂79cm

DN New Caledonia. **HT** Coral reefs; to 49m. **ID** Fairly slender, elongated and cyclindrical body. Narrowly rounded head; nasal flaps do not reach mouth. Tall, equal-sized dorsal fins, first dorsal origin over pelvic fins origin. **CR** Dark grey with variegated pattern of large dark and white blotches; white fin margins **Status: V.**

7 Blackspotted Catshark *Aulohalaelurus labiosus*   67cm

DN Southwestern Australia. **HT** Shallow coastal waters and offshore reefs; to 4m+. **ID** Fairly slender, elongated and cyclindrical body. Relatively narrow head; narrowly rounded snout; nasal flaps do not reach mouth. Equal-sized dorsal fins, first dorsal origin over or slightly in front of pelvic fin insertions. **CR** Light greyish to yellowish-brown with variegated pattern of dark saddles, small to large black spots and blotches; few fine white spots; white dorsal, caudal and anal fin tips highlighted by dark blotches. **Status: LC.**

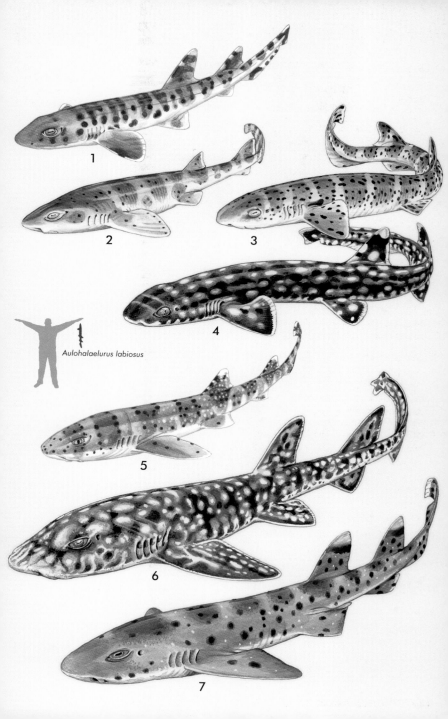

Aulohalaelurus labiosus

Plate 44: CATSHARKS VII

1 **Dusky Catshark** *Bythaelurus canescens* 70cm

DN Southeast Pacific. **HT** Upper continental slope, muddy and rocky deepwater; 250–700m. **ID** Short, rounded snout. Long arched mouth reaches to slightly in front of the large cat-like eyes. Two small dorsal fins, first dorsal fin base over pelvic fin bases; anal fin almost as large as second dorsal fin. **CR** Uniform dark brown adults, young have white fin tips. **Status:** DD.

2 **Broadhead Catshark** *Bythaelurus clevai* about 42cm

DN West Indian Ocean, Madagascar. **HT** Upper insular slopes; 400–500m. **ID** Longish snout, bell-shaped viewed from above. Long arched mouth reaches to slightly in front of the small cat-like eyes. Two small dorsal fins, first dorsal fin base mostly over pelvic fin bases; anal fin larger than second dorsal fin. **CR** Grey above with large conspicuous dark brown blotches and spots; white below. **Status:** DD.

3 **New Zealand Catshark** *Bythaelurus dawsoni* about 42cm

DN New Zealand. **HT** Upper slopes, on or near bottom ; 240–992m. **ID** Short, rounded snout; elongate lobate nasal flaps. Long arched mouth reaches past front of the large cat-like eyes. First dorsal fin smaller than second, first dorsal fin base over pelvic fin bases; anal fin as large as second dorsal fin. **CR** Light brown or grey above; white fin tips; dark bands on caudal fin, line of white spots on sides of smaller individuals; paler below. **Status:** DD.

4 **Jaguar Catshark** *Bythaelurus giddingsi* at least 45cm

DN Galapagos Islands. **HT** Insular slopes, bottom; 428–562m. **ID** Short, flattened, rounded snout. Long arched mouth reaches past front of the cat-like eyes. Two medium-sized dorsal fins, first dorsal fin base over rear of pelvic fin bases; anal fin much longer than second dorsal fin. **CR** Grey with variegated pattern of large white blotches and spots. **Status:** NE.

5 **Bristly Catshark** *Bythaelurus hispidus* 29cm

DN Northern Indian Ocean. **HT** Upper continental slope, bottom; 293–766m. **ID** Very small with bristly skin. Short rounded snout. Long arched mouth reaches to slightly in front of the large cat-like eyes. Two small dorsal fins, first dorsal fin base over pelvic fin bases; anal fin almost as large as second dorsal fin. **CR** Pale brown to whitish, sometimes with faint grey crossbands and white or dusky spots. **Status:** DD.

6 **Spotless Catshark** *Bythaelurus immaculatus* 76cm

DN South China Sea. **HT** Continental slope, bottom; 534–1020m. **ID** Long abdomen. Rounded snout. Long arched mouth reaches to the large cat-like eyes. First dorsal fin smaller than second, first dorsal fin base over pelvic fin bases; anal fin much smaller than second dorsal fin. **CR** Uniform yellow-brownish similar to *B. dawsoni* but no markings. **Status:** DD.

7 **Dusky Catshark** *Bythaelurus incanus* immature ♂45cm

DN Northwestern Australia. **HT** Continental slope; 900–1000m. **ID** Long soft body. Very broad, flattened head with short, rounded snout. Long arched mouth reaches to the large cat-like eyes. Two well separated similar-sized dorsal fins, first dorsal fin base over pelvic fin bases; anal fin smaller than dorsal fin. **CR** Uniform dark greyish-brown; few pale blotches below. **Status:** DD.

8 **Mud Catshark** *Bythaelurus lutarius* about 39cm

DN East Africa. **HT** Tropical continental slope, deepwater on or just above muddy bottom; 338–766m. **ID** Short rounded snout. Long arched mouth reaches past front of the cat-like eyes. Two small dorsal fins, first dorsal larger than second, first dorsal base roughly over pelvic fins insertions; anal fin much longer than second dorsal fin. **CR** Grey-brown, sometimes with dusky saddle bands; light below. **Status:** DD.

Bythaelurus dawsoni

1

2

3

4

5

6

7

8

Plate 45: CATSHARKS VIII

1 Whitefin Swellshark *Cephaloscyllium albipinnum* at least 110cm

DN Southern Australia. **HT** Upper continental slope; 125–555m. **ID** Large and stocky. Broad head. Rough skin. Ridges over eyes. Pectoral fins relatively large. **CR** Medium brown or grey with dark blotches and saddles; usually five pre-dorsal bars. **Status:** NT.

2 Reticulated Swellshark *Cephaloscyllium fasciatum* at least 42cm

DN Western Pacific: Vietnam to Philippines. **HT** Uppermost slopes, on or near muddy bottom; 219–450m. **ID** Small. Broad head. Ridges over eyes. Pectoral fins relatively small and narrow. **CR** Light grey with a striking variegated pattern of dark lines and spots. **Status:** DD.

3 Draughtsboard Shark *Cephaloscyllium isabellum* 150cm

DN New Zealand. **HT** Rocky to sandy bottom; shore to 673m. **ID** Large and stocky. Broad head. Ridges over eyes. Pectoral fins relatively large and broad. **CR** Up to 11 dark brown irregular saddles and alternating blotches in a chequerboard pattern. **Status:** LC.

4 Australian Swellshark *Cephaloscyllium laticeps* at least 150cm

DN Southern Australia. **HT** Continental shelf, inshore; to 60m or more. **ID** Large and stocky. Very broad, short head. Pectoral fins relatively large and broad. **CR** Light grey or chestnut with strongly variegated pattern of dark brown to grey saddles and blotches. **Status:** LC.

5 Speckled Swellshark *Cephaloscyllium speccum* 69cm

DN Northwestern Australia. **HT** Continental shelf and slope; 150–455m. **ID** Stocky. Broad, short head. Ridges over eyes. Pectoral fins relatively small. **CR** Pale grey with intense mottling of small and large dark blotches and saddles; white spots. **Status:** DD.

6 Balloon Shark *Cephaloscyllium sufflans* at least 110cm

DN Western Indian Ocean. **HT** Continental shelf and uppermost slopes, sand and mud bottom; 40–440m. **ID** Large. Broad head. Ridges over eyes. Pectoral fins relatively large and broad. **CR** Light grey with seven light grey-brown obscure (in adults) saddles, sometimes absent; no obvious light fin margins. **Status:** LC.

7 Japanese Swellshark *Cephaloscyllium umbratile* at least 120cm

DN Western Pacific. **HT** Continental shelf; less than 18m to about 220m. **ID** Large and stocky. Broad head. Ridges over eyes. Pectoral fins relatively large. **CR** Pale brown with regular dark brown saddles and dense mottling separated by light reddish-brown areas; scattered small white and dark spots. **Status:** DD.

8 Saddled Swellshark *Cephaloscyllium variegatum* at least 74cm

DN Northeastern Australia. **HT** Continental shelf and slope; 115–605m. **ID** Medium-sized and elongate. Slender head. Ridges over eyes. Pectoral fins relatively large and broad. **CR** Medium brownish or greyish with obvious dark saddles, usually five predorsal; fin margins sometimes pale. **Status:** NT.

9 Swellshark *Cephaloscyllium ventriosum* at least 100cm

DN Eastern Pacific. **HT** Continental shelf and upper slopes, rocky bottom in kelp beds; inshore to 457m. **ID** Large and stocky. Broad head. Ridges over eyes. Pectoral fins relatively large. **CR** Light yellow-brown with strongly variegated close-set dark brown saddles and blotches; numerous dark spots. **Status:** LC.

10 Narrowbar Swellshark *Cephaloscyllium zebrum* mature ♂44.5cm

DN Northeastern Australia. **HT** Upper continental slope; 440m. **ID** Small and stocky. Broad head. Relatively smooth skin. Ridges over eyes. Pectoral fins medium-sized and relatively broad. **CR** Dark brown to cream with distinctive, numerous, closely spaced, narrow, dark bars. **Status:** DD.

Cephaloscyllium ventriosum

Plate 46: CATSHARKS IX

1 Cook's Swellshark *Cephaloscyllium cooki*   at least 30cm

DN Eastern Indian Ocean, Arafura Sea. **HT** Upper continental slope; 225–300m. **ID** Small and stocky. Broad, short head. Pectoral fins relatively small. **CR** Greyish-brown with a pattern of eight dark brown saddles outlined in white; ventrally pale grey. **Status:** DD.

2 Australian Reticulated Swellshark *Cephaloscyllium hiscosellum*   at least 52cm

DN Western Australia. **HT** Upper continental slope; 294–420m. **ID** Small and stocky. Broad, short head. Pectoral fins relatively small and narrow. **CR** Pale greyish or brownish with a striking pattern of dark brown narrow transverse lines forming open centered saddles and blotches. **Status:** DD.

3 Spotted Swellshark *Cephaloscyllium maculatum*   holotype ♀19cm

DN Taiwan. **HT** Nearshore. **ID** Small and slender. Short snout. Pectoral fins medium-sized. **CR** Brownish with a pattern of eight dorsal saddles, four predorsal; saddles are open with dark outlined lateral blotches between paired fins. **Status:** DD.

4 Leopard-spotted Swellshark *Cephaloscyllium pardelotum*   holotype ♀20cm

DN Taiwan. **HT** Nearshore. **ID** Small and slender. Very short snout. Pectoral fins medium-sized. **CR** Brownish with an elaborate pattern of speckled dorsal saddles with three clusters arranged into rosettes between the paired fins. **Status:** DD.

5 Painted Swellshark *Cephaloscyllium pictum*   72cm

DN Eastern Indonesia. **HT** Only known from fish markets. **ID** Medium-sized and stocky. Broad, rounded head. Pectoral fins relatively large. **CR** Brownish with a strongly variegated colour pattern of prominent dark blotches, saddles and spots; paler below. **Status:** NE.

6 Sarawak Swellshark *Cephaloscyllium sarawakensis*   44cm

DN Western Pacific: Taiwan to Malaysia. **HT** 118–165m. **ID** Small. Broad head. Pectoral fins relatively large. **CR** Adult light brown with six darker brown saddles on back; juveniles brownish with a striking patterns of distinct dark brown polka dots. **Status:** DD.

7 Flagtail Swellshark *Cephaloscyllium signourum*   74cm

DN Western South Pacific. **HT** Continental slopes; from 480–700m. **ID** Large and heavy bodied. Very broad, short head. Pectoral fins relatively large and broad. **CR** Medium brown with a variegated pattern of nine to ten poorly defined dark brown saddles; ventrally pale grey or white. **Status:** DD.

8 Indian Swellshark *Cephaloscyllium silasi*   ♂36cm

DN Indian Ocean: off north-central India. **HT** Uppermost continental shelf, bottom; 300m. **ID** Small. Broad head. Ridges over eyes. Pectoral fins relatively large and broad. **CR** Light brown with seven dark brown saddles, dark blotch over pectoral fins; ventrally light brown, unspotted. **Status:** DD.

9 Steven's Swellshark *Cephaloscyllium stevensi*   66cm

DN Western Pacific: Papua New Guinea. **HT** Continental slope; 240–274m. **ID** Medium-sized and moderately stocky. Short snout. Pectoral fins relatively large. **CR** Grey-brown with eight large dark brown saddles; dark brown blotches; numerous scattered small white spots. **Status:** NE.

Cephaloscyllium signourum

1 Antilles Catshark *Galeus antillensis* — 46cm

DN Straits Florida, Hispaniola to Martinique. **HT** Upper insular slopes, deepwater on or near bottom; 293–658m. **ID** Medium-sized pectoral fins; first dorsal fin slightly larger than second; anal fin relatively short. Dermal denticle crest along upper margin of tail. Very similar to *G. arae*, but larger. **CR** Dark mouth lining; usually less than eleven saddle blotches; dark bands on tail; no black marks on dorsal fin tips; caudal fin with light web. **Status:** DD.

2 Roughtail Catshark *Galeus arae* — about 33cm

DN North Carolina to Gulf of Mexico, Cuba and Belize to Costa Rica, and adjacent islands. **HT** Upper continental and insular slopes, on or near bottom; 292–732m. **ID** Very similar to *G. antillensis*, but smaller. **CR** Very similar to *G. antillensis*. **Status:** LC.

3 Atlantic Sawtail Catshark *Galeus atlanticus* — about 46cm

DN Northeast Atlantic and Mediterranean. **HT** Continental slope; 330–790m. **ID** Large pectoral fins; equally-sized, dissimilarly shaped dorsal fins; anal fin very long and low. Dermal denticle crest along upper margin of tail. **CR** Grey above white below with dark grey blotches and saddles. **Status:** NT.

4 Blackmouth Catshark *Galeus melastomus* — ♀90cm ♂61cm

DN Northeast Atlantic and Mediterranean. **HT** 55–1000m. **ID** Large pectoral fins; equally-sized dorsal fins; anal fin very long and low. Dermal denticle crest along upper margin of tail. **CR** Black mouth lining. Striking pattern of 15 to 18 dark saddles, blotches and spots, white-edged fins. **Status:** LC.

5 Southern Sawtail Catshark *Galeus mincaronei* — at least 43cm

DN Southern Brazil. **HT** Upper continental slope, deep reefs; 495m. **ID** Medium-sized pectoral fins; equally-sized, dissimilarly shaped dorsal fins; anal fin moderately long. Dermal denticle crest along upper margin of tail. **CR** Striking pattern eleven dark oval saddles and spots outlined in white. **Status:** V.

6 Mouse Catshark *Galeus murinus* — 63cm

DN Northeast Atlantic (west of Iceland to Faeroes Channel. **HT** Continental slopes, on or near bottom; 380–1250m. **ID** Moderately large pectoral fins; first dorsal fin larger than second; anal fin moderately long. Dermal denticle crest along upper margin of tail and ventral midline of caudal peduncle. **CR** Brown above; paler below, no markings. **Status:** LC.

7 Broadfin Sawtail Catshark *Galeus nipponensis* — reported 65.5cm

DN Northwest Pacific (Japan, Kyushu-Palau Ridge). **HT** Deepwater, bottom; 362–540m. **ID** Large pectoral fins; equally-sized, dissimilarly shaped dorsal fins; anal fin very long and low. Dermal denticle crest along upper margin of tail. **CR** Numerous obscure dusky saddles and blotches, white below. **Status:** DD.

8 Peppered Catshark *Galeus piperatus* — 30cm

DN Mexico and northern Gulf of California. **HT** Bottom; 275–1326m. **ID** Similar to *G. arae* and *G. antillensis*, but smaller and different patternation. **CR** Black dots all over body and tail, with or without saddles. **Status:** LC.

9 African Sawtail Catshark *Galeus polli* — ♀43cm ♂36cm

DN Eastern Atlantic (southern Morocco to South Africa). **HT** Upper continental slope;159–720m. **ID** Large pectoral fins; equally-sized dorsal fins; anal fin long and low. Dermal denticle crest along upper margin of tail. **CR** Usually eleven or less, well-defined dark saddle blotches outlined in white or uniform dark. **Status:** LC.

10 Blacktip Sawtail Catshark *Galeus sauteri* — 45cm

DN Japan to Philippines. **HT** Continental shelves; 60–90m. **ID** Medium-sized pectoral fins; equally-sized dorsal fins; anal fin long. Dermal denticle crest along upper margin of tail. **CR** Not patterned; often dorsal fins and caudal fin lobes with prominent black tips. **Status:** DD.

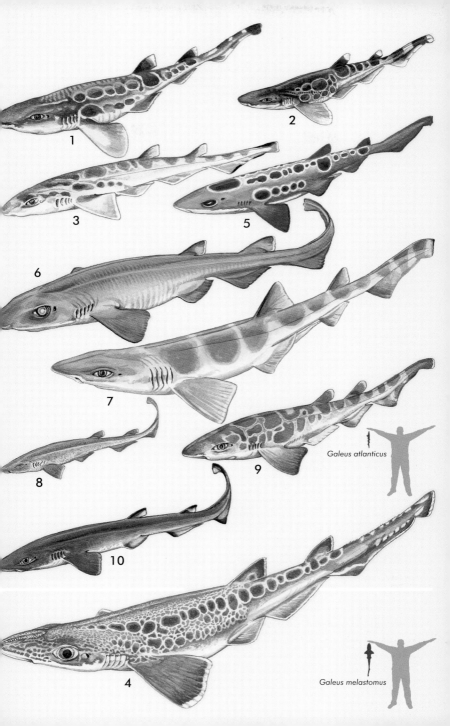

Galeus atlanticus

Galeus melastomus

Plate 48: CATSHARKS XI

1 Australian Sawtail Catshark *Figaro boardmani* 61cm

DN Australia (SE Queensland to Western Australia). **HT** Outer continental shelf and upper slope, on or near bottom; 150–640m. **ID** Medium-sized pectoral fins; equal-sized dorsal fins; anal fin moderately long. Dermal denticle crest along upper margin of tail and along ventral midline of caudal peduncle. **CR** Dark grey-brown saddles and bars, three pre- and three postdorsal. **Status:** LC.

2 Northern Sawtail Catshark *Figaro striatus* at least 42cm

DN Northeast Australia. **HT** Bottom; 300–420m. **ID** Relatively small pectoral fins; first dorsal fin slightly larger than second; anal fin relatively short. Dermal denticle crest along upper margin of tail. **CR** 10 to 16 predorsal pale-edged saddles and bars; pale centred bars below dorsal fins. **Status:** DD.

3 Longfin Sawtail Catshark *Galeus cadenati* 35cm

DN Southwest Caribbean off Panama and Colombia. **HT** Upper continetal slopes; 439–548m. **ID** Very similar to *G. arae* and *G. antillensis* but with notceably longer shallower anal fin. **CR** Very similar to *G. arae* and *G. antillensis*. **Status:** DD.

4 Gecko Catshark *Galeus eastmani* possibly 50cm

DN Japan and East China Sea, possibly Vietnam. **HT** Deepwater, on or near bottom. **ID** Moderately large pectoral fins; first dorsal fin slightly smaller than second; anal fin relatively short. Dermal denticle crest along upper margin of tail. **CR** Obscure saddles, white-edged dorsal and caudal fins. **Status:** LC.

5 Slender Sawtail Catshark *Galeus gracilis* at least 34cm

DN Northern Australia. **HT** Continental slope, on or near bottom; 290–470m. **ID** Short and broad pectoral fins; first dorsal fin slightly larger than second; anal fin relatively short. Dermal denticle crest along upper margin of tail. **CR** Four dusky saddles, one beneath each dorsal fin and two on caudal fin. **Status:** DD.

6 Longnose Sawtail Catshark *Galeus longirostris* at least 80cm

DN Japan (southern islands). **HT** Upper insular slopes, on or near bottom; 350–550m. **ID** Large pectoral fins; first dorsal fin larger than second; anal fin relatively high. Dermal denticle crest along upper margin of tail. **CR** Greyish white mouth lining. Grey above white below; young with obscure saddle blotches. **Status:** DD.

7 Phallic Catshark *Galeus priapus* 46cm

DN Western South Pacific (New Caledonia). **HT** Mainly on insular slopes; 262–830m. **ID** Medium-sized pectoral fins; first dorsal fin larger than second; anal fin relatively short. Adult male has extremely long claspers. Dermal denticle crest along upper margin of tail. **CR** Dark grey with four predorsal saddles, one under each dorsal fin and two saddles on caudal fin. **Status:** LC.

8 Dwarf Sawtail Catshark *Galeus schultzi* 30cm

DN Philippines (off Luzon). **HT** Mainly insular slope; 329–431m. **ID** Medium-sized pectoral fins; first dorsal fin larger than second; anal fin long. Dermal denticle crest along upper margin of tail. **CR** Light or dusky mouth lining. Obscure dark saddles below dorsal fins and two bands on tail. **Status:** DD.

9 Springer's Sawtail Catshark *Galeus springeri* ♀44cm

DN Caribbean Sea. **HT** Upper insular slopes; 457–699m. **ID** Medium-sized pectoral fins; first dorsal fin larger than second; anal fin long. Dermal denticle crest along upper and lower margin of tail. **CR** Only *Galeus* with predorsal dark longitudinal stripes outlined in white. **Status:** DD.

Galeus priapus

1 Speckled Catshark *Halaelurus boesemani* — 48cm

DN Indo-west Pacific (Somalia, Gulf of Aden). **HT** Continental and insular shelves; 37–91m. **ID** Pointed snout. Eyes raised above head; gills on upper surface of head above level of mouth. **CR** Yellow-brown above with eight dark saddles separated by narrower bars; dark blotches on dorsal and caudal fins; numerous small scattered dark spots; broad pale bands on edge of pectoral fins; pale below. **Status:** DD

2 Blackspotted Catshark *Halaelurus buergeri* — 49cm

DN Northwest Pacific (Japan to Philippines). **HT** Continental shelf; 80–100m. **ID** Pointed snout. Eyes raised above head; gills on upper surface of head above level of mouth. **CR** Light-coloured with variegated pattern of dusky bands outlined by large black spots. **Status:** DD.

3 Lined Catshark *Halaelurus lineatus* — 56cm

DN West Indian Ocean (South Africa to Mozambique). **HT** Continental shelf; surfline to 290m. **ID** Narrow head with upturned knob on snout. Eyes raised above head; gills on upper surface of head above level of mouth. **CR** Pale brown above with about 13 pairs of narrow dark brown stripes outlining dusky saddles; numerous small spots and squiggles; cream below. **Status:** DD.

4 Indonesian Speckled Catshark *Halaelurus maculosus* — 53cm

DN Western Indo-Pacific (Eastern Indonesia). **HT** Coastal on shallow reefs. **ID** Narrow head with upturned knob on snout. Eyes raised above head; gills on upper surface of head above level of mouth. **CR** Pale brown above with 13 pairs of narrow dark brown stripes outlining dusky saddles; many small spots and squiggles; cream below. **Status:** LC.

5 Tiger Catshark *Halaelurus natalensis* — ♀50cm

DN Southeast Atlantic and western Indian Ocean. **HT** Continental shelf, on or near bottom; inshore to 114m. **ID** Broad head with pointed upturned snout tip. Eyes raised above head; gills on upper surface of head above level of mouth. **CR** Yellow-brown above with ten pairs of broad dark brown bars enclosing lighter reddish saddles; no spots; cream below. **Status:** DD.

6 Quagga Catshark *Halaelurus quagga* — 35cm

DN Indian Ocean (Somalia, India). **HT** Continental shelf, offshore, on or near bottom; 54–186m. **ID** Pointed snout. Eyes raised above head; gills on upper surface of head above level of mouth. **CR** Light brown above with more than 20 dark brown narrow vertical stripes; pairs of bars form saddles under the dorsal fins; no spots; lighter below. **Status:** DD.

7 Rusty Catshark *Halaelurus sellus* — 42cm

DN Indian Ocean (NW Australia). **HT** Outer continental shelf; 62–164m. **ID CR** Yellowish-brown above with ten rusty brown saddles outlined by narrow dark brown lines with narrower saddles between them. **Status:** LC.

Halaelurus sellus

Plate 50: CATSHARKS XIII

1 Puffadder Shyshark *Haploblepharus edwardsii* — 60cm

DN South Africa. **HT** Continental shelf, on or near sand and rock bottom; 0–288m. **ID** Slender body. Stocky, broad head. Very large nostrils with greatly expanded nasal flaps reaching mouth. Gills on upper sides of body. **CR** Pale to dark brown or grey-brown above with prominent golden brown or reddish saddles with darker brown margins; numerous white spots; white below. **Status:** NT.

2 Brown Shyshark *Haploblepharus fuscus* — 69cm

DN South Africa. **HT** Continental shelf, inshore, on or near sand and rock bottom; 0–35m. **ID** Stocky body. Stocky, broad head. Very large nostrils with greatly expanded nasal flaps reaching mouth. Gills on upper sides of body. **CR** Brown above sometimes with obscure saddles or small white or black spots; white below. **Status:** V.

3 Natal Shyshark *Haploblepharus kistnasamyi* — at least 50cm

DN South Africa. **HT** Continental shelf; close inshore. **ID** Slender body. Stocky, broad head. Very large nostrils with greatly expanded nasal flaps reaching mouth. Gills on upper sides of body. **CR** Brown above with H-shaped saddle markings with conspicuous dark margins, dotted with numerous small white spots; interspaces between saddles and fins with dark mottling; white below. **Status:** CE.

4 Dark Shyshark *Haploblepharus pictus* — 60cm

DN Namibia to South Africa. **HT** Continental shelf, kelp, sand and rock reefs; close inshore to 35m. **ID** Slender body when juvenile, stocky when mature. Stocky, broad head. Very large nostrils with greatly expanded nasal flaps reaching mouth. Gills on upper sides of body. **CR** Light brown to dark, even blackish above with dorsal saddles without obvious darker edges; sparsely dotted with large white spots; white below. **Status:** LC.

5 Pyjama Shark *Poroderma africanum* — 97cm

DN Southeast Atlantic and western Indian Ocean. **HT** Continental shelf to upper slope; surfline to 100m. **ID** Prominent, short nasal barbels. Dorsal fins set far back; first dorsal fin much larger than second. **CR** Greyish to brownish above with unmistakable colour pattern of striking longitudinal stripes; no spots. **Status:** NT.

6 Leopard Catshark *Poroderma pantherinum* — 77cm

DN Southeast Atlantic and western Indian Ocean. **HT** Continental to upper slope; surfline to 256m. **ID** Long nasal barbels that reach mouth. Dorsal fins set far back; first dorsal much larger than second. **CR** Pale to almost black above with a striking colour pattern of leopard-like rosettes of dark spots and lines around light centres; variations to this pattern include dense spots to very large spots and partial longitudinal stripes. **Status:** DD.

Haplobelpharus edwardsii

Poroderma africanum

Plate 51: CATSHARKS XIV

1 Honeycomb Izak Catshark *Holohalaelurus favus* — at least 52cm

DN West Indian Ocean. **HT** Upper continental slope; 200–740m. **ID** Very broad head with short snout. Long, very wide mouth. Dorsal fins short and angular; slender tail. **CR** Brown above, with a very distinctive honeycomb pattern of irregular reticulations and spots; no white spots; below uniformly grey-brown. **Status:** E.

2 Grinning Izak *Holohalaelurus grennian* — at least 27cm

DN Western Indian Ocean (Mozambique to Somalia). **HT** Continental slope; 238–353m. **ID** Very broad head with short snout. Long, very wide mouth. Dorsal fins short and angular; tail slender. Enlarged rough denticles on middle of back. **CR** Yellow-brown above densely covered with small close-spaced dark brown spots; no dark reticulations, blotches, horizontal stripes, or tear marks; a few large conspicuous white spots above pectoral fin insertions; highlighted narrow dark bar on webs of dorsal fins; lighter below with scattered tiny black dots under head. **Status:** DD.

3 Crying Izak Catshark *Holohalaelurus melanostigma* — at least 38cm

DN West Indian Ocean (Tanzania to southern Kenya). **HT** Continental slope; 607–658m. **ID** Very broad head with short snout. Long mouth. Dorsal fins short and angular; slender tail. Slightly enlarged rough denticles on middle of back. **CR** Grey-brown above with many large dark brown spots some fused to form reticulations, blotches and horizontal stripes; horizontal 'tear-marks' on snout in front of eyes; dark lines and 'C'-shaped marks on dorsal fins; lighter below with scattered tiny black dots under head. **Status:** DD.

4 African Spotted Catshark *Holohalaelurus punctatus* — 34cm

DN West Indian Ocean (South Africa, Mozambique, Madagascar). **HT** Continental shelf and upper slope; 220–420m. **ID** Very broad head with short snout. Long mouth. Dorsal fins short and angular; slender tail. **CR** Yellow-brown to dark brown above densely covered with small dark brown spots; few white spots scattered on back and dorsal fin inserts; faint saddles sometimes present; no reticulations, blotches or tear-marks; 'C' or 'V'-shaped dark marks on dorsal fin webs; whitish below with tiny black dots underneath head. **Status:** EN.

5 Izak Catshark *Holohalaelurus regani* — 69cm

DN Namibia to South Africa. **HT** Continental shelf and upper slopes; 40–910m, mainly about 100–300m. **ID** Very broad head with short snout. Long mouth. Dorsal fins short and angular; slender tail. **CR** Yellowish to yellow-brown covered with dark brown reticulations bars and blotches; no white spots or tear-marks; white below; young dark and slender with line of white spots on sides and black bars on fins and tail. **Status:** LC.

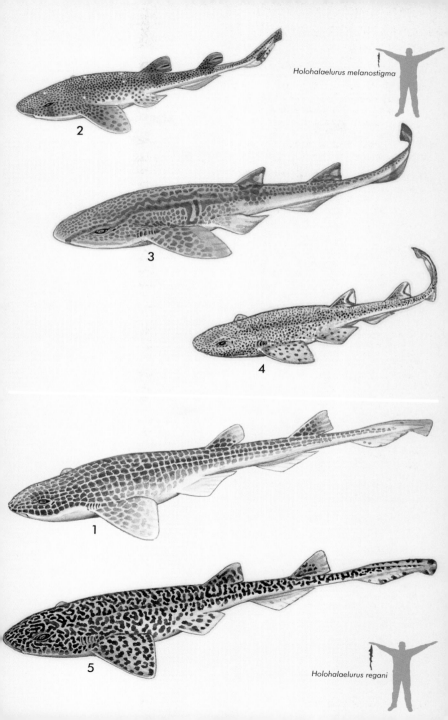

Holohalaelurus melanostigma

Holohalaelurus regani

Plate 52: CATSHARKS XV

1 Whitetip Catshark *Parmaturus albimarginatus*   holotype ♂58cm

DN Western Pacific: New Caledonia. **HT** Insular slope, on or near bottom; 590–732m. **ID** Slender, soft-bodied Snout short. Large and high anterior nasal flaps. Ridges under eyes; gills relatively long. Velvety skin with greatly enlarged denticles on upper and lower caudal fin lobes. First dorsal fin much smaller than second with origin behind pelvic fin insert, second dorsal about as large as anal fin with insertion well behind that of the anal fin. **CR** Uniform brown above with prominent white fin edges; light below. **Status:** DD.

2 White-clasper Catshark *Parmaturus albipenis*   holotype ♂41.5cm

DN Western Pacific: New Caledonia. **HT** Insular slope, on or near bottom; 688–732m. **ID** Slender, soft-bodied. Snout short. Large and high anterior nasal flaps. Ridges under eyes; gills relatively long. Soft velvety skin with caudal crests present, but denticles not greatly enlarged; crest nearly extending to second dorsal fin. First dorsal fin about same size as second with origin just behind pelvic fin origin second dorsal about as large as anal fin with insertion well behind that of the anal fin. **CR** Uniform brown above; lighter below; contrasting white pelvic fins. **Status:** DD.

3 Beige Catshark *Parmaturus bigus*   holotype ♀71cm

DN Northeastern Australia. **HT** Continental slope, on or near bottom; 590–606m. **ID** Slender, soft-bodied. Snout short. Large and high anterior nasal flaps. Gills short. Velvety skin on midflanks with greatly enlarged denticles on upper and lower caudal fin lobes. First dorsal fin smaller than second with origin over pelvic fin midbases, second dorsal slightly smaller than anal fin with insertion well behind that of the anal fin. **CR** Uniform pale yellowish-brown above; light below. **Status:** DD.

4 Campeche Catshark *Parmaturus campechiensis*   holotype immature ♀16cm

DN Gulf of Mexico. **HT** Continental slope, on or near bottom; 1097m. **ID** Slender, flabby. Snout short. Very small and low anterior nasal flaps. Ridges under eyes; gills not greatly enlarged. Velvety skin with enlarged denticles on upper caudal fin lobe, apparently not lower. First dorsal fin slightly smaller than second with origin in front of pelvic fin origin, second dorsal about as large as anal fin with insertion well behind that of the anal fin. **CR** Grey above; dusky on abdomen, around gills and on fin webs. **Status:** DD.

5 Velvet Catshark *Parmaturus lanatus*   holotype juvenile ♂36cm

DN Indonesia. **HT** ontinental slope, on or near bottom; 84–855m. **ID** Sender, soft-bodied, tadpole-shaped. Snout short. Large and high anterior nasal flaps. Ridges under eyes; gills not greatly enlarged. Velvety skin with enlarged denticles on upper and lower caudal fin lobes. First dorsal fin smaller than second with origin behind pelvic fin origin, second dorsal about larger than anal fin with insertion well behind that of the anal fin. **CR** Uniform brown with darker gill regions and fin margins. **Status:** DD.

6 New Zealand Filetail *Parmaturus macmillani*   at least 53cm

DN New Zealand. **HT** Deepwater; 950–1003m or more. **ID** Soft, flabby-bodied. Snout very short and blunt. Elongate, lobate anterior nasal flaps. Ridges under eyes; gills not greatly enlarged. First dorsal fin about same size as second, first dorsal origin opposite or just behind pelvic fin origin, second dorsal fin smaller than anal fin, insertion slightly behind that of anal fin. **CR** Uniform grey above; lighter below; fins with dusky webs. **Status:** DD.

7 Filetail Catshark *Parmaturus xaniurus*   61cm

DN Northeast Pacific. **HT** Outer continental shelf and upper slope, on or near bottom; 91–1251m. **ID** Soft, flabby bodied. Snout moderately long and blunt. Large, triangular anterior nasal flaps. Ridges under eyes; gills enlarged. First dorsal fin same size as second, first dorsal origin just behind pelvic fin origin, second dorsal fin much smaller than anal fin, insertion well in front of anal fin insertion. **CR** Brownish-black above; fins dark, lighter below. **Status:** DD.

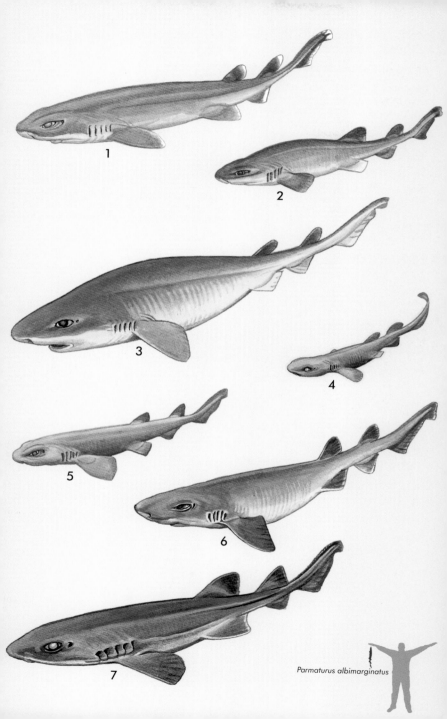

Parmaturus albimarginatus

Plate 53: CATSHARKS XVI

1 Blackgill Catshark *Parmaturus melanobranchius* (possibly adult) ♀85cm

DN Northwest Pacific (South China Sea). **HT** Upper continental and insular slopes, mud bottom, 540–835m. **ID** Soft, flabby-bodied. Snout moderately long and blunt. Elongated, pointed anterior nasal flaps. Ridges under eyes; gills not greatly enlarged. First dorsal fin smaller than second, first dorsal origin well behind pelvic fin origin, second dorsal fin about the same size as anal fin with origin well behind pelvic fin origins and opposite their midbases or insertions. **CR** Grey to dark brown above, blackish on gill speta; lighter below. **Status:** DD.

2 Salamander Catshark *Parmaturus pilosus* at least 64cm

DN Northwest Pacific (Japan to Taiwan). **HT** 358–895m. **ID** Soft, flabby bodied. Snout moderately long and blunt. Elongate, narrowly lobate anterior nasal flaps. Ridges under eyes; gills not greatly enlarged. First dorsal fin about same size as second, first dorsal origin approximately opposite pelvic fin origin, second dorsal fin much smaller than anal fin with insertion about opposite anal insertion. **CR** Reddish above with darker fin webs; white below. **Status:** DD.

3 Lollipop Catshark *Cephalurus cephalus* about 30cm

DN Southern Baja California, Gulf of California and possibly south to Peru and Chile. **HT** Upper continental slope and outermost shelf, on or near bottom; 155–927m. **ID** Unmistakable tadpole-shaped catshark. Small, slender, very soft, thin skinned body and tail. Expanded, flattened, rounded head and gill region;. Dorsal fins small, first dorsal slightly ahead pelvic fin origins. **CR** Uniform brownish-grey often with lighter fin margins. **Status:** DD.

4 Onefin Catshark *Pentanchus profundicolus* ♂51cm

DN Philippines. **HT** Insular slope, on bottom; 673–1070m. **ID** Only shark species with five gill slits and one dorsal fin. Unusually short abdomen. Snout broadly rounded. Short mouth. Short gills with incised gill septa. Pectoral and pelvic fins very close together; very long, shallow anal fin; long, narrow caudal fin. **CR** Uniform brownish. **Status:** DD.

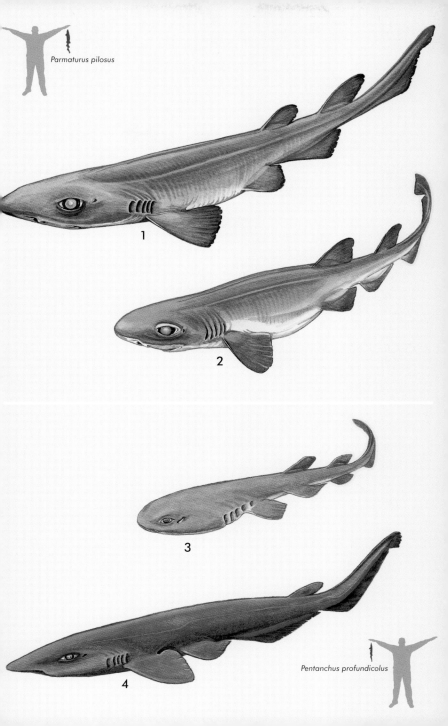

Parmaturus pilosus

1

2

3

Pentanchus profundicolus

4

1 **Narrowmouth Catshark** *Schroederichthys bivius* ♀70cm ♂82cm

DN Central Chile to southern Brazil. **HT** Temperate continental shelf and upper slope; 14–359m. **ID** Fairly slim body. Snout short, narrow and rounded. Narrow, lobate anterior nasal flaps. First dorsal origin slightly in front of pelvic insertions; short tail. Adult males longer and lighter, with much larger teeth and longer narrower mouths than females; mouths of young even longer and more slender. **CR** Grey-brown above with seven to eight dark brown saddles, two conspicuous interdorsal saddles, few scattered large dark and small white spots, dark spots do not border the saddles. **Status:** DD.

2 **Redspotted Catshark** *Schroederichthys chilensis* 70cm

DN Peru to south-central Chile. **HT** Temperate inshore continental shelf, on or near bottom; 1–50m. **ID** Moderately slim body. Snout short, broad and rounded; very broad; wide mouth. Broad, triangular anterior nasal flaps. First dorsal origin in front of pelvic insertions; short tail. Young more slender than adults. **CR** Dark reddish-brown above with conspicuous dark saddles, two interdorsal saddles; numerous dark spots and sometimes a few white spots; creamy-white below often with red spots. **Status:** DD.

3 **Narrowtail Catshark** *Schroederichthys maculatus* 35cm

DN Carribean. **HT** Tropical outer shelf and upper slope, deepwater, shelly or sandy bottom; 190–410m. **ID** Very slender body with elongated trunk region and tail in juveniles and adults. Snout rounded; long, wide mouth. Long, broad, triangular anterior nasal flaps. First dorsal fin origin slightly behind pelvic fin insertions; long tail. **CR** Dark tan to grey above; juveniles with six to nine inconspicuous brown saddles three interdorsal saddles; these fade in adult; juvenile and adult both with numerous, scattered, small white spots; no dark spots. **Status:** LC.

4 **Lizard Catshark** *Schroederichthys saurisqualus* at least 70cm

DN South Brazil; deep reef. **HT** Outer shelf and upper slope; 122–435m, mostly below 250m on deep-reef habitat. **ID** Slender trunk and tail. Snout rounded; moderately wide mouth. Long, narrow and lobate anterior nasal flaps. First dorsal fin origin slightly behind pelvic fin insertions. **CR** Adults and sub-adults light grey or brown above with ten conspicuous dusky saddles, four interdorsal saddles; numerous, scattered dark and small white spots. **Status:** V.

5 **Slender Catshark** *Schroederichthys tenuis* 47cm

DN Surinam to north Brazil. **HT** Outer continental shelf and upper continental slope, on or near bottom; 72–450m. **ID** Very slender. Snout broad; narrow mouth. Narrow, lobate anterior nasal flaps. First dorsal origin slightly behind pelvic insertions. Males have much larger teeth and a longer more angular mouth than females (may reach a larger size). **CR** Light brown above with seven to eight conspicuous dark saddles, four interdorsal saddles, outlined by many small dark spots; no white spots. **Status:** DD.

Schroederichthys bivius

1 Boa Catshark *Scyliorhinus boa* ♂54cm

DN South Caribbean to Surinam. **HT** Insular and continental slopes, on or near bottom; 200–700m. **ID** Moderately sized, slender catshark. Narrow, slender head. Anterior nasal flaps do not reach mouth; no nasoral grooves; lower labial furrows only. First dorsal fin much larger than second. **CR** Greyish above with inconspicuous saddles and flank markings, outlined by many black spots, some reticulating rows and broken lines; occasionally a few white spots. **Status:** LC.

2 Smallspotted Catshark *Scyliorhinus canicula* Med. Sea 60cm; N. Sea 100cm

DN Northeast Atlantic and Mediterranean. **HT** Continental shelves and upper slopes; nearshore to 110m. **ID** Relatively large, slender catshark. Blunt head. Anterior nasal flaps greatly expanded and reach mouth; shallow nasoral grooves; lower labial furrows only. First dorsal fin much larger than second. **CR** Greyish-brown above with eight to nine dusky saddles which may be inconspicuous; numerous, small dark spots; a few scattered white spots may be present; lighter below. **Status:** LC.

3 Yellowspotted Catshark *Scyliorhinus capensis* 122cm

DN Namibia and South Africa. **HT** Continental shelf and upper slope, bottom; 26–695m. **ID** Fairly large, slender catshark. Head slender but deep. Anterior nasal flaps small and do not reach mouth; no nasoral grooves; lower labial furrows only. First dorsal fin much larger than second. **CR** Light grey above with eight to nine irregular dark grey saddles; numerous small bright yellow spots; no dark spots. **Status:** NT.

4 West African Catshark *Scyliorhinus cervigoni* 76cm

DN Tropical west Africa. **HT** Continental shelf and upper slope, rocky to mud bottom; 45–500m. **ID** Moderately large, very stout catshark. Narrow, flattened in profile head. Anterior nasal flaps just reach mouth; no nasoral grooves; lower labial furrows only. First dorsal fin much larger than second; interdorsal space slightly less than anal fin base. **CR** Greyish or brownish above with eight to nine dark saddles centred on midline dark spots; few relatively large dark spots; no white spots. **Status:** DD.

5 Comoro Catshark *Scyliorhinus comoroensis* ♂46cm

DN Southwest Indian Ocean: Comoro Islands. **HT** Insular slopes, bottom; 200–400m. **ID** Small catshark. Moderately broad head. Anterior nasal flaps very large, reaching mouth; no nasoral grooves; lower labial furrows only. First dorsal fin much larger than second. **CR** Light grey patterned with bold, sharply defined dark grey-brown saddles centred on dark spots on the midline of the back and large blotches; numerous, scattered small white spots; no dark spots. **Status:** DD

6 Nursehound *Scyliorhinus stellaris* 162cm

DN Northeast Atlantic and Mediterranean. **HT** Continental shelf, rocky or seaweed-covered bottom; 1–125m. **ID** Very large, stocky catshark. Head broad and rounded. Anterior nasal flaps do not reach mouth and are widely separated; no nasoral grooves; lower labial furrows only. First dorsal fin much larger than second. **CR** Light grey or brown above; saddles faint to absent; numerous small back spots, large black spots may be irregular, occasionally expand into large blotches totally covering the body; sometimes white spots. **Status:** NT.

Scyliorhinus canicula

Scyliorhinus stellaris

1 Polkadot Catshark *Scyliorhinus besnardi* ♂ 47cm

DN North Uruguay to southern Brazil. **HT** Outer continental shelf, on bottom; 140–90m. **ID** Fairly small slender catshark. Anterior nasal flaps small and do not reach mouth; no nasoral grooves; lower labial furrows only. First dorsal fin much larger than second. **CR** No prominent saddles; sparse almost round black spots; no white spots. **Status:** DD.

2 Brownspotted Catshark *Scyliorhinus garmani* immature 24cm

DN Indo-western Pacific, possibly Philippines. **HT** Unknown depth. **ID** Relatively stocky catshark. Anterior nasal flaps broad but do not reach mouth; no nasoral grooves; lower labial furrows only. First dorsal fin much larger than second; anal fin base shorter than interdorsal space. **CR** Seven indistinct saddles; scattered large round brown spots; no white spots. **Status:** DD.

3 Freckled Catshark *Scyliorhinus haeckelii* 50cm

DN Venezuala to Uruguay. **HT** Continental shelf and upper slope, on or near bottom; 37–439m. **ID** Small, slender catshark. Anterior nasal flaps small and do not reach mouth; no nasoral grooves; lower labial furrows only. First dorsal fin much larger than second. **CR** Seven to eight dusky saddles which may be inconspicuous; dark bar under eye; small black spots; no light spots. **Status:** DD.

4 Whitesaddled Catshark *Scyliorhinus hesperius* ♀ at least 47cm

DN Caribbean Honduras to Colombia. **HT** Upper continental slope, on or near bottom; 274–457m. **ID** Fairly small, slender catshark. Anterior nasal flaps small but nearly reach mouth; no nasoral gooves; lower labial furrows only. First dorsal fin much larger than second. **CR** Seven to eight well defined dark saddles covered by large white spots; no black spots. **Status:** DD.

5 Blotched Catshark *Scyliorhinus meadi* immature 49cm

DN North Carolina to Yucatan. **HT** Continental slope, on or near bottom; 329–548m. **ID** Stocky catshark. Anterior nasal flaps small nearly reach mouth; no nasoral grooves; lower labial furrows only. First dorsal fin much larger than second. **CR** Seven to eight darker saddles may be obscure; no spots. **Status:** DD.

6 Chain Catshark *Scyliorhinus retifer* 59cm

DN Massachusetts to Florida, Gulf of Mexico and Caribbean. **HT** Outer continental shelf and upper slope, on or near bottom; 73–754m. **ID** Anterior nasal flaps do not reach mouth; no nasoral grooves; lower labial furrows well developed. First dorsal fins set well back, first much larger than second. **CR** Distinctive black chain patterning outlines faint dusky saddles; no spots. **Status:** LC.

7 Izu Catshark *Scyliorhinus tokubee* at least 41cm

DN Japan and Taiwan. **HT** Continental shelf, offshore; 100m or more. **ID** Narrow anterior nasal flaps nearly reach mouth; no nasoral grooves; lower labial furrows only. First dorsal fin much larger than second. **CR** Bold, sharply defined red-brown saddles on midline of back and large lateral blotches; very numerous, conspicuous, densely set, small, yellow spots in saddles and spaces between; no dark spots. **Status:** DD.

8 Cloudy Catshark *Scyliorhinus torazame* 48cm

DN Japan to possibly south Taiwan and the Philippines. **HT** Continental shelf and upper slope; close inshore to at least 320m. **ID** Rough skin. Anterior nasal flaps small and do not reach mouth; no nasoral grooves; lower labial furrows only. First dorsal fin much larger than second. **CR** Six to nine darker saddles and, in larger specimens, many irregular, large, dark and light spots. **Status:** LC.

9 Dwarf Catshark *Scyliorhinus torrei* 32cm

DN Bahamas, Cuba, and Virgin Islands. **HT** Upper continental slope, on or near bottom; 229–550m. **ID** Anterior nasal flaps small and do not reach mouth; no nasoral grooves; lower labial furrows only. First dorsal fin much larger than second. **CR** Seven to eight darker brown saddles, obscure in adults; scattered large, regular, white spots; no black spots. **Status:** LC.

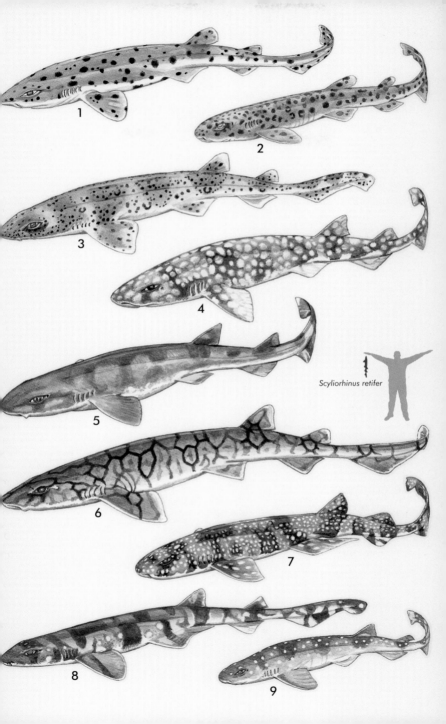

Scyliorhinus retifer

1 Harlequin Catshark *Ctenacis fehlmanni* ♀46cm

DN Somalia and Oman. **HT** Outer continental shelf; deeper than 300m. **ID** Stoutish body and tail. Nictitating eyelids; anterior nasal flaps do not reach large triangular mouth; very short labial furrows. **CR** Unique pattern of large red-brown saddle blotches; smaller round spots and vertical bars. **Status:** DD.

2 Cuban Ribbontail Catshark *Eridacnis barbouri* 34cm

DN Florida Straits to north Cuba. **HT** Upper continental and insular slopes, bottom; 430–613m. **ID** Small; slender. Nictitating eyelids; anterior nasal flaps do not reach triangular mouth; short but well-developed labial furrows. Anal fin two-thirds dorsal fin heights; long, narrow, ribbon-like caudal fin. **CR** Light greyish-brown with faint dark bands on caudal fin; light edging on dorsal fins. **Status:** DD.

3 Pygmy Ribbontail Catshark *Eridacnis radcliffei* ♀24cm

DN Patchy Indo-west Pacific. **HT** Upper continental, insular slopes and outer shelves, mud bottom; 71–766m. **ID** Extremely small; slender. Nictitating eyelids; anterior nasal flaps do not reach broad triangular mouth; no labial furrows. Anal fin less than half dorsal fin heights; long, narrow, ribbon-like caudal fin. **CR** Dark brown with prominent dark bands on caudal fin, blackish markings on dorsal fins. **Status:** LC.

4 African Ribbontail Catshark *Eridacnis sinuans* 37cm

DN Mozambique to Tanzania. **HT** Upper continental slope and outer shelf; 180–480m. **ID** Dwarf; slender. Fairly long snout; nictitating eyelids; anterior nasal flaps do not reach triangular mouth, short labial furrows. Anal fin half dorsal fin height. **CR** Greyish-brown with faint dark bands on caudal fin; light margins on dorsal fins. **Status:** LC.

5 Graceful Catshark *Proscyllium habereri* 65cm

DN West Pacific. **HT** Continental and insular shelves; 50–100m. **ID** Slender. Large eyes; nictitating eyelids; large anterior nasal flaps nearly reach triangular mouth which extends past eyes, short labial furrows. Long tail. **CR** Indistinct dusky saddle blotches; small to large dark brown spots; occasionally small white. **Status:** DD.

6 Magnificent Catshark *Proscyllium magnificum* 49cm

DN Andaman Sea. **HT** Near edge outer continental shelf; known from 141–144m. **ID** Slender. Large eyes; nictitating eyelids; large anterior nasal flaps nearly reach triangular mouth which extends past eyes, very short labial furrows. Long tail. **CR** Similar to *P. habereri* but more variegated pattern of large and small spots, including two spots and bar forming 'clown face' pattern below dorsal fins. **Status:** NE.

False catsharks

7 Slender Smoothhound *Gollum attenuatus* 110cm

DN New Zealand. **HT** Outermost continental shelf, upper slope and adjacent seamounts; 129–724m. **ID** Slender. Very long, angular snout; nictitating eyelids; anterior nasal flaps short; triangular mouth extends behind eyes; short labial furrows. Second dorsal slightly larger than first. **CR** Greyish above, light below. **Status:** LC.

8 Sulu Gollumshark *Gollum suluensis* ♀at least 65cm

DN Philippines. **HT** Upper continental slope or upper shelf, deepwater; from about 730m. **ID** Shorter snout than other gollumshark. **CR** Dark grey-brown above; lighter below; dorsal, pectoral and pelvic fins with paler posterior margins; terminal caudal lobe light with dark to black edge. **Status:** NE.

9 Whitemarked Gollumshark *Gollum* sp. B about 60cm

DN New Caledonia. **HT** Presumably deepwater on upper continental slope or upper shelf. **ID** Snout same size or slightly larger than *G. attenuatus*. **CR** Grey-brown above; pale brown below; characteristic conspicuous row of white spots on tail; bold white marks on head and fins. **Status:** NE.

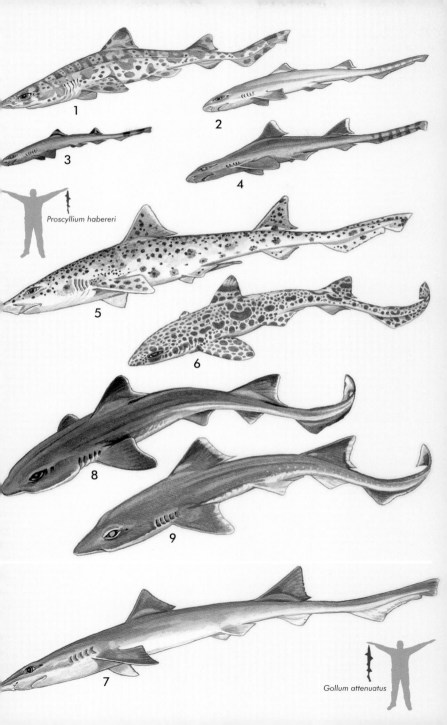

Proscyllium habereri

Gollum attenuatus

FINBACK CATSHARKS: Proscylliidae – page 172

A small family containing three genera, with six described species included here: *Ctenacis* (one species), *Eridacnis* (three species) and two species of *Proscyllium*. A fourth undescribed species of (probably) *Eridacnis* has been collected from the Philippines.

Identification Dwarf to small sharks (adults 15–65cm) with narrowly rounded head and rounded or subangular snout, no deep groove in front of elongated, cat-like eyes. Rudimentary nictitating eyelids. No barbels or nasoral grooves, internarial space less than 1.3 times nostril width, long angular arched mouth reaching past anterior ends of eyes, small papillae on palate and edges of gill arches, labial furrows very short or absent. First dorsal fin base short and well ahead of pelvic fin bases, but closer to pelvic bases than pectoral bases, no precaudal pits, cauda fin without a strong ventral lobe or lateral undulations on its dorsal margin. Body and fin colour usually variegated, but *Eridacnis* species with plain bodies and striped caudal fins.

Biology Most are viviparous, except for oviparous *Proscyllium habereri*, and feed on small fishes and invertebrates.

Status Poorly known deepwater sharks of outer continental and insular shelves and upper slopes, on or near bottom, 50–766m. Disjunct distribution, mostly in Indo-west Pacific but also in tropical northwest Atlantic.

FALSE CATSHARKS: Pseudotriakidae – pages 172 and 176

This poorly known family of deepwater sharks contains at least five species in three genera, although some of the smaller species, one of which is also a new genus, were still undescribed as this book went to print.

Identification Small to large sharks (adults 56–295cm) with narrowly rounded head and more or less elongated bell-shaped snout, a deep groove in front of elongated, cat-like eyes. Rudimentary nictitating eyelids. No barbels or nasoral grooves, internarial space over 1.5 times nostril width, long angular arched mouth reaching past anterior ends of eyes, no papillae inside mouth and none on edges of gill arches, labial furrows short but always present. First dorsal fin more or less elongated, base closer to pectoral fin bases than to pelvic fin bases, no precaudal pits, caudal fin with a weak ventral lobe or none, no lateral undulations on its dorsal margin. Colour usually plain grey to brown or blackish (white spots and fin margins on some *Gollum* species).

Biology Viviparous as far as known, at least two species are known to be oophagous, with foetuses eating nutritive eggs. Probably prey upon small fishes and invertebrates.

Status Poorly-known deepwater sharks of outer continental and insular shelves and slopes, on or near the bottom, 129–1890m. The large *Pseudotriakis microdon* is wide-ranging but small species have restricted distributions in western Indian Ocean and western Pacific. Absent from the South Atlantic and eastern Pacific.

BARBELED HOUNDSHARKS: Leptochariidae – page 176

One genus, one species *Leptocharias smithii*.

HOUNDSHARKS: Triakidae – pages 176–188

One of the largest families of sharks, with over 40 species, distributed worldwide in warm and temperate coastal seas. Most species occur in continental and insular waters, from the shoreline and intertidal to the outermost shelf, often close to the bottom, with many in sandy, muddy and rocky inshore habitats, enclosed bays and near river mouths. A few deepwater species range down continental slopes to great depths, possibly deeper than 2000m. Many are endemic with a very restricted distribution.

Identification Small to medium-sized sharks with two medium to large spineless dorsal fins, the first dorsal base well ahead of pelvic bases, and an anal fin. Horizontally oval eyes with nictitating eyelids, no nasoral grooves, anterior nasal flaps not barbel-like (except in *Furgaleus*), a long, angular or arched mouth reaching past the front of the eyes, moderate to very long labial furrows. Caudal fin without a strong ventral lobe or lateral undulations on its dorsal margin. Some (e.g. *Mustelus*) can be very hard to identify without vertebral counts and many species are undescribed.

Biology Some species are very active and swim almost continuously, others can rest on the bottom, and many swim close to the seabed. Some are most active by day, others at night. Houndsharks are viviparous, with or without a yolk sac placenta, bearing litters from one or two to 52 pups. They feed mainly on bottom and midwater invertebrates and bony fishes; some take largely crustaceans, some mainly fishes, and a few primarily cephalopods; none feed on birds or mammals.

Status Houndsharks are generally fairly common and some are very abundant in coastal waters, fished extensively for their meat, liver oil and fins (e.g. *Galeorhinus* and *Mustelus*). Some of the smaller coastal species reproduce rapidly and can support well-managed fisheries. Others have a history of stock collapse where fisheries are unregulated and require much more careful management. Some species are extremely rare. None are harmful to people.

WEASEL SHARKS: Hemigaleidae – page 190

There are four genera in this family, containing eight described species. *Chaenogaleus* and *Hemipristis* contain one species each, *Hemigaleus* two species, and *Paragaleus* at least four, although there is probably at least a fifth undescribed species in the latter.

Identification Small to medium-sized sharks with horizontal oval eyes with nictitating eyelids, small spiracles, long labial furrows, precaudal pits, spiral intestinal valves, and large second dorsal fins. Caudal fin with a strong ventral lobe and wavy dorsal edge.

Biology Live-bearing (viviparous), with yolk sac placenta. Some are specialist feeders on cephalopods, others have a very varied diet.

Status Worldwide in fossil record, now restricted to shallow tropical continental and insular shallow shelf waters of east Atlantic and Indo-west Pacific. Common and important in inshore fisheries.

Plate 58: FALSE CATSHARKS, BARBELED HOUNDSHARKS AND HOUNDSHARKS

1 **Pygmy False Catshark** *Planonasus parini* — at least 56cm

DN Arabian Sea and Maldives. **HT** Continental and insular slopes; 560–1120m. **ID** Moderately stocky; soft body. Short snout, bell-shaped; nictitating eyelids; anterior nasal flaps short; angular mouth extends behind eyes; short labial furrow; small spiracles. Relatively short subtriangular first dorsal fin; second dorsal fin larger than first. **CR** Dark grey-brown with dark fins. **Status:** NE.

2 **False Catshark** *Pseudotriakis microdon* — 295cm

DN Patchy worldwide except south Atlantic and east Pacific. **HT** Continental and insular slopes; bottom 100–1890m. **ID** Large shark with stocky soft body. Short snout, bell-shaped; nictitating eyelids; anterior nasal flaps short; huge angular mouth; short labial furrows; very large spiracles. Long, low, keel-like first dorsal fin; second much higher. **CR** Uniform dark brown to blackish. **Status:** DD.

Barbeled houndsharks

3 **Barbeled Houndshark** *Leptocharias smithii* — 82cm

DN Angola to Mauritania possibly Mediterranean. **HT** Continental shelf, near bottom; 10–75m. **ID** Relatively small; slender. Horizontal oval eyes, internal nictitating eyelids; nostrils with slender barbels; long arched mouth reaching past eyes; very long labial furrows. **CR** Light grey-brown above; light below. **Status:** NT.

Houndsharks

4 **Whiskery Shark** *Furgaleus macki* — 160cm

DN Australia. **HT** Shallow temperate continental shelf, on or near bottom. **ID** Stocky, almost humpbacked. Conspicuous subocular ridges; dorsolateral eyes; only houndshark with anterior nasal flaps forming barbels; very short, arched mouth. **CR** Grey above with variegated dark blotches and saddles that fade with age; lighter below. **Status:** LC.

5 **Sailback Houndshark** *Gogolia filewoodi* — ♀74cm

DN North New Guinea. **HT** Only known specimen probably near bottom; 73m. **ID** Small. Preoral snout long. First dorsal fin very large and triangular (length about the same as caudal fin). **CR** Grey-brown above; lighter below. **Status:** DD.

6 **Blacktip Topeshark** *Hypogaleus hyugaensis* — at least 130cm

DN West Indian Ocean, northwest and southwest Pacific. **HT** Tropical and warm temperate seas, near bottom; 40–480m. **ID** Medium-sized; fairly slender. Snout long and broadly pointed; large oval eyes with subocular ridges; small anterior nasal flaps; arched mouth. First dorsal fin larger than second; second dorsal larger than anal fin; relatively short terminal caudal lobe. **CR** Bronze to grey-brown above; lighter below; dusky dorsal and upper caudal fin tips, especially in young. **Status:** NT.

7 **Tope** *Galeorhinus galeus* — ♀195cm ♂175cm

DN Worldwide most temperate waters. **HT** Continental shelf, often on or near bottom; 2–471m. **ID** Large slender houndshark. Snout long and conical; no obvious subocular ridges; small anterior nasal flaps; large arched mouth. First dorsal fin much larger second; second dorsal same size as anal fin; very long terminal caudal lobe. **CR** Grey above; white below; black fin markings in young; sometimes few dusky spots. **Status:** V.

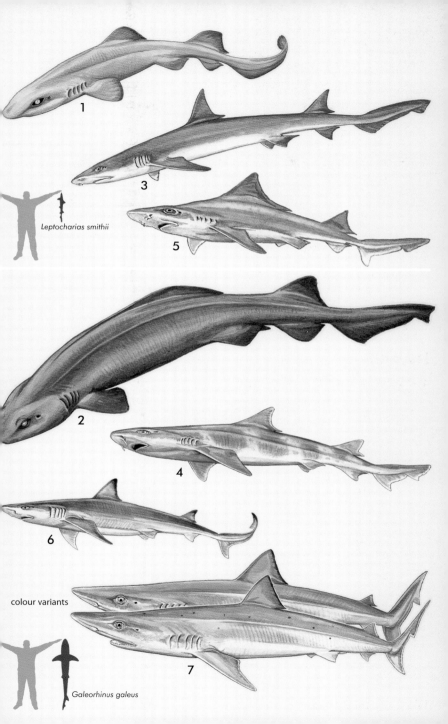

1

3

Leptocharias smithii

5

2

4

6

7

colour variants

Galeorhinus galeus

1 Deepwater Sicklefin Houndshark *Hemitriakis abdita*   more than 80cm

DN Australia, possibly New Caledonia. **HT** Upper continental slope, deepwater; 225–400m. **ID** Slender houndshark. Snout long and parabolic; small anterior nasal flaps; arched mouth; long upper labial furrows, shorter lowers. Falcate dorsal, pectoral and anal fins; first dorsal fin same size as second. **CR** Grey-brown above; distinct white dorsal, pectoral and anal fin tips; paler below with dark stripe under snout; juveniles prominent dark bars and saddles. **Status:** DD.

2 Striped Topeshark *Hemitriakis complicofasciata*   93cm

DN Southern Japanese Islands and Taiwan. **HT** Inshore; from about 90–100m. **ID** Slender houndshark. Snout short and blunt; prominent sub-ocular ridge; small anterior nasal flaps; moderately arched mouth; long upper labial furrows, shorter lowers. Falcate dorsal, pectoral and anal fins; first dorsal fin higher than second. **CR** Greyish-brown above with vague saddles; caudal fin with white posterior margins; whitish below, no stripe under snout; near term young distinctly patterned with dark O-shaped spots, bars and saddles which fade with age. **Status:** DD.

3 Sicklefin Houndshark *Hemitriakis falcata*   77cm

DN Northwest Australia. **HT** Outer continental shelf, temperate to subtropical; 110–200m. **ID** Slender houndshark. Snout long and blunt; small anterior nasal flaps, arched mouth; long upper labial furrows, shorter lowers. Strongly falcate dorsal, pectoral and anal fins; first dorsal fin same size as second; first dorsal fin origin over to behind pectoral fin rear tips. **CR** Grey-brown above; prominent white dorsal fin tips, thin white tips to pectoral, pelvic and lower caudal fin; upper caudal fin tip dusky; paler below with no stripe under snout; juveniles with saddles and large spots. **Status:** LC.

4 Indonesian Houndshark *Hemitriakis indroyonoi*   120cm

DN Eastern Indonesia. **HT** Outer continental shelf; to 60m or more. **ID** Slender houndshark. Snout long and narrow; rounded anterior nasal flaps, arched mouth; long upper labial furrows, shorter lowers. Falcate dorsal fins, pectoral fins semifalcate and anal fins strongly falcate; first dorsal fin slightly lager than second; first dorsal fin origin behind pectoral fin rear tips. **CR** Greyish-brown above; lighter below; adults plain grey with prominent white fin tips; newborns with dark blotches and bars. **Status:** NE.

5 Japanese Topeshark *Hemitriakis japanica*   ♀ at least 120cm ♂110cm

DN Northwestern Pacific, China to Japan. **HT** Continental shelf, temperate to subtropical inshore; to over 100m. **ID** Snout moderately long and parabolic; short anterior nasal flaps; broad arched mouth; moderately long upper labial furrows, shorter lowers. Fins not strongly falcate; first dorsal fin about same size as second; first dorsal fin origin over to behind pectoral fin rear tips; first dorsal fin much larger than anal fin. **CR** Grey above with conspicuous white-edged fins; lighter below, no dark stripe under snout. **Status:** LC.

6 Whitefin Topeshark *Hemitriakis leucoperiptera*   ♀96cm

DN Philippines. **HT** Coastal; to about 48m. **ID** Snout moderately long and parabolic; small anterior nasal flaps; broadly arched mouth; moderately long uppler labial furrows, shorter lowers. Fins strongly falcate, first dorsal fin larger than second; first dorsal fin origin over to behind pectoral fin rear tip; first dorsal fin much larger than anal fin. **CR** Grey above with conspicuous white-edged fins; lighter below, no dark stripe under snout. **Status:** E.

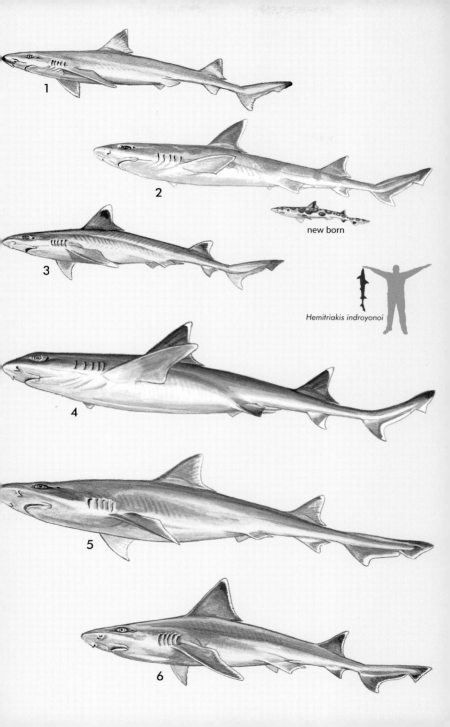

new born

Hemitriakis indroyonoi

Plate 60: HOUNDSHARKS III

1 Longnose Houndshark *Iago garricki* 75cm

DN Southwest Pacific. **HT** Upper continental and insular slopes, deepwater tropical; 250–475m. **ID** Slender houndshark. First dorsal fin slightly larger than second dorsal; first dorsal fin origin over pectoral fin inner margins. **CR** Grey-brown above with conspicuous black dorsal fin tips and upper posterior margins; pale tips and posterior margins to pectoral and caudal fins; pale below. **Status:** LC.

2 Mangalore Houndshark *Iago mangalorensis* more than 41cm

DN Gulf of Aden to southwest India. **HT** Outer continental shelf and upper slope, also semipelagic; 0–183m. **ID** Very slender houndshark. Short head; large eyes; large gills. Dorsal fins small and low; first dorsal fin origin over pectoral fin bases; pectoral fins small; ventral caudal fin lobe small. **CR** Dark brown above; lighter below. **Status:** NE.

3 Bigeye Houndshark *Iago omanensis* ♀58cm ♂ much smaller

DN Red and Arabian Sea. **HT** Continental shelf and slope, on or near bottom; shallower than 110–1000m, possibly much deeper. **ID** Slender houndshark. Large eyes; large gills. Dorsal fins small; first dorsal fin origin over pectoral fin bases; ventral caudal fin lobe small. **CR** Grey-brown above, sometimes with darker dorsal fin posterior margins; lighter below. **Status:** LC.

4 Flapnose Houndshark *Scylliogaleus quecketti* 102cm

DN South Africa. **HT** Inshore continental shelf, surfline and close offshore. **ID** Short blunt snout; large fused anterior nasal flaps, covers mouth. First dorsal fin same size as second; second dorsal fin much larger than anal fin. **CR** Grey above; cream below; newborns white posterior margins to dorsal, anal and caudal fins. **Status:** V.

5 Sharpfin Houndshark *Triakis acutipinna* mature ♀102cm ♂90cm

DN Ecuador. **HT** Tropical continental waters. **ID** Snout broadly rounded; widely separated anterior nasal flaps do not reach mouth; long upper labial furrows reach lower symphysis. Narrow fins; pectoral fins falcate; first dorsal fin with abrupt vertical posterior margin. **CR** Greyish above; paler below. **Status:** E.

6 Spotted Houndshark *Triakis maculata* 180cm, possibly 240cm

DN Peru to north Chile and Galapagos. **HT** Inshore temperate continental shelf. **ID** Stout. Snout broadly rounded; widely separated lobate anterior nasal flaps do not reach mouth; long upper labial furrows reach lower symphasis. Broad fins; pectoral fins falcate with straight posterior margins; first dorsal fin with backward sloping posterior margin. **CR** Greyish above with many black spots; paler below. **Status:** V.

7 Spotted Gully Shark *Triakis megalopterus* possibly 208cm

DN South Angola to South Africa. **HT** Surfline to shallow inshore. **ID** Snout broad and blunt; widely separated, small, lobate anterior nasal flaps do not reach mouth; upper labial furrow does not reach lower symphasis. Broad large fins; pectoral fins falcate with concave posterior margins; first dorsal fin almost vertical. **CR** Grey-bronze above with usually many small black spots; white below. **Status:** NT.

8 Banded Houndshark *Triakis scyllium* 150cm

DN South Siberia to China. **HT** Continental and insular inshore, on or near bottom. **ID** Fairly slender. Short snout, broadly rounded; widely separated lobate anterior nasal flaps do not reach mouth; long upper labial furrow reach lower symphysis. Pectoral fins almost triangular; first dorsal fin almost vertical. **CR** Grey above with usually sparsely scattered small black spots; dusky saddles in young. **Status:** LC.

9 Leopard Shark *Triakis semifasciata* 180cm, est. 210cm

DN Oregon to Gulf of California. **HT** Inshore and offshore continental shelf, on or near bottom; 0–20m, records to 91m. **ID** Snout broadly rounded; widely separated anterior nasal flaps do not reach mouth; upper labial furrow reach lower symphysis. Broad large fins; pectoral fins falcate. **CR** Pale tan to greyish above with a unique colour pattern of saddles and spots; whitish below. **Status:** LC.

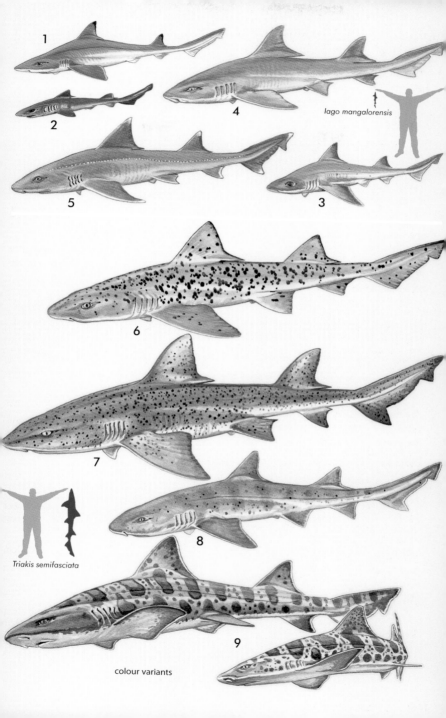

Iago mangalorensis

Triakis semifasciata

colour variants

Plate 61: HOUNDSHARKS IV

1 Starry Smoothhound *Mustelus asterias* 140cm

DN North Sea to Mauritania, Canary Islands and Mediterranean. **HT** Continental and insular shelves, on or near sand and gravel; intertidal to 100m or more. **ID** Large, slender houndshark. Rounded snout; nostrils closer together than similar species in region; upper labial furrows long, much shorter lowers. Unfringed high dorsal fins, first dorsal origin over pectoral fin inner margins, first dorsal slightly larger than second; pectoral and pelvic fins fairly small. **CR** Grey to grey-brown above, only European smoothhound with numerous white spots, however these spots can fade in some individuals; white below. **Status:** LC.

2 Dusky Smoothhound *Mustelus canis* 150cm

DN Canada to Argentina. **HT** Continental shelf subspecies and island subspecies, widely separated discrete populations; shallower than 18–200m, maximum 360m. **ID** Large, slender houndshark. Short head and snout; large close-set eyes; nostrils widely spaced; upper labial furrows moderately long, shorter lowers. Unfringed high dorsal fins, first dorsal origin over pectoral fin free rear tips, first dorsal fin larger than second. **CR** Grey above, usually unspotted; white below; newborn with dusky tip to dorsal and caudal fins. **Status:** NT.

3 Smoothhound *Mustelus mustelus* ♀164cm ♂ at least 110cm

DN Temperate eastern Atlantic. **HT** Continental shelves and upper slopes, intertidal to 350m. **ID** Large, fairly slender houndshark. Short head and snout; large close-set eyes; nostrils widely spaced; upper labial furrows moderately long, shorter lowers. Unfringed high dorsal fins, first dorsal origin over pectoral fin inner margins, first dorsal slightly larger than second; pectoral and pelvic fins fairly small. **CR** Grey to grey-brown above, usually unspotted, occasionally dark spots; white below. **Status:** V.

4 Whitespot Smoothhound *Mustelus palumbes* 113cm

DN Namibia to south Mozamique. **HT** Continental shelf and upper slope, on or near sand and gravel; intertidal to 360m. **ID** Fairly large houndshark. Short head and snout; nostrils relatively widely spaced, upper labial furrows long, shorter lowers. Unfringed moderately high dorsal fins, first dorsal origin over pectoral fin inner margins, first dorsal slightly larger than second; large pectoral fins (larger than *M. asterias*, *M. manazo* and *M. mustelus*). **CR** Grey to grey-brown above, usually white-spotted (only South African smoothhound with white spots); white below. **Status:** DD.

5 Blackspot Smoothhound *Mustelus punctulatus* less than 95cm

DN West Sahara and Mediterranean. **HT** Inshore continental shelf, on bottom. **ID** Medium-sized, slender houndshark. Short, narrow head; short snout; large eyes; nostrils close together; upper labial furrows moderately long, slightly shorter lowers. Prominently fringed dorsal fins, first dorsal origin over pectoral fin inner margins, first dorsal larger than second; moderately-sized pectoral fins. **CR** Grey above, usually black-spotted; light below; often mistaken for *M. mustelus*. **Status:** DD.

6 Narrownose Smoothhound *Mustelus schmitti* 109cm

DN South Brazil to north Argentina. **HT** Offshore continental shelf; 60–195m. **ID** Medium-sized, fairly slender houndshark. Short head; snout moderately long; nostrils close together; upper labial furrows moderately long; much shorter lowers. Prominently fringed high dorsal fins give dark frayed appearance, first dorsal origin well over pectoral fin inner margins, first dorsal much larger than second; moderately-sized pectoral fins. **CR** Grey above with white spots; easily distinguished from other white-spotted *Mustelus*; white below. **Status:** E.

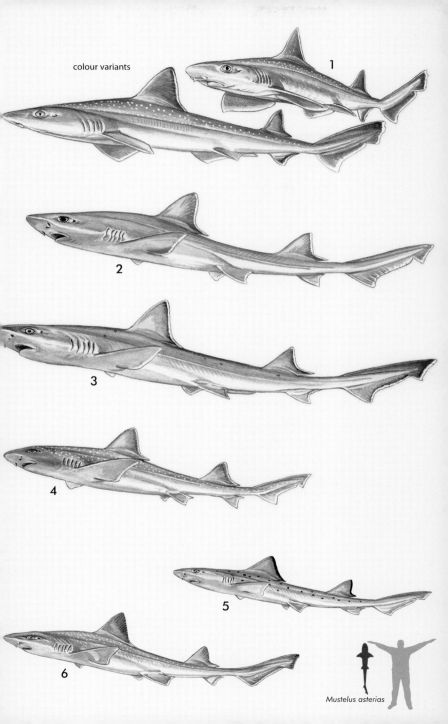

colour variants

1

2

3

4

5

6

Mustelus asterias

Plate 62: HOUNDSHARKS V

1 Grey Smoothhound *Mustelus californicus* ♀125cm ♂116cm

DN Northern California to Gulf of California. **HT** Continental shelves, bottom, warm temperate to tropical; inshore and offshore. **ID** Relatively large, slender houndshark. Short, narrow head; fairly small eyes; nostrils widely spaced; short mouth; upper labial furrows same length as lowers. Triangular dorsal fins, first closer to pelvic fins than pectorals, first dorsal larger than second; ventral caudal fin lobe poorly developed. **CR** Uniform grey above, no spots; light below. **Status:** LC.

2 Sharptooth Smoothhound *Mustelus dorsalis* 64cm

DN Eastern Pacific: Mexico to Ecuador. **HT** Tropical continental shelf; inshore. **ID** Small, fairly slender houndshark. Long, acutely pointed snout; very small, wide-set eyes; large nostrils, moderately spaced; upper labial furrows moderately long; shorter lowers. Broadly triangular, unfringed dorsal fins, first dorsal origin over pectoral fin free rear tips, first dorsal larger than second. **CR** Uniform grey or grey-brown above, no spots; light below. **Status:** DD.

3 Spotless Smoothhound *Mustelus griseus* ♀101cm ♂87cm

DN Japan to Vietnam. **HT** Continental shelf; intertidal to 51m or more. **ID** Medium-sized, slender houndshark. Short head and snout; small eyes; nostrils widely spaced; upper labial furrow about same length as lower, or slightly shorter. Unfringed roughly equally-sized dorsal fins, first dorsal midbase about equidistant between pectoral and pelvic bases; ventral caudal fin lobe semifalcate. **CR** Above uniform grey or grey-brown, no spots; light below. **Status:** DD.

4 Brown Smoothhound *Mustelus henlei* 100cm

DN Northern California to Mexico, and Ecuador to Peru. **HT** Continental shelf; intertidal to 200m or more. **ID** Medium-sized, slender houndshark. Short head; moderately long snout; large close-set eyes; nostrils widely spaced; upper labial furrows moderately long, shorter lowers. Caudal peduncle long. Dark broadly fringed dorsal fins, first dorsal broadly triangular with its midbase closer to pelvic bases than to pectorals. **CR** Usually iridescent bronze-brown occasionally grey above, no spots; white below. **Status:** LC.

5 Starspotted Smoothhound *Mustelus manazo* ♀117cm ♂96cm

DN South Siberia to Vietnam, and Kenya. **HT** Temperate to tropical continental shelf, mud and sand; inshore. **ID** Relatively large, fairly slender. Short head; moderately long snout; large close-set eyes; nostrils fairly close-set; upper labial furrows long, much shorter lowers. Unfringed dorsal fins; relatively small pectoral and pelvic fins. **CR** Grey to grey-brown above with white spots (only spotted houndshark in range); light below. **Status:** DD.

6 Speckled Smoothhound *Mustelus mento* 130cm

DN Galapagos to Peru and Argentina. **HT** Temperate continental and insular shelves, inshore and offshore; 16 to 50m. **ID** Large, stocky houndshark. Fairly short head; short, blunt, angular snout; fairly small moderately spaced eyes; nostrils widely spaced; upper labial furrows long; shorter lowers. Caudal peduncle short. Unfringed large dorsal fins; anal fin much smaller than second dorsal. **CR** Grey to grey-brown above with numerous white spots; light below. **Status:** NT.

7 Arabian Smoothhound *Mustelus mosis* 150cm

DN West Indian Ocean, Red Sea and Gulf. **HT** Continental shelf, bottom, coral reefs; inshore and offshore. **ID** Large, fairly slender. Short head and snout; large fairly close-set eyes; nostrils widely spaced; upper labial furrow same length as lower. Unfringed fairly large dorsal fins; ventral caudal fin lobe semifalcate. **CR** Uniform grey or grey-brown above, no spots; light below; in South Africa first dorsal fin tip white, second dorsal and caudal fin tips black. **Status:** DD.

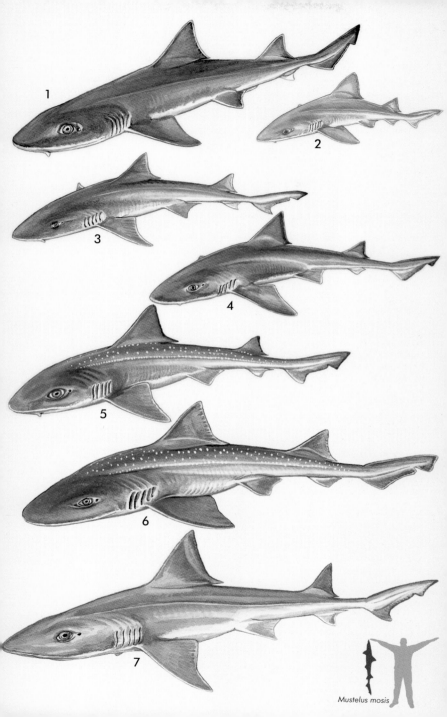

Mustelus mosis

1 White-margin Fin Houndshark *Mustelus albipinnis* 118cm

DN Gulf of Mexico to possibly Ecuador and Galapagos. **HT** Deepwater; from 100–226m. **ID** A fairly large, slender-bodied houndshark. Head and snout short; widely separated nostrils; upper labial furrows very long, shorter lowers, but still long. Unfringed dorsal fins, first larger than second. **CR** Distinguished from other species by a combination of uniform dark grey-brown above, lighter below, and with distinctive white fin edges on the posterior margins of the dorsal, pectoral, anal, and caudal fins. **Status:** DD.

2 Striped Smoothhound *Mustelus fasciatus* 155cm

DN South Brazil to north Argentina. **HT** Temperate continental shelf and uppermost slope, bottom; possibly intertidal to 70m, rarely to 500m. **ID** Large, fairly stocky houndshark. Long head; long angular pointed snout; very small eyes; nostrils widely spaced; upper labial furrow moderately long, lowers much shorter. Caudal peduncle short. Broadly triangular unfringed dorsal fins. **CR** Grey or grey-brown above with vertical dark bars in juveniles, fades in most adults, unspotted. **Status:** CE.

3 Smalleye Smoothhound *Mustelus higmani* 64cm

DN North Gulf of Mexico to Brazil. **HT** Continental shelf and upper slope, mud, sand and shell bottom; close inshore to 1281m. **ID** Small, fairly slender houndshark. Long acutely pointed snout; very small wide-set eyes; nostrils widely spaced; upper labial furrows same length as lowers. Unfringed dorsal fins, falcate first dorsal fin only slightly larger than second. **CR** Uniform grey or grey-brown above, no spots; light below. **Status:** LC.

4 Sicklefin Smoothhound *Mustelus lunulatus* possibly 175cm

DN Southern California to Panama. **HT** Warm temperate to tropical continental shelf; close inshore to well offshore. **ID** Distinguished from similar *M. californicus* by more pointed snout, more widely separated eyes, shorter mouth, shorter upper labial furrows and strongly falcate dorsal fins. **CR** Uniform grey to grey-brown above, no spots; light below. **Status:** LC.

5 Venezuelan Dwarf Smoothhound *Mustelus minicanis* ♀ at least 57cm

DN Colombia and Venezuela. **HT** Offshore, outer continental shelf; 71–183m. **ID** Small, stout houndshark. Short head and snout; very large close-set eyes; nostrils widely spaced; upper labial furrow slightly longer than lower. Unfringed dorsal fins; ventral caudal fin lobe poorly developed. **CR** Uniform grey above, no spots; light below; newborn dorsal and caudal fin tips dusky. **Status:** DD.

6 Narrowfin Smoothhound *Mustelus norrisi* 98cm

DN Gulf of Mexico- USA, Columbia, Venezuela and South Brazil. **HT** Continental shelf, sand and mud bottom; close inshore to 84m or more. **ID** Medium-sized, slender houndshark. Short narrow head; relatively large eyes; nostrils close-set; relatively long mouth; upper labial furrow longer than lower. Strongly falcate fins. **CR** Uniform grey above, no spots; light below; newborn dorsal and caudal fin tips dusky. **Status:** DD.

7 Gulf of Mexico Smoothhound *Mustelus sinusmexicanus* about 140cm

DN Gulf of Mexico- USA and Mexico. **HT** Offshore continental shelf and upper slope; 36 to 229m. **ID** Large houndshark. Short head and snout; large close-set eyes; nostrils widely spaced; upper labial furrow longer than lower. Unfringed dorsal fins, large first dorsal fin; ventral caudal fin lobe moderately expanded. **CR** Uniform grey above, no spots; light below; newborn dorsal and caudal fin tips dusky. **Status:** DD.

8 Humpback Smoothhound *Mustelus whitneyi* at least 87cm

DN Peru to south Chile. **HT** Continental shelf; 16 to 211m, prefers island rocky bottom. **ID** Stocky, almost humpbacked. Fairly long head and snout; fairly large eyes; nostrils widely spaced; upper labial furrow much longer than lower. Short caudal peduncle. Dark, fringed dorsal fins; ventral caudal fin lobe very slightly falcate. **CR** Uniform grey above, no spots; light below. **Status:** V.

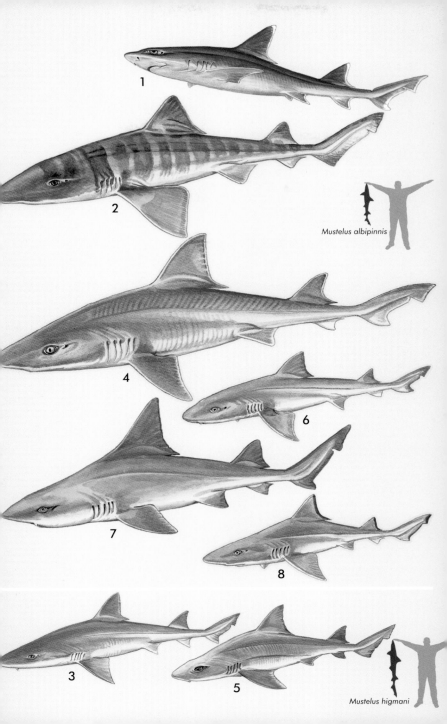

Mustelus albipinnis

Mustelus higmani

1 Gummy Shark *Mustelus antarcticus* ♀185cm ♂148cm

DN Australia. **HT** Mainly continental shelf, on or near bottom; shore to 350m, only *Mustelus* in Australian temperate waters. **ID** Large, slender houndshark. Snout relatively long; large nostrils widely spaced; angular mouth; long upper labial furrows, slightly longer than lower. Unfringed dorsal fins, first dorsal fin slightly larger than second; relatively small pectoral and pelvic fins. **CR** Bronze to grey-brown above with white spots, sometimes black spots; pale below. **Status:** LC.

2 Rig *Mustelus lenticulatus* ♀151cm ♂126cm

DN New Zealand. **HT** Cold temperate, insular shelf; close inshore to 220m. **ID** Large, fairly slender houndshark. Short head; moderately long snout; fairly large wide-set eyes; nostrils widely spaced; long upper labial furrow longer than lowers. Unfringed dorsal fins, first dorsal fin larger than second; relatively large pectoral and pelvic fins. **CR** Grey or grey-brown above with numerous white spots (only one in range); light below. **Status:** LC.

3 Australian Grey Smoothhound *Mustelus ravidus* 101cm

DN Northern (Tropical) Australia. **HT** Deep continental shelf; 100–300m. **ID** Moderately-sized, slender houndshark. Snout relatively long; relatively close-set eyes; nostrils widely spaced; upper labial furrows shorter than lowers. Unfringed dorsal fins, first fin dorsal larger than second; pectoral fins moderately broad; deeply notched caudal fin. **CR** Uniform bronze to grey-brown above, unspotted, second dorsal and upper caudal fin tips with dark margins; paler below. **Status:** LC.

4 Whitespotted Gummy Shark *Mustelus stevensi* 103cm

DN Northern (Tropical) Australia. **HT** Deep continental shelf; 120–400m, possibly deeper. **ID** Moderately-sized, slender houndshark, very similar to *M. antarcticus* but range does not overlap; snout relatively long; large nostrils widely spaced; relatively broad mouth; long upper labial furrows, longer than lower. Unfringed dorsal fins, first dorsal fin larger than second; relatively small pectoral and pelvic fins. **CR** Yellowish-grey to grey-brown above with numerous white spots, dorsal fins sometimes have dark tips; paler below; juveniles more strongly marked, other fins have pale tips and posterior margins; slight variance between east and west forms. **Status:** LC.

5 Eastern Spotted Gummy Shark *Mustelus walkeri* at least 122cm

DN Tropical eastern Australia. **HT** Continental shelf and upper slope; 50–400m. **ID** A fairly large, slender houndshark. Snout relatively long; relatively close-set eyes; large nostrils widely spaced; relatively broad mouth; long upper labial furrows, longer than relatively long lowers. Unfringed dorsal fins, first dorsal fin larger than second; relatively large, broad pectoral fins. **CR** Uniformly grey above, with numerous small indistinct spots; lighter below. **Status:** DD.

6 Whitefin Smoothhound *Mustelus widodoi* at least 110cm

DN Eastern Indonesia. **HT** Inshore; 60–120m. **ID** A fairly large, slender houndshark. Narrow snout; relatively narrow mouth; upper labial furrows about the same length as lowers. Unfringed relatively high dorsal fins, first dorsal fin tip rounded, second dorsal pointed. **CR** Uniform grey above with a broad white margin on the first dorsal fin and a distinct black margin on the second dorsal fin apex. **Status:** DD.

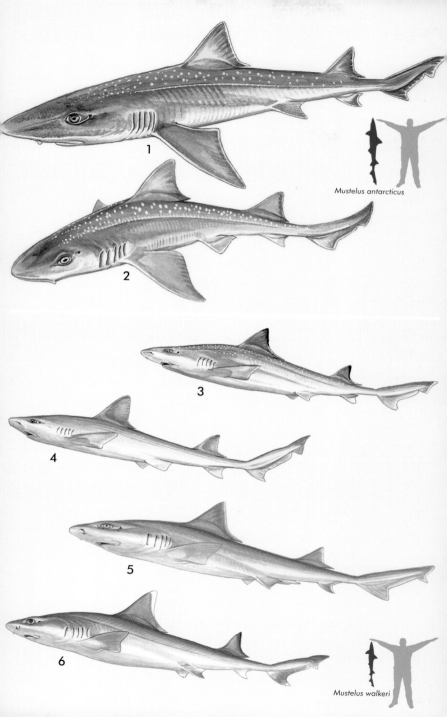

Mustelus antarcticus

Mustelus walkeri

Plate 65: WEASEL SHARKS

1 Hooktooth Shark *Chaenogaleus macrostoma* about 100cm

DN Gulf to Indonesia and China. **HT** Continental and insular shelves; to 59m. **ID** Fairly long angular snout; large lateral eyes with nictitating eyelid; small spiracles; very long mouth; gills more than twice eye length. Second dorsal fin two-thirds the size of first and opposite to slightly ahead of, smaller, anal fin origin. **CR** Light grey or bronze above, occasionally black second dorsal tip and caudal fin posterior tip. **Status:** V

2 Australian Weasel Shark *Hemigaleus australiensis* 110cm

DN North Australia, possibly Papua New Guinea. **HT** Continental shelf, on or near bottom; 12–170m. **ID** Very similar to *H. microstoma* but has different coloration. **CR** Light grey or bronze above; unmarked first dorsal fin, dark second dorsal tip and margin, dark caudal fin posterior tip, no white spots. **Status:** LC.

3 Sicklefin Weasel Shark *Hemigaleus microstoma* 91–94cm

DN India to Philippines and China, possibly Red Sea. **HT** Bottom continental shelf. **ID** Fairly long rounded snout; eyes with nictitating eyelid; small spiracles; very short arched mouth; gills short. Dorsal, pectoral, pelvic fins and ventral caudal lobe strongly falcate; second dorsal fin three quarters the size of first and opposite, equally sized, anal fin origin. **CR** Light grey or bronze above; dorsal fins with light tips and margins; occasionally white spots on sides. **Status:** V.

4 Snaggletooth Shark *Hemipristis elongata* 230–240cm

DN South Africa to north Australia, Philippines and China. **HT** Continental and insular shelve; to 132m. **ID** Long broadly rounded snout; large lateral eyes with nictitating eyelid; small spiracles; teeth protrude from mouth; gills more than three times eye length. Strongly curved concave fins; second dorsal fin two-thirds first and ahead of, smaller, anal fin origin. **CR** Light grey or bronze above; dusky second dorsal tip and caudal fin posterior tip. **Status:** V.

5 Whitetip Weasel Shark *Paragaleus leucolomatus* ♀96cm

DN East coast South Africa. **HT** Tropical coastal; to 20m. **ID** Long snout; large eyes with nictitating eyelid; small spiracles; fairly long mouth; gills about twice eye length. Dorsal, pectoral and ventral caudal fin lobe not falcate; second dorsal fin height about the same as first and ahead of, smaller, anal fin origin. **CR** Dark grey above, prominent white tips and margins on most fins except black-tipped second dorsal; white below, underside snout with broad dusky patches. **Status:** DD.

6 Atlantic Weasel Shark *Paragaleus pectoralis* 138cm

DN Cape Verdes, Mauritania to Angola and south to Namibia, possibly north to Morocco. **HT** Tropical shelf; to 100m. **ID** Moderately long snout; large oval eyes with nictitating eyelid; small spiracles; short small mouth; gill slits less than 1.5 times eye length. Second dorsal fin two-thirds the size of first and ahead of, much smaller, anal fin origin. **CR** Light grey or bronze above with striking longitudinal yellow bands; white below. **Status:** DD.

7 Slender Weasel Shark *Paragaleus randalli* more than 81cm

DN Arabian Sea. **HT** Inshore continental shelf; shallow water to 18m. **ID** Snout with narrowly rounded tip; large lateral eyes with nictitating eyelid; small spiracles; long mouth; gills about the same as eye length. Concave fins; second dorsal fin two-thirds the size of first and slightly ahead of, smaller, anal fin origin. **CR** Grey to grey-brown above, dark fins with inconspicuous light posterior margins; light below, underside snout with narrow black lines. **Status:** NT.

8 Straighttooth Weasel Shark *Paragaleus tengi* ♂70–88cm

DN Gulf of Thailand to South China, including Malaysia, and Japan. **HT** Inshore; to 20m. **ID** Moderately long rounded snout; large lateral eyes with nictitating eyelid; small spiracles; short arched mouth; gill slits about 1.2 to 1.3 times eye lengths. Second dorsal fin two-thirds the size of first and slightly ahead of, smaller, anal fin origin. **CR** Light grey above with no prominent markings. **Status:** DD.

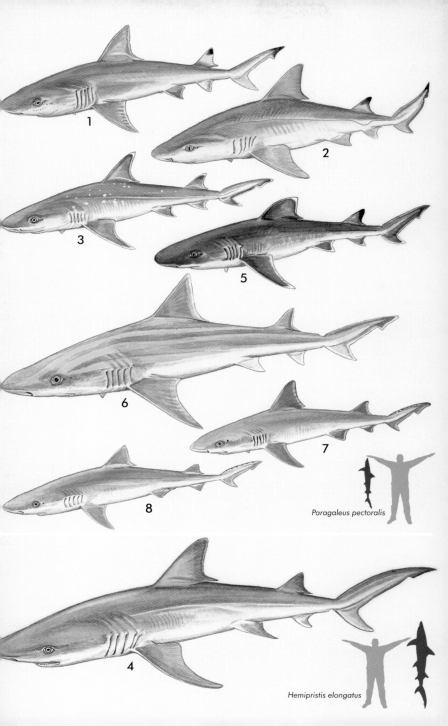

Paragaleus pectoralis

Hemipristis elongatus

REQUIEM SHARKS: Carcharhinidae – pages 194–218

The requiem shark family (Carcharhinidae) comprises 12 genera and at least 56 described species worldwide. This is one of the largest, most important shark families, with many common and wide-ranging species. Requiem sharks are the dominant group of sharks found in tropical waters, often both in biodiversity and in abundance and biomass, on continental shelves and offshore, but they are also found in subtropical and warm temperate seas. Most species inhabit tropical continental coastal and offshore marine waters, with a few occurring in freshwater rivers and lakes. Several members of this family prefer coral reefs and oceanic islands, while other species range far into ocean basins. One pelagic requiem shark, the Blue Shark, has one of the greatest geographic ranges of any shark or marine vertebrate, ranging from high latitude, cool temperate waters to the tropics. A few other species range into temperate waters and some even occur to great depths, but none are truly specialised deepwater sharks (compared with many species of the families Squalidae and Scyliorhinidae). Although members of other families may enter river mouths and ascend rivers for a short distance, a few requiem shark species (the little-known river sharks and the Bull Shark) appear to be the only living sharks that can live in freshwater for extended periods. The Bull Shark has a wide range in tropical and temperate rivers and lakes around the world and is remarkable for the apparent ease with which it can move from saline to freshwater conditions and back again.

Identification Although some species are relatively small (70–100cm), most are medium to large in size, with maximum lengths ranging to 740cm. They have a long arched mouth with blade-like teeth (often broader in upper jaw), most with short labial furrows (except *Galeocerdo* and *Rhizoprionodon*), no nasoral grooves or barbels. Usually round (to horizontal) eyes with internal nictitating eyelids, usually no spiracles. Two dorsal fins, one anal fin, first dorsal fin medium to large with base well ahead of pelvic bases, second usually much smaller. Precaudal pits, caudal fin with a strong ventral lobe and lateral undulations on dorsal margin. Mostly unpatterned (particularly in *Carcharhinus*). The extremely rare river sharks (*Glyphis* species), the only freshwater shark species, are very difficult to distinguish without tooth and vertebral counts.

Biology Most requiem sharks are viviparous with a yolk sac placenta (the exception is the Tiger Shark, which exhibits yolk sac viviparity), and have litters ranging in size from just one or two pups to 135 in the Blue Shark. They are active, strong swimmers, occurring singly or in small to large schools. Some species are 'ram-ventilators' needing to swim continually to oxygenate their gills, while others are capable of resting motionless for extended periods on the bottom. Many are more active at night, or dawn and dusk, than during the daytime. Some are solitary or socialize in small groups, some are social schooling species. The requiem sharks are major predators, feeding on a wide variety of prey, including bony fishes, elasmobranchs, cephalopods, and crustaceans, as well as sea birds, turtles, sea snakes, marine mammals, benthic invertebrates, and carrion. Smaller species tend to select for a narrower range of prey, but certain very large species, especially the Tiger Shark, are virtually omnivorous and will eat just about any and everything, including carrion and rubbish, but none are obligate scavengers. At least some of the species have been shown to give specialised displays when confronted by divers or other sharks, which may be indicative of aggressive or defensive threat. There is a clear hierarchical dominance between certain species: Oceanic Whitetip Sharks are dominant over Silky Sharks of the same size, which in turn can dominate Grey Reef Sharks; Galapagos Sharks are dominant over Blacktip Sharks but subordinate to the Silvertip.

Status The requiem sharks are by far the most important family in tropical shark fisheries: commercial, subsistence and sports. They are utilised for food and for fins (requiem shark fins are the most common in international fin trade), also for liver oil, cartilage and skin. Their importance in fisheries has had serious consequences for their conservation status: 28% of requiem sharks have been assessed as threatened (10% Critically Endangered, 6% Endangered, 12% Vulnerable) in the IUCN Red List of Threatened Species; 41% are Near Threatened, and only 18% are Least Concern (these include most of the *Rhizoprionodon* spp., smaller more fecund species of *Carcharhinus* and some Australian endemics); the remainder being presently Data Deficient or Not Evaluated. This family contains more dangerous species than any other shark group. Several of the larger requiem sharks have attacked people and boats and a few are among the most dangerous of shark species. Several are popular in public aquaria as display animals, and have bred in large aquaria. These and some others (including dangerous species) have also gained popularity as attractive subjects for viewing underwater by divers. A few (particularly Lemon and Blue Sharks) are the subject of intensive research activity.

HAMMERHEAD SHARKS: Sphyrnidae – pages 220–222

A small family containing two genera, with eight described species. Genus *Eusphyra* contains one very distinctive species, and there are seven described species in genus *Sphyrna*. An eighth cryptic species of *Sphyrna* (visually indistinguishable from the Scalloped Hammerhead and apparently widespread in the western Atlantic) has been identified through genetic analysis of tissue samples.

Identification Unmistakable hammer-shaped heads. These function as a submarine-like bow plane to improve manoeuvrability, and increase sensory capacity by enhancing stereoscopic vision and the sharks' ability to triangulate sources of scent and electromagnetic signals.

Biology Live-bearing (viviparous), with yolk sac placenta. Feed on bony fishes, smaller sharks, rays, cephalopods and invertebrates, but not on marine mammals or other large vertebrates.

Status Found worldwide in tropical and warm temperate seas, on or adjacent to continental and insular shelves and seamounts, from the surface to at least 275m, sometimes in large schools. Target and bycatch fisheries have depleted many populations. The fins are particularly valuable (making up over 6% of large shark fins identified in international trade during the early 2000s) and hammerheads die very quickly when hooked or entangled; live release of bycatch is therefore unusual. Increased concern over hammerhead population declines has resulted in the Scalloped Hammerhead and the other two similar large species (Great and Smooth Hammerheads) being listed in Appendix II of CITES. Large hammerhead species are also protected in the Mediterranean and prohibited species in ICCAT fisheries (although developing countries may continue to take them for domestic consumption). The largest species (Great Hammerhead and possibly Scalloped and Smooth Hammerheads) have occasionally bitten divers and swimmers, but most are shy and very difficult to approach, not aggressive.

1 Bull Shark *Carcharhinus leucas*   about 340cm

DN Worldwide subtropical and tropical seas. **HT** Usually close inshore, hypersaline lagoons and river mouths; 1–30m, can be found at 152m or more and 100s km up warm rivers and freshwater lakes. **ID** Large, robust shark. Large, broad head. Very short, broad, bluntly rounded snout; small eyes; upper labial furrows very short; no spiracles. Weak caudal keels; no interdorsal ridge. Large angular pectoral fins; broad, triangular first dorsal fin less than 3.2 times height of second; both dorsal fins with short rear tips. **CR** Grey to grey-brown above with dusky fin tips, but not conspicuously marked except in young; white below. **Status:** NT.

2 Oceanic Whitetip Shark *Carcharhinus longimanus*   possibly 350–395cm

DN Worldwide warm temperate and tropical seas. **HT** Oceanic-epipelagic, usually far offshore in open seas of 18–28°C; surface–184m or more. **ID** Large, stocky shark. Short, bluntly rounded snout; small eyes; upper labial furrows very short; no spiracles. Weak caudal keels; interdorsal ridge low. Long paddle-like pectoral fins; huge rounded first dorsal fin much larger than second. **CR** Bronze, grey or brown above with first dorsal fin, pectoral fins and sometimes caudal fin tips conspicuously mottled white; juveniles with black tips on some fins and black patches on caudal peduncle; white below. **Status:** V.

3 Tiger Shark *Galeocerdo cuvier*   at least 550cm

DN Worldwide temperate and tropical seas. **HT** On or near continental and insular shelves; surface and intertidal, possibly to 140m. **ID** Very large shark, the anterior portion of the body is stout becoming more slender behind the first dorsal fin. Large, broad head; very short, broad, bluntly rounded snout; eyes fairly large; big mouth with very long labial furrows, upper much longer than lowers; large spiracles. Low caudal keels; interdorsal ridge very prominent. Moderately broad, semifalcate pectoral fins; first dorsal fin more than 2.5 times height of second; both dorsal fins have very long rear tips, first dorsal fin's almost half fin height; upper caudal fin lobe tapers to a thin pointed tip. **CR** Grey above with vertical black to dark grey bars and blotches, bold in young, fading in adults; white below. **Status:** NT

Carcharhinus longimanus

young

juvenile

1

2

3

young

1 Silky Shark *Carcharhinus falciformis*   about 330cm

DN Worldwide tropical seas. **HT** Oceanic and epipelagic; surface–500m or more, commonest in water less than 200m near continental and insular shelf edge and over deepwater reefs and seamounts. **ID** Large, slim shark. Fairly long, flat, rounded snout; large eyes; small mouth, labial furrows short and inconspicuous. No caudal keels; narrow interdorsal ridge present. Long narrow pectoral fins (comparatively shorter in young); first dorsal fin behind pectoral fins; second dorsal fin low with greatly elongated inner margin and rear tip; anal fins with similar long inner margins and rear tip. **CR** Dark grey, grey-brown to dark brown or nearly black above with inconspicuous pale flank bands, often with subtle dusky fin tips except first dorsal fin; white below. **Status:** NT

2 Blue Shark *Prionace glauca*   380cm

DN Worldwide temperate and tropical seas, possibly most wide-ranging shark. **HT** Oceanic and epipelagic, usually off the edge of the continental shelf; surface to 350m. **ID** Large, graceful, slim shark. Narrow head; long conical snout; large eyes; small mouth, small labial furrows confined to corners of mouth; no spiracles. Weak caudal keels; no interdorsal ridge. Long, narrow, scythe-shaped pectoral fins; first dorsal fin well behind pectoral fins, closer to pelvic fin base; second dorsal fin less than a third the size of first. **CR** Usually dark blue back with bright blue flanks grading to silvery blue; well defined, white below. **Status:** NT.

Prionace glauca

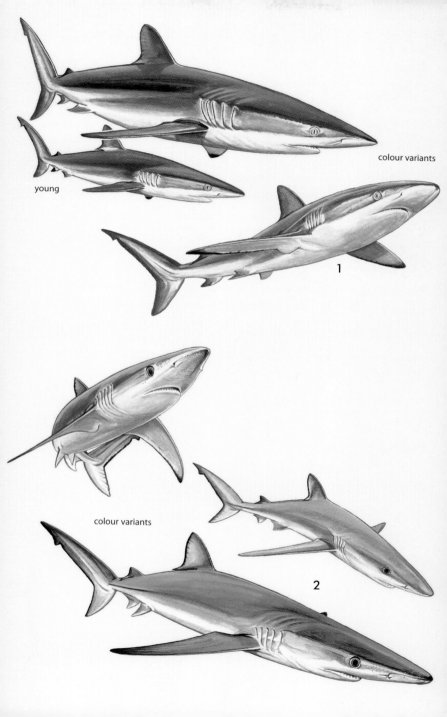

young

colour variants

1

colour variants

2

Plate 68: REQUIEM SHARKS III

1 Silvertip Shark *Carcharhinus albimarginatus*   about 300cm

DN Tropical Indo-Pacific, wide ranging, patchy distribution. **HT** Continental shelf, offshore islands, coral reefs and offshore banks, not an oceanic species; surface–800m. **ID** Moderately large shark; smaller adults slim, very large adults stocky. Moderately long, broadly rounded snout; eyes round; labial furrows small and inconspicuous. Interdorsal ridge present. Pectoral fins with narrow tips; first dorsal fin apex narrowly rounded or pointed; second dorsal fin small less than half the height of first. **CR** Dark grey above occasionally bronze-tinged with inconspicuous pale flank bands, striking white tips and posterior margins on all fins; white below. **Status:** NT.

2 Grey Reef Shark *Carcharhinus amblyrhynchos*   possibly 233–255cm

DN Indo-Pacific. **HT** Continental and insular shelves and adjacent oceanic waters, coastal-pelagic and inshore; to140m, deeper than *C. melanopterus*. **ID** Medium-sized shark. Moderately long, broadly rounded snout; eyes usually round; labial furrows short and inconspicuous. No interdorsal ridge. Pectoral fins narrow and falcate; first dorsal fin apex narrowly rounded or pointed; second dorsal fin relatively large with short rear tip. **CR** Bronze-grey to grey above, first dorsal fin plain or irregularly marked to prominent white edge, obvious broad black posterior margin to entire caudal fin, blackish tips to other fins; white below. **Status:** NT.

3 Blacktip Reef Shark *Carcharhinus melanopterus*   smaller than 200cm

DN West Pacific, Indian Ocean and east Mediterranean. **HT** Very shallow water around coral reefs, rarely offshore or brackish water. **ID** Medium-sized shark. Short, broadly rounded snout; horizontally oval eyes; labial furrows short and inconspicuous. No interdorsal ridge. Pectoral fins narrow and falcate; first dorsal fin apex rounded; second dorsal fin relatively large with short rear tip. **CR** Yellow-brown to brown-grey or grey above with inconspicuous pale flank bands, distinct black fin tips highlighted by white; white below. **Status:** NT.

Carcharhinus albimarginatus

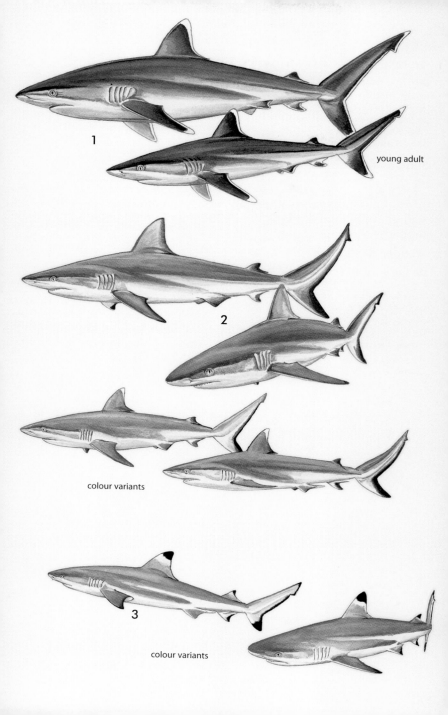

1

young adult

2

colour variants

3

colour variants

Plate 69: REQUIEM SHARKS IV

1 Graceful Shark *Carcharhinus amblyrhynchoides* — at least 178cm

DN Gulf of Aden to Philippines and northwest Australia. **HT** Continental and insular shelves, coastal-pelagic; inshore to at least 50m. **ID** Medium-sized, tubby shark. Fairly short, wedge-shaped, pointed snout; fairly large eyes; labial furrows small and inconspicuous; large gills. No interdorsal ridge. Moderately large pectoral fins; large triangular first dorsal fin, moderately large second dorsal, both with short rear tips. **CR** Bronze-coloured above with conspicuous white flank band, often with all black-tipped fins; pale below. **Status:** NT.

2 Sharptooth Lemon Shark *Negaprion acutidens* — 310cm

DN Tropical Indo-west and central Pacific. **HT** Inshore, on or near bottom; 0–30m, prefers turbid still water bays, estuaries, outer reef shelves and lagoons. **ID** Large, stocky shark. Broad blunt snout; fairly small eyes; labial furrows relatively short and confined to corners of mouth; moderately large gills. No interdorsal ridge. Very similar to *N. brevirostris,* usually dorsal, pectoral and anal fins more falcate; first dorsal fin about same size as second. **CR** Pale yellow-brown to light brown or grey above; white below. **Status:** V.

3 Whitetip Reef Shark *Triaenodon obesus* — at least 160cm

DN Indo-Pacific. **HT** Continental shelves and island terraces, usually on or near bottom, in crevices or caves in coral reefs and lagoons; from 1–330m deep. **ID** Relatively small, slender shark. Very short, broad snout; oval eyes; labial furrows relatively short and confined to corners of mouth; moderately large gills. No interdorsal ridge. Fairly broad triangular pectoral fins; first dorsal fin well behind pectoral fins; second dorsal fin about half to three-quarters the size of first, about same size as anal fin. **CR** Grey-brown to grey above, usually with scattered dark spots on sides, brilliant very conspicuous white tips on first dorsal and terminal caudal fin; lighter below. **Status:** NT.

Triaenodon obesus

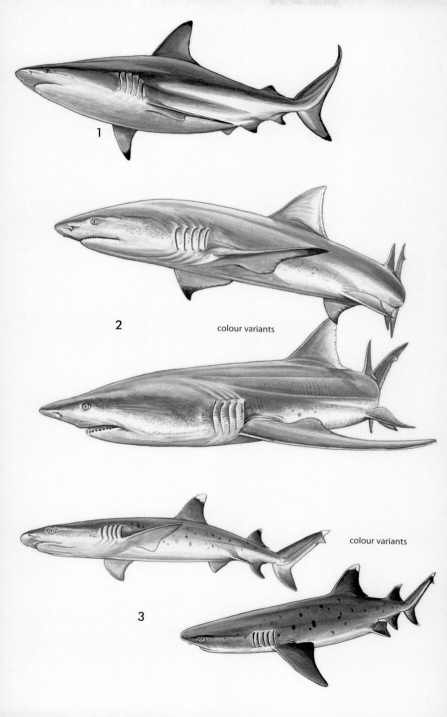

1

2

colour variants

colour variants

3

1 Galapagos Shark *Carcharhinus galapagensis*   possibly 370cm

DN Worldwide, patchy, mainly around warm-temperate to tropical oceanic islands. **HT** Coastal-pelagic shallow inshore to well offshore; 0–180m. **ID** Large, slender shark. Fairly long, broad snout; fairly large eyes low anterior nasal flaps. Low interdorsal ridge. Large semifalcate pectoral fins; moderately large first dorsal fin with short rear tip, first dorsal origin over pectoral fins inner margin. **CR** Grey-brown to dark grey above most fins with inconspicuous dusky tips, inconspicuous white flank stripe; white below. **Status:** NT.

2 Dusky Shark *Carcharhinus obscurus*   360–400cm

DN Possibly worldwide in tropical and warm temperate seas. **HT** Continental and insular shelves, shoreline to adjacent oceanic waters; 0–400m. **ID** Large, slender shark. Broadly rounded snout; fairly large eyes; low poorly developed anterior nasal flaps. Low interdorsal ridge. Moderately large, curved pectoral fins; moderately large, falcate first dorsal fin, first dorsal origin over to ahead of pectoral fin free rear tips **CR** Grey to bronze above, most fins with inconspicuous dusky tips, inconspicuous white flank stripe; white below. **Status: V,** NW and W central Atlantic: E.

3 Sandbar Shark *Carcharhinus plumbeus*   240cm, possibly 300cm

DN Possibly worldwide in tropical and warm temperate seas. **HT** Common in bays, harbours and river mouths, also offshore, usually near bottom; 1–280m. **ID** Moderately large, stout shark. Moderately long rounded snout; fairly large eyes; low short anterior nasal flaps. Interdorsal ridge present. Large pectoral fins; very large erect first dorsal fin, first dorsal origin over to slightly ahead pectoral fin inserts. **CR** Grey-brown to bronze above, tips and posterior margins of fins often inconspicuously dusky, inconspicuous white flank stripe; white below. **Status: V.**

Carcharhinus obscurus

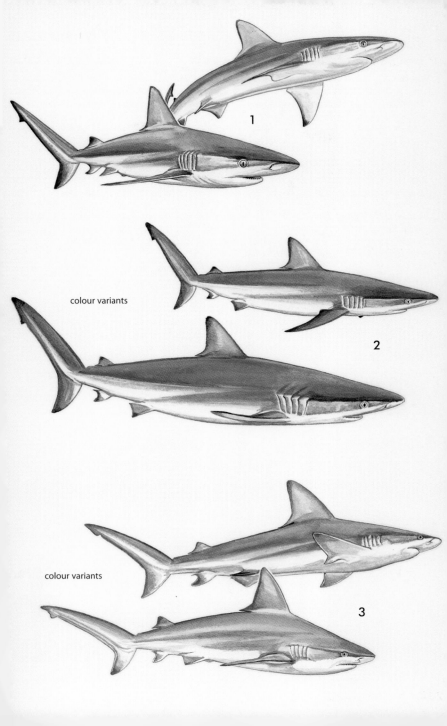

colour variants

colour variants

1

2

3

Plate 71: REQUIEM SHARKS VI

1 Bignose Shark *Carcharhinus altimus* possibly to 300cm

DN Probably worldwide in tropical and warm seas. **HT** Offshore deep continental and insular shelf edges and uppermost slopes; 80–430m or more, sometimes at surface. **ID** Moderately large, heavy cylindrical-bodied shark. Large, long, broad snout; circular moderately large eyes; long anterior nasal flaps; upper labial furrows short and inconspicuous; moderately long gills. Prominent, high interdorsal ridge. Large, straight pectoral and dorsal fins; first dorsal fin relatively high. **CR** Grey, occasionally bronze, above with obscure dusky fin tips except pelvic fins, inconspicuous white flank stripe; white below. **Status:** DD.

2 Spinner Shark *Carcharhinus brevipinna* 278cm

DN Warm temperate and tropical Atlantic, Mediterranean and Indo-west Pacific. **HT** Coastal-pelagic on continental and insular shelves and close inshore; surface to bottom, 75m or more. **ID** Moderately large, slender shark. Long narrow pointed snout; circular small eyes; short relatively inconspicuous anterior nasal flaps; prominent labial furrows; long gills;. No interdorsal ridge. Relatively small pectoral and first dorsal fins; second dorsal fin moderately large, both dorsal fins with short rear tips. **CR** Bronze to grey above, all fins, except the pelvic fins, have a conspicuous black tip in adults and juveniles (but not young), inconspicuous white flank stripe; white below. **Status:** NT.

3 Blacktip Shark *Carcharhinus limbatus* 255cm

DN Widespread tropical and subtropical seas. **HT** Continental and insular shelves; usually close inshore rarely deeper than 30m, tolerates reduced salinity. **ID** Moderately large, stout shark. Long narrow pointed snout; circular small eyes; low triangular anterior nasal flaps; upper labial furrows short and inconspicuous; long gills. No interdorsal ridge. Moderately large, falcate pectoral fins; high first dorsal fin, second dorsal moderately large. **CR** Grey to grey-brown and bronze above, black fin tips to pectorals, dorsals, pelvics and ventral caudal lobe, sometimes pelvic fin is plain and very occasionally anal fin is black-tipped (like the Spinner), usually black edges on first dorsal apex and dorsal caudal lobe, conspicuous white flank stripe; white below. **Status:** NT.

Carcharhinus altimus

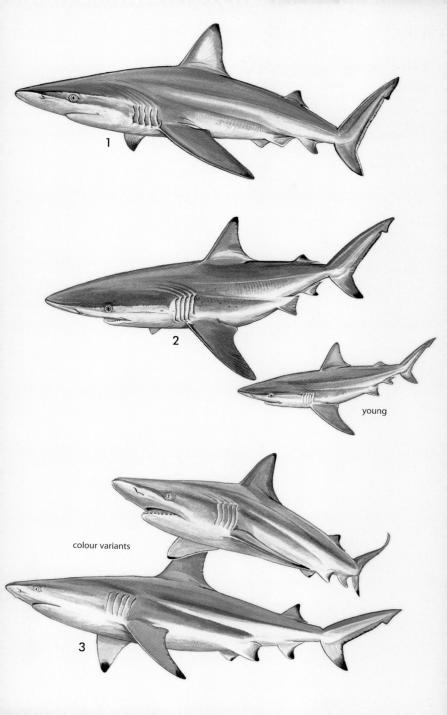

young

colour variants

1 Bronze Whaler *Carcharhinus brachyurus* 294cm

DN Most warm temperate waters in Indo-Pacific, Atlantic and Mediterranean. **HT** Close inshore to 100m or more offshore. **ID** Moderately large, slender shark. Bluntly pointed, broad snout; labial furrows are small and inconspicuous. No interdorsal ridge. Long pectoral fins; small dorsal fins with short rear tips. **CR** Olive-grey to bronze above, most fins with inconspicuous darker margins and dusky tips, fairly prominent white flank stripe; white below. **Status:** NT.

2 Caribbean Reef Shark *Carcharhinus perezi* 295cm

DN West Atlantic, south United States to Brazil including Caribbean. **HT** Commonest Caribbean coral reef shark; near bottom to 30m or more; on hard bottom and mud near river deltas in Brazil. **ID** Moderately large, heavy-bodied shark. Short, bluntly rounded snout; small anterior nasal flaps; relatively large round eyes. Interdorsal ridge present. Large narrow pectoral fins; small first dorsal fin and moderately large second dorsal with short rear tip. **CR** Dark grey or grey-brown above, inconspicuous white flank stripe; white below, underside of pectoral, pelvic, anal fins and ventral caudal lobe dusky, but not prominent marked. **Status:** NT.

3 Lemon Shark *Negaprion brevirostris* 340cm

DN Tropical western Atlantic, west Africa and east Pacific (Mexico to Ecuador). **HT** Inshore and coastal surface; intertidal to 92m or more, adapted to low oxygen shallow water environments. **ID** Large, stocky shark. Short-nosed; fairly small eyes; labial furrows relatively short and confined to corners of mouth; moderately large gills. No interdorsal ridge; dorsal, pectoral and pelvic fins weakly falcate; first dorsal fin about the same as second. **CR** Pale yellow-brown to olive-grey above with no fin markings and no flank stripe; light below. **Status:** NT.

Negaprion brevirostris

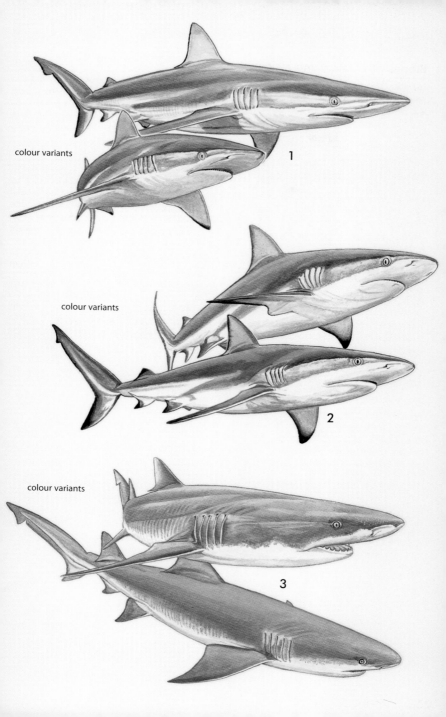

colour variants

1

colour variants

2

colour variants

3

PLATE 73: REQUIEM SHARKS VIII

1 Blacknose Shark *Carcharhinus acronotus* — at least 137cm

DN West Atlantic, south United States to south Brazil including Caribbean. **HT** Coastal continental and insular shelves, mainly over sand, shell and coral; 18 to 64m. **ID** Relatively small, slender shark. Long rounded snout; moderately large eyes; short inconspicuous upper labial furrows; short gills. No interdorsal ridge. Small pectoral fins; dorsal fins with short rear tips, first dorsal small; second dorsal moderately large (but still half the size of the first), second dorsal fin origin approximately over anal fin origin. **CR** Greenish- to brownish-grey above with dark tip to snout, second dorsal and terminal caudal fin tips dark; white to creamy below. **Status:** NT.

2 Finetooth Shark *Carcharhinus isodon* — possibly 200cm

DN West Atlantic, south United States to south Brazil including Caribbean. **HT** Warm temperate to tropical inner continental shelf; intertidal to about 20m. **ID** Medium-sized, slender shark. Long pointed snout; moderately large eyes; short inconspicuous upper labial furrows; very long gills. No interdorsal ridge. Small pectoral fins; dorsal fins with short rear tips, first dorsal relatively small, second dorsal moderately large (but about a third the size of the first), second dorsal fin origin over to posterior of anal fin origin. **CR** Dark blue-grey above with no prominent fin markings, inconspicuous white flank stripe; white below. **Status:** LC.

3 Smoothtooth Blacktip *Carcharhinus leiodon* — 142cm

DN Gulf of Aden to Persian Gulf. **HT** Inshore to 30–40m deep, water temperature is from 19° to 30°C. **ID** Relatively small, stocky shark. Similar to *C. amblyrhynchoides*. Short, bluntly pointed snout; moderately large eyes; long gills. No interdorsal ridge. Small pectoral fins; dorsal fins with short rear tips; moderately large first dorsal and second dorsal fins. **CR** Greenish-grey above with conspicuous black tips on all fins; white below. **Status:** V.

4 Night Shark *Carcharhinus signatus* — 280cm

DN Tropical and warm temperate Atlantic. **HT** Deepwater coastal and semi-oceanic, on or along outer continental and insular shelves and off upper slopes; 0 to 600m. **ID** Moderately large, slim shark. Long pointed snout; large eyes; short inconspicuous upper labial furrow. Interdorsal ridge present. Small pectoral fins; first dorsal fin small with moderately long rear tip, first dorsal fin origin over pectoral fins; second dorsal fin low with long rear tip. **CR** Grey-brown above with no conspicuous fin markings; white below. **Status:** V.

5 Australian Blacktip Shark *Carcharhinus tilstoni* — 200cm

DN Tropical Australia. **HT** Continental shelf, close inshore; to about 150m. **ID** Medium-sized, moderately robust shark. Similar to *C. limbatus*. Long snout; fairly large eyes; labial furrows small and inconspicuous. No interdorsal ridge. Moderately large pectoral fins; dorsal fins with short rear tips; first dorsal large, second dorsal moderately large, first dorsal fin origin approximately over pectoral fin insertions. **CR** Grey to bronze above with black tipped fins, pelvic and anal fins occasionally plain, pale flank stripe; pale below. **Status:** LC.

Carcharhinus leiodon

Plate 74: REQUIEM SHARKS IX

1 Borneo River Shark *Glyphis fowlerae*   possibly more than 200cm

DN Borneo. **HT** Turbid brackish to freshwater rivers. **ID** Medium-sized, stocky shark. Short, broadly rounded snout; tiny eyes. No interdorsal ridge; longitudinal upper precaudal pit. Pectoral fins large and comparatively narrow; first dorsal fin origin over posterior third of pectoral fin base; second dorsal fin large, slightly more than half the height of first; anal fin with deep notch. **CR** Grey-brown above with dusky to blackish fin margins and tips, conspicuous dusky blotch on each flank and pectoral fin base, white below. **Status:** NE.

2 Ganges Shark *Glyphis gangeticus*   at least 204cm probably larger

DN Ganges–Hooghly river system. **HT** Freshwater rivers; possibly estuaries and inshore. **ID** Moderately large, stocky shark. Short, broadly rounded snout; tiny eyes. No interdorsal ridge; longitudinal upper precaudal pit. Pectoral fins large and broad; first dorsal fin origin over posterior third of pectoral fin base; second dorsal fin about half height of first; deeply notched anal fin. **CR** Grey above with no conspicuous markings; white below. **Status:** CE.

3 New Guinea River Shark *Glyphis garricki*   250 to 300cm

DN North Australia and Papua New Guinea. **HT** Turbid brackish to freshwater rivers and adjacent marine waters. **ID** Large, slender shark. Flat-headed; short, broadly rounded snout; tiny eyes. No interdorsal ridge; longitudinal upper precaudal pit. Pectoral fins large and broad; first dorsal fin origin over posterior third of pectoral fin base; second dorsal large about two-thirds the height first; anal fin with deep notch. **CR** Grey above with dusky fin margins; whitish below. **Status:** CE.

4 Speartooth Shark *Glyphis glyphis*   possibly 200 to 300cm

DN Indo-west Pacific: Papua New Guinea and Bay of Bengal. **HT** Inshore possibly rivers and estuaries. **ID** Large, stocky shark. Short, broadly rounded snout; tiny eyes. No interdorsal ridge; longitudinal upper precaudal pit. Pectoral fins large and weakly falcate; first dorsal fin origin over rear pectoral fin base; second dorsal fin large, about three fifths height of first; anal fin with deep notch. **CR** Grey-brown above with no conspicuous markings; white below. **Status:** E.

5 Irrawaddy River Shark *Glyphis siamensis*   unknown, probably 100 to 300cm

DN Irrawaddy River mouth. **HT** Rivers and/or estuaries. **ID** Large?, stocky shark. Short, broadly rounded snout; tiny eyes. No interdorsal ridge; longitudinal upper precaudal pit. Pectoral fins large; first dorsal fin origin over rear pectoral fin base; second dorsal fin about half height of first; anal fin with deep notch. **CR** Grey-brown above with no conspicuous markings; white below. **Status:** CE.

Glyphis glyphis

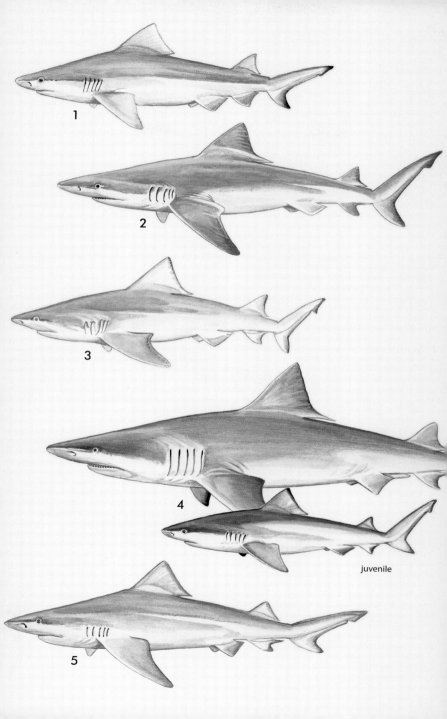

juvenile

1 Pigeye Shark *Carcharhinus amboinensis* 280cm

DN Indo-west Pacific: South Africa to Australia and east Atlantic: Nigeria. **HT** Continental and insular shelves; 0 to 60m. **ID** Moderately large, stout shark. Large, thick head; very short, broad, blunt snout; small eyes; short labial furrows. No interdorsal ridge. Large angular pectoral fins; high erect triangular first dorsal fin, second dorsal fin less than a third the size of first, both with short rear tips. **CR** Grey above with dusky fin tips in juveniles, fading in adults, not conspicuous marked; white below. **Status:** DD.

2 Smalltail Shark *Carcharhinus porosus* less than 150cm

DN West Atlantic and east Pacific. **HT** Shallow continental shelf and estuaries, near mud bottom; 0 to 36m. **ID** Relatively small, slender shark. Long pointed snout; large circular eyes; short labial furrows. No interdorsal ridge. Small pectoral fins; first dorsal fin relatively large and falcate; second dorsal fin small, origin over anal fin midbase; deeply notched anal fin. **CR** Grey above, pectoral, dorsal and caudal fin tips frequently dusky but not conspicuously marked, inconspicuous white flank band; light below. **Status:** DD.

3 Daggernose Shark *Isogomphodon oxyrhynchus* possibly 200 to 244cm

DN Tropical north South America. **HT** Turbid water in estuaries, mangroves, river mouths and shallow banks; 4 to 40m. **ID** Medium-sized to moderately large, unmistakable shark. Extremely long, flat, pointed snout; tiny circular eyes; short prominent labial furrows. No interdorsal ridge. Large, broad, paddle-shaped pectoral fins; first dorsal fin origin over pectoral fins; small second dorsal fin about half the size of first, notched anal fin. **CR** Uniform grey or yellow-grey above; light below. **Status:** CE.

4 Caribbean Sharpnose Shark *Rhizoprionodon porosus* about 110cm

DN Caribbean and tropical South America. **HT** Usually close inshore on continental and insular shelves, also offshore; to 500m. **ID** Small, slender shark. Long snout; fairly large eyes; small wide-spaced nostrils, long labial furrows; no spiracles. No interdorsal ridge. Moderately large pectoral fins; first dorsal fin origin usually over or slightly behind pectoral fin free rear tips; small second dorsal fin, origin over anal fin midbase. **CR** Brown or grey-brown above, sometimes with white spots on sides, white-edged fins; white below. **Status:** LC.

5 Atlantic Sharpnose Shark *Rhizoprionodon terraenovae* at least 110cm

DN Northwest Atlantic. **HT** Coastal; from intertidal–280m, usually deeper than 10m, often close to surf zone off sandy beaches. **ID** Small, slender shark. Similar to *R. porosus*. Long snout; fairly large eyes; small wide-spaced nostrils; long labial furrows; no spiracles. No interdorsal ridge. Moderately large pectoral fins; first dorsal fin origin usually over to slightly in front pectoral fin free rear tips; small second dorsal fin, origin over anal fin midbase inserts. **CR** Grey to grey-brown above with small white spots on sides in larger specimens, pectoral fins with white margins, dorsal fin tips dusky; white below. **Status:** LC.

Isogomphodon oxyrhynchus

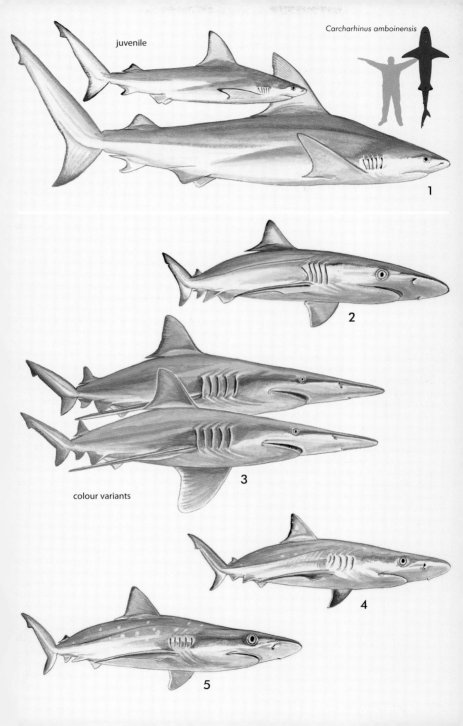

juvenile

Carcharhinus amboinensis

1

2

colour variants

3

4

5

Plate 76: REQUIEM SHARKS XI

1 Whitecheek Shark *Carcharhinus dussumieri*   about 100cm

DN Western Indian Ocean, Persian Gulf to India. **HT** Tropical inshore continental and insular shelves. **ID** Small, slender shark. Often confused with *C. tjutjot*. Moderately long, rounded snout; small wide-spaced nostrils; fairly large, horizontally oval eyes; upper labial furrows short and inconspicuous. Interdorsal ridge present. Small semifalcate pectoral fins; small, triangular first dorsal fin; short rear tips to dorsal fins; no preanal ridge. **CR** Grey to grey-brown above with black or dusky spot on second dorsal fin, other fins with pale posterior margins, inconspicuous light flank stripe; white below. **Status:** NT.

2 Pondicherry Shark *Carcharhinus hemiodon*   about 102cm

DN Indo-west Pacific. **HT** Tropical coastal on continental and insular shelves. **ID** Small, stocky shark. Moderately long, pointed snout; small wide-spaced nostrils; fairly large eyes; upper labial furrows short and inconspicuous. Interdorsal ridge present. Small pectoral fins; moderately large first and second dorsal fins, short rear tips to both; no preanal ridge. **CR** Grey above with black tips to pectorals, second dorsal and caudal fins, conspicuous white flank stripe; white below. **Status:** CE.

3 Milk Shark *Rhizoprionodon acutus*   178cm (usually less than 110cm)

DN East Atlantic, Mediterranean and Indo-west Pacific. **HT** Continental shelf, midwater to near bottom; 1 to 200m. **ID** Relatively small, slender shark. Long narrow snout; small wide-spaced nostrils; large eyes; only requiem shark in range with long upper and lower labial furrows. Interdorsal ridge present. Small pectoral fins; first dorsal fin origin well behind pectoral fin origin; small, low second dorsal behind, larger, anal fin origin; long preanal ridge. **CR** Bronze to grey above, white below; most fin tips slightly pale, juvenile dorsal and terminal caudal fin tips dark, occasionally occurs in adults. **Status:** LC.

4 Pacific Sharpnose Shark *Rhizoprionodon longurio*   110cm, possibly 154cm

DN Eastern Pacific, southern California to Peru. **HT** Littoral to continental and insular shelves inshore and offshore; inshore to at least 27m deep. **ID** Relatively small, slender shark. Long snout; small wide-spaced nostrils; large eyes; long upper and lower labial furrows. Interdorsal ridge present. Small pectoral fins; first dorsal fin origin usually over or slightly in front pectoral fin free tip; second dorsal origin well behind, larger, anal fin origin; long preanal ridge. **CR** Grey or grey-brown above, light edged pectoral fins, dusky-tipped dorsal fins; white below. **Status:** DD.

Carcharhinus dussumieri

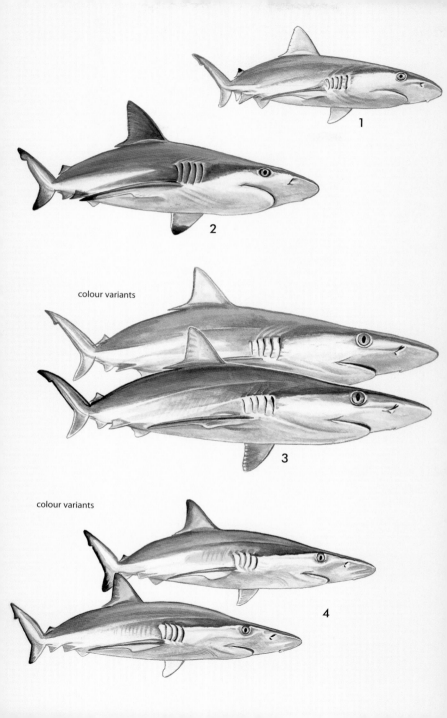

colour variants

colour variants

1 Nervous Shark *Carcharhinus cautus* 150cm

DN East Indian Ocean and southwest Pacific. **HT** Shallow inshore water on continental and insular shelves, coral reefs and estuaries, occasionally deeper water. **ID** Relatively small, stoutish shark. Short bluntly rounded snout; horizontally oval eyes; nipple-like anterior nasal flaps; short labial furrow; moderately large gills. No interdorsal ridge. Moderately large second dorsal fin with short rear tip. **CR** Grey to light brown above with black dorsal and caudal fin margins; caudal and pectoral fins with black tips; conspicuous white flank stripe; white below. **Status:** DD.

2 Coates's Shark *Carcharhinus coatesi* 88cm

DN Northern Australia and New Guinea. **HT** Continental and insular shelves; shallow inshore to 123m. **ID** Small, slender shark. This species has only recently been distinguished from the similar-looking *C. sealei* (page 218). **CR** Grey above with black marking on upper one-third of second dorsal fin, well defined from the rest of the fin colour and not extending onto fin base. **Status:** NE.

3 Creek Whaler *Carcharhinus fitzroyensis* 135cm

DN North Australia. **HT** Mainly inshore; intertidal to 40m or more. **ID** Relatively small, stocky shark. Long, parabolic snout; moderately large round eyes; lobate anterior nasal flaps; short labial furrow; short gills. No interdorsal ridge. Broad triangular fins; first dorsal fin origin over pectoral fin rear tips; second dorsal approximately over anal fin origin. **CR** Grey-brown to bronze above, lacks any conspicuous markings; light below. **Status:** LC.

4 Spottail Shark *Carcharhinus sorrah* 160cm

DN Tropical Indo-west Pacific. **HT** Shallow water on continental and insular shelves and coral reefs; 0–140m. **ID** Relatively small, stocky shark. Long, rounded snout; large round eyes; long narrow nipple-like anterior nasal flaps; short inconspicuous labial furrow; moderately short gills. Interdorsal ridge present. Very low, long second dorsal fin. **CR** Medium grey above, large conspicuous black tips to pectoral, second dorsal and terminal caudal fins, conspicuous white flank stripe; white below. **Status:** NT.

5 Indonesian Whaler Shark *Carcharhinus tjutjot* at least ♀94cm ♂92cm

DN Western North Pacific from Indonesia to Taiwan. **HT** Inshore; 100m or less. **ID** Small, slender shark. Recently separated from *C. dussumieri* (p.214) by a narrower, distinctly falcate pectoral fin and differences in biogeography. **CR** Greyish to pale brown above with prominent black fin blotch on second dorsal fin; lighter below. **Status:** NE.

6 Broadfin Shark *Lamiopsis temmincki* 168cm

DN Scattered in the Indian Ocean, western Pacific records of a different species. **HT** Inshore continental shelf. **ID** Medium-sized, fairly stout shark. Moderately long snout about the same as mouth width; small round eyes. Short, broadly triangular anterior nasal flaps; short labial furrow; fifth gill slit about half the size the first. No interdorsal ridge. Very broad triangular pectoral fins; anal fin posterior margin approximately straight. **CR** Light grey or tan above, lacks any conspicuous markings; light below. **Status:** E.

7 Borneo Broadfin Shark *Lamiopsis tephrodes* at least 145cm

DN Indonesia to China. **HT** Inshore continental shelf. **ID** & **CR** Similar in appearance to *L. temminckii* except upper teeth triangular and lower teeth with fine serrations. **Status:** NE.

8 Whitenose Shark *Nasolamia velox* at least 150cm

DN East Pacific, Baja California to Peru. **HT** Inshore and offshore continental shelf; 15–192m. **ID** Relatively small, fairly slender shark. Very long conical snout; moderately large round eyes; close-set nostrils, width nostril about the same as the space between; very short labial furrow. No interdorsal ridge. Moderately broad triangular pectoral fins; first dorsal fin much larger than second; anal fin slightly larger than second dorsal fin. **CR** Grey-brown to light brown above with prominent black spot outlined with white on upper snout; light below. **Status:** DD.

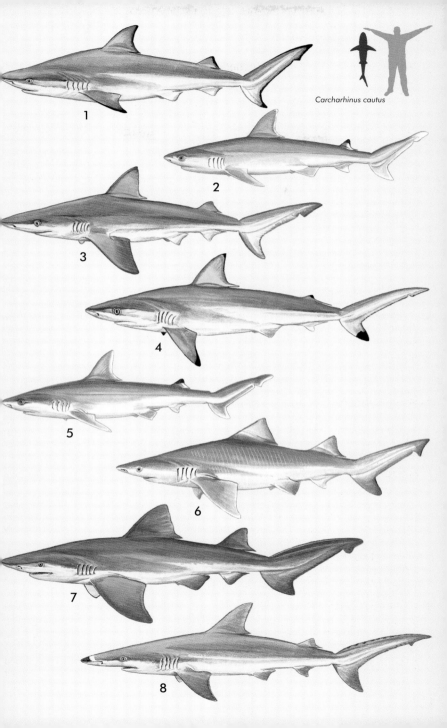

Carcharhinus cautus

1

2

3

4

5

6

7

8

Plate 78: REQUIEM SHARKS XIII

1 Borneo Shark *Carcharhinus borneensis* estimated 70

DN Indo-west Pacific. **HT** Tropical inshore/coastal. **ID** Small, slender shark. Long pointed snout; large e
No interdorsal ridge. Small pectoral fins; small dorsal fins with short tips. **CR** Brown above with
markings on second dorsal and upper caudal fin tips; pectoral, pelvic and anal fins with light marg
lighter below. **Status:** E.

2 Hardnose Shark *Carcharhinus macloti* 110

DN Indo-west Pacific. **HT** Close inshore to 170m. **ID** Relatively small, slender shark. Long, pointed, h
snout; moderately large eyes. No interdorsal ridge. Small dorsal fins; second dorsal fin very low with
long rear tip; anal fin with long reat tip. **CR** Grey to grey-brown above, fins with light margins but
conspicuously marked, inconspicuous flank stripe; white below. **Status:** NT.

3 Blackspot Shark *Carcharhinus sealei* 95

DN Indo-west Pacific. **HT** Surfline to 40m. **ID** Small, slender shark. Long, rounded snout; large oval e
No or very low interdorsal ridge. Small pectoral and first dorsal fins. **CR** Grey or tan above wit
conspicuous dusky to black tip on second dorsal fin, other fins with light margins, light flank stripe; lig
below. **Status:** NT.

4 Sliteye Shark *Loxodon macrorhinus* 99

DN Indo-west Pacific. **HT** Clear water; 7 to 100m. **ID** Small, very slim shark. Long, narrow snout; large e
with rear notch; short labial furrows. No rudimentary interdorsal ridge. First dorsal fin much larger t
second, second dorsal fin low with long free posterior margin. **CR** Grey to brown above with black mar
on first dorsal and caudal fins, other fins with inconspicuous light rear edges; white below. **Status:** LC

5 Brazilian Sharpnose Shark *Rhizoprionodon lalandei* 77

DN Western Atlantic. **HT** Continental shelf; 3 to 70m. **ID** Small, slender shark. Long snout; large eyes; w
spaced nostrils; only requiem shark in its range with long upper and lower labial furrows. Small seco
dorsal fin well behind anal fin origin; long anal ridge. **CR** Dark grey to grey-brown above with li
margins to pectoral fins and dusky margins to dorsal fins. **Status:** DD.

6 Grey Sharpnose Shark *Rhizoprionodon oligolinx* 70

DN Tropical Indo-west Pacific. **HT** Continental and insular shelves, littoral to offshore. **ID** Very sm
slender shark. Long snout; large eyes; small wide-spaced nostrils; short labial furrows. Small second do
fin well behind anal fin origin; long anal ridge. **CR** Grey to bronze above with pale pectoral fin marg
and inconspicuous dusky caudal fin margins; pale below. **Status:** LC.

7 Australian Sharpnose Shark *Rhizoprionodon taylori* 67

DN Australia. **HT** Tropical, inshore continental shelf. **ID** Very small, slender shark. Very similar to *R. oligo*
(see above). **CR** Grey to bronze above with dark margins to dorsal and caudal fins, upper caudal fin
dark, other fins with light margins; pale below. **Status:** LC.

8 Spadenose Shark *Scoliodon laticaudus* 74

DN Western Indian Ocean. **HT** Close inshore. **ID** Small, stocky, unmistakable shark. Very long, flatter
snout; small eyes. No interdorsal ridge. Short broad triangular pectoral fins; first dorsal fin much lar
than second. **CR** Bronze-grey above with no conspicuous markings; white below. **Status:** NT.

9 New Spadenose Shark *Scoliodon macrorhynchos* 71

DN Western Central Pacific. **HT** Close inshore. **ID** Small, stocky, unmistakable shark. Appearance simila
S. laticaudus; main difference is that the origins of the second dorsal and anal fins are nearer in *S. laticau*
(4.6–6.2% total length) than *macrorhynchos* (6–9.1% total length). **CR** As above. **Status:** NE.

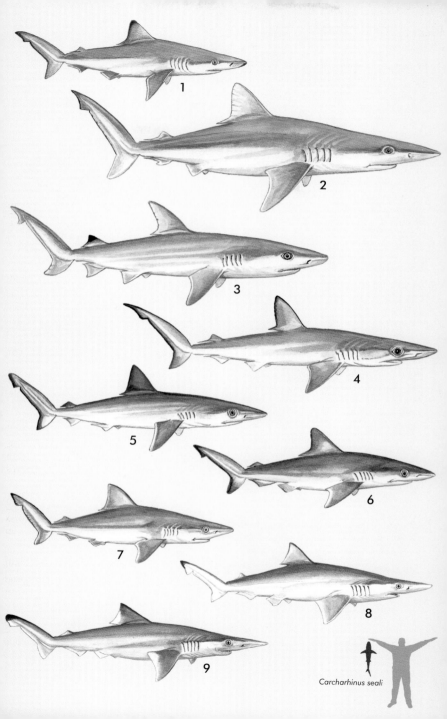

Carcharhinus seali

1 Winghead Shark *Eusphyra blochii* 186cm

DN North Indian Ocean to Australia and China. **HT** Shallow water, continental and insular shelves **ID** Moderately large, slender , unmistakable shark. Immense wing-shaped head with narrow blades; width between eyes about half body length; nostrils greatly enlarged. First dorsal fin origin over pectoral fin bases, further forward than other hammerheads. Upper precaudal pit longitudinal not crescent-shaped **CR** Grey to brownish above with no dark fin markings; pale to white below. **Status: NT.**

2 Scalloped Bonnethead *Sphyrna corona* 92cm

DN East Pacific: Gulf of California to Peru. **HT** Continental shelf, mostly a coastal species. **ID** Small shark, probably the smallest hammerhead. Moderately broad anterior arched mallet-shaped head with medial and lateral indentation on anterior edge and transverse posterior margin; no prenarial grooves; snout rather long about two-fifths head width; small strongly arched mouth. First dorsal fin free rear tip is over pelvic fin insertion; anal fin posterior margin approximately straight. Upper precaudal pit transverse crescentic. **CR** Grey above with no prominent fin markings; white below extending to back of head. **Status: NT.**

3 Scoophead Shark *Sphyrna media* 150cm

DN West Atlantic, Panama to south Brazil and east Pacific, Gulf of California to north Peru. **HT** Continental shelf. **ID** Relatively small shark. Moderately broad anterior arched mallet-shaped head with weak medial and lateral indentation on anterior edge and transverse posterior margin; no prenarial grooves; snout moderately short about a third the head width; moderately large broadly arched mouth. First dorsal fin free rear tip over pelvic fin insertion. Upper precaudal pit transverse crescentic. **CR** Grey-brown above with no prominent fin markings; light below. **Status: DD.**

4 Bonnethead Shark *Sphyrna tiburo* 150cm

DN West Atlantic: Rhode island, USA, to southern Brazil. East: southern California to Ecuador. **HT** Continental and insular shelves; 0 to 80m. **ID** Relatively small shark. Unique, very narrow, smooth shovel-shaped head with no indentations; no prenarial grooves; snout moderately long about two fifths the head width; broadly arched mouth. First dorsal fin free rear tip anterior to pelvic fin origins; anal fin posterior margin shallowly concave. Upper precaudal pit tranverse crescentic. **CR** Grey or grey-brown above often with small dark spots, no prominent fin markings; light below. **Status: LC.**

5 Smalleye Hammerhead *Sphyrna tudes* 150cm

DN West Atlantic, Venezuela to Uruguay. **HT** Continental shelf; to 12m or more. **ID** Relatively small shark. Broad anterior arched mallet-shaped head with medial and lateral deep indentation on anterior edge none on posterior margin; no prenarial grooves; snout short, less than a third the head width; moderately large, broadly arched mouth. First dorsal fin free rear tip over pelvic fin insertion; anal fin posterior margin moderately concave. Upper precaudal pit transverse crescentic. **CR** Grey-brown to golden above with no prominent fin markings; light below. **Status: V.**

Eusphyra blochii

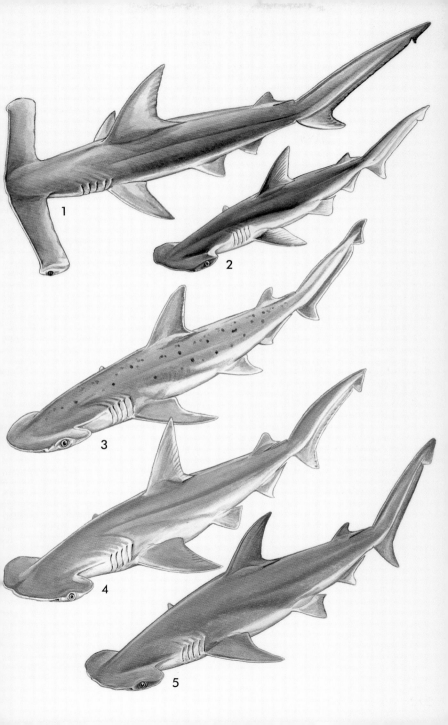

1 Scalloped Hammerhead *Sphyrna lewini* 420cm

DN Worldwide warm temperate and tropical seas. **HT** Over continental and insular shelves and adjacent water surface; to 275m or more. **ID** Large, moderately slender shark. Broad, narrow-bladed head, arched anterior margin with prominent median indentation and lateral indentation; well-developed prenarial grooves; snout short, a fifth to a third the head width; broadly arched mouth. First dorsal fin moderately high; second dorsal and pectoral fins low. Upper precaudal pit transverse crescentic. **CR** Light grey or bronze above with dusky pectoral fin tips and dark blotch on lower caudal fin lobe; white below. **Status:** E.

2 Great Hammerhead *Sphyrna mokarran* at least 610cm

DN Worldwide tropical seas. **HT** Coastal-pelagic and semi-oceanic, close inshore to well offshore; 1 to 80m or more. **ID** Very large shark. Broad, narrow-bladed head, nearly straight anterior margin with prominent median indentation and lateral indentation; no or weakly developed prenarial grooves; snout short, less than a third the head width; broadly arched mouth. First dorsal fin very high and falcate; second dorsal and pectoral fins high. Upper precaudal pit transverse crescentic. **CR** Light grey or grey-brown above, adult with no prominent fin markings; white below. **Status:** E.

3 Smooth Hammerhead *Sphyrna zygaena* 400cm

DN Worldwide warm temperate and tropical seas. **HT** Continental and insular shelves, close inshore to well offshore; 0 to 20m or more. **ID** Large shark. Broad narrow-bladed head with broadly arched anterior margin, no median indentation but prominent lateral indentations; well-developed prenarial grooves; snout short, a fifth to less than a third the head width; broadly arched mouth. First dorsal fin moderately high; second dorsal and pectoral fins low. Upper precaudal pit transverse crescentic. **CR** Olive-grey or dark grey-brown above; white below with undersides of pectoral fin tips dusky. **Status:** V.

Sphyrna mokarran

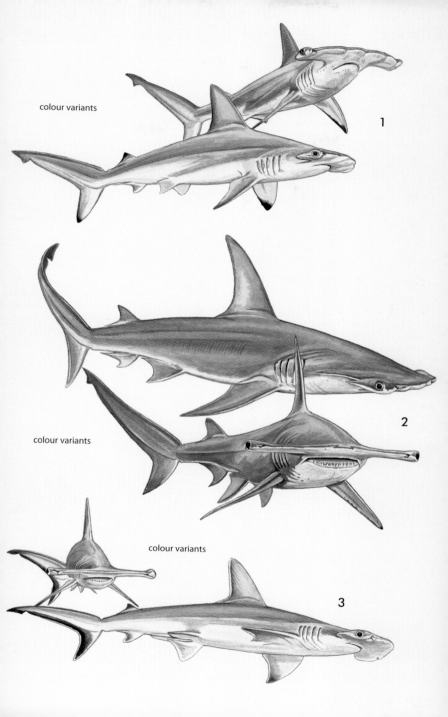

colour variants

1

colour variants

2

colour variants

3

Glossary

Abdominal ridges or keels. In some sharks, paired longitudinal dermal ridges that extend from the bases of the pectoral fins to the pelvic fin bases.

Abyss. See page 229.

Abyssal plain. See page 229.

Anal fin. See page 11.

Anterior. Forward, in the [longitudinal] direction of the snout tip.

Anterior margin. See page 12.

Anterior nasal flap. See page 13.

Apex (plural, Apices). In precaudal fins, the distal tip, which can be acutely pointed to broadly rounded.

Apical. In oral teeth, towards the tip of the crown or cusp. Can also be used as indicating direction towards the apex or tip of a fin, fin-spine, etc.

Barbels. Long conical paired dermal lobes on the snouts of sharks, which may serve to locate prey. Sawsharks have barbels on the underside of the snout in front of the nostrils (as in sturgeon), but most barbelled sharks have them associated with the nostrils.

Base. In precaudal fins, the proximal part of the fin between the origin and insertion, extending distally, and supported by the cartilaginous fin skeleton. In the caudal fin, that thickened longitudinal part of the fin enclosing the vertebral column and between the epaxial and hypaxial lobes or webs of the fin. In oral teeth, the proximal root and crown foot, in apposition to the distal cusp. In denticles, the proximal anchoring structures, often with four or more lobes, holding the denticles in the skin.

Bathyal. See page 229.

Bathypelagic zone. See page 229. The sunless zone. Some oceanic sharks may transit the epipelagic, mesopelagic and bathypelagic zones to the bottom while migrating vertically.

Benthic or Demersal. Referring to organisms that are bottom-dwelling.

Bioluminscence. Light produced by biochemical means in some organisms.

Blade. In oral teeth, an arcuate, convex-edged section of the cutting edge of the crown foot, without cusplets.

Body ridges. Elongated longitudinal dermal ridges on the sides of the trunk and precaudal tail in certain carpet sharks (Orectolobiformes), in the Whale, Zebra, and some bamboosharks.

Body. Can refer to an entire shark, sometimes restricted to the trunk and precaudal tail.

Bycatch. The part of a catch taken incidentally in addition to the target species towards which fishing effort is directed. In a broad context, this includes all non-targeted catch including byproduct, discards and other interactions with gear.

Carcharhinoid. A ground shark, a member of the order Carcharhiniformes, and including the catsharks, false catsharks, finbacked catsharks, barbeled houndsharks, houndsharks, weasel sharks, requiem sharks, and hammerheads.

Cartilaginous fishes. Members of the class Chondrichthyes.

Caudal crest. A prominent saw-like row of enlarged pointed denticles along the dorsal caudal margin and sometimes along the ventral caudal margin of the caudal fin. Found in certain sharks including hexanchoids and some carcharhinoids.

Caudal fin. See page 11.

Caudal keels. See page 11.

Caudal peduncle. See page 11.

Ceratotrichia. Slender soft or stiff filaments of an elastic protein, superficially resembling keratin or horn (from the Greek keratos, horn, and trichos, hair). Ceratotrichia run in parallel and radial to the fin base and support the fin webs. The prime ingredient of shark-fin soup.

Chondrichthyan. Referring to the class Chondrichthyes.

Chondrichthyes. The class Chondrichthyes (from Greek chondros, cartilage, and ichthos, fish), a major taxonomic group of aquatic, gill-breathing, jawed, finned vertebrates with primarily cartilaginous skeletons, one to seven external gill openings, oral teeth in transverse rows on their jaws, and mostly small, toothlike scales or dermal denticles. Chondrichthyes include the living elasmobranchs and holocephalans and their numerous fossil relatives, and also can be termed shark-like fishes or simply sharks.

Circumglobal. Occurring around the world.

Circumnarial fold. A raised semicircular, lateral flap of skin around the incurrent aperture of a nostril, in heterodontoids, orectoloboids, and a few batoids, defined by a circumnarial groove.

Circumnarial groove. A shallow groove defining the lateral bases of the circumnarial folds.

Circumtropical. Occurring around the tropical regions of the world.

CITES. Convention on International Trade in Endangered Species of Fauna and Flora. An international agreement which aims to ensure that international trade in specimens of wild fauna and flora does not threaten the survival of species. Appendix II of CITES includes 'species not necessarily threatened with extinction, but in which trade must be controlled in order to avoid utilisation incompatible with their survival' (www.cites.org).

Claspers. Paired copulatory organs present on the pelvic fins of male cartilaginous fishes, for internal fertilisation of eggs.

Class. One of the taxonomic groups of organisms, containing related orders; related classes are grouped into phyla.

Classification. The ordering of organisms into groups on the basis of their relationships, which may be by similarity or common ancestry.

Common name. The informal vernacular name for an organism, which may vary from location to location.

Continental rise. The gently sloping base of the continental shelf made up of sediment deposits; see also Rise. (See page 229).

Continental shelf. See page 229.

Continental slope. See page 229.

Cusp. A usually pointed large distal projection of the crown. A primary cusp is situated on the midline of the crown foot. Multicuspid refers to oral teeth or denticles with more than one cusp. In lateral trunk denticles, the posterior ends of the crown may have medial and lateral cusps, sharp or blunt projections associated with the medial and lateral ridges.

Cusplet. As with a cusp, but a small projection in association with a cusp, and usually mesial and distal but not medial on the crown foot.

Cutting edge. In oral teeth, the compressed sharp longitudinal ridge on the mesiodistal edges of the crown.

Demersal. Occurring or living near or on the bottom of the ocean (cf. pelagic).

Dermal denticle. A small tooth-like scale found in cartilaginous fishes, covered with enameloid, with a core and base of dentine and usually small and often close-set to one another and covering the body. A few non-batoid sharks, many batoids, and chimaeroids generally have them enlarged and sparse or reduced in numbers.

Dermal lobes. In wobbegongs, family Orectolobidae, narrow or broad-based, simple or branched projections of skin along the horizontal head rim and on the chin.

Distal. In any direction, at the far end of a structure. In oral teeth, used in a special sense for structures on the teeth towards the posterolateral mouth corners or rictuses. See apical and basal.

Dorsal. Upwards, in the vertical direction of the back. See ventral.

Dorsal fin spine. See page 11.

Dorsal fin. See page 11.

Dorsal lobe. See page 12.

Dorsal margin. See page 12.

Drop-off. Steep or sheer underwater cliff or precipice.

Ecosystem. The living community of different species, interdependent on each other, together with their non-living environment.

Eggcase. A stiff-walled elongate-oval, rounded rectangular, conical, or dart-shaped capsule that surrounds the eggs of oviparous sharks, and is deposited by the female shark on the substrate. It is analogous to the shell of a bird's egg and is made of protein, which is a type of collagen that superficially resembles horn or keratin. Eggcases often have pairs of tendrils or hornlike structures on their ends, or flat flanges on their sides or spiral flanges around their lengths, which anchor the cases to the bottom. As the egg travels from the ovaries into the oviducts and through the nidamental glands, the eggcase is secreted around it and the egg is fertilised. Live-bearing sharks may retain eggcases, and these vary from being rigid and similar to those of oviparous sharks to soft, bag like, degenerate and membranous. Soft eggcases may disintegrate during the birth cycle.

Elasmobranch. Referring to the subclass Elasmobranchii.

Elasmobranchii. The subclass Elasmobranchii, (from Greek elasmos, plate, and branchos, gills, in allusion to their platelike gill septa), the shark-like fishes other than the Holocephali or chimaeras, and including the living non-batoid sharks, batoids, and a host of fossil species. They differ from holocephalans in having five to seven pairs of gill openings open to the exterior and not covered by a soft gill cover, oral teeth separate and not formed as tooth plates, a fixed first dorsal fin with or without a fin spine, and a short spined or spineless second dorsal.

Embryo. An earlier development stage of the young of a live-bearing shark, ranging from nearly microscopic to moderate-sized but not like a miniature adult. See foetus.

Endemic. A species or higher taxonomic group of organisms that is only found in a given area. It can include national endemics found in a river system or along part or all of the coast of a given country, but also regional endemics, found off or in adjacent countries with similar habitat, but not elsewhere.

Epibenthic zone. The area of the ocean just above and including the sea bottom, from shallow seas to deep abysses, epibenthic sharks live on or near the bottom. See page 229.

Epipelagic zone. That part of the oceans beyond the continental and insular shelves, in oceanic waters, from the surface to the limits of where most sunlight penetrates, about 200m. Also known as the sunlit sea or 'blue water'. Most epipelagic sharks are found in the epipelagic zone, but may penetrate the mesopelagic zone. See page 229.

Euryhaline. An organism that is able to tolerate a large variance in salinity found mainly in and around estuaries.

Excurrent apertures. See page 13.

Extant. Applied to a group that has all or some living representatives.

Extinct. Applied to a group that has no living representatives.

Eye notch. See page 13.

Eyespots or ocelli. Large eye-like pigment spots located on the dorsal surface of the pectoral fins or bodies of some sharks including rays, angelsharks, and some bamboo sharks, possibly serving to frighten potential enemies.

Falcate. Sickle-shaped.

Family. One of the taxonomic groups of organisms, containing related genera; related families are grouped into orders.

FAO. United Nations Food and Agricultural Organisation.

Fauna. The community of animals peculiar to a region, area, specified environment or period.

Fecundity. A measure of the capacity of the maternal adult to produce young.

Filter-feeding. A form of feeding whereby suspended food particles are extracted from the water using the gill rakers.

Fin base. See base.

Fin insertion. See insertion.

Fin origin. See origin.

Fin web. See page 12.

Finning. The practice of slicing off a shark's valuable fins and discarding the body at sea.

First dorsal fin. See page 11.

Flank. Sides of the shark excluding the head and tail regions.

FL. Fork length. A standard morphometric measurement used for sharks, from the tip of the snout to the fork of the caudal fin.

Free rear tips. The pectoral, pelvic, dorsal, and anal fins all have a movable rear corner or flap, the free rear tip, that is separated from the trunk or tail by a notch and an inner margin. In some sharks the rear tips of some fins are very elongated.

Fusiform. Spindle- or torpedo-shaped, elongated with tapering ends.

Genus (plural, Genera). One of the taxonomic groups of organisms, containing related species; related genera are grouped into families. The first of two scientific names assigned to each species.

Gestation period. The period between conception and birth in live-bearing animals.

Gill openings or slits. In elasmobranchs, the paired rows of five to seven transverse openings on the sides or underside of the head for the discharge of water through the gills. Chimaeras have their four gill openings hidden by a soft gill cover and discharge water through a single external gill opening.

Habitat. The locality or environment in which an animal lives.

Hadal. See page 229.

Hadopelagic zone. The pelagic zone inside the deep trenches, 6000 to about 11,000m, from which no chondrichthyans have been observed or recorded. See page 229.

Head. That part of a cartilaginous fish from its snout tip to the last (or in chimaeras only) gill slits.

Heterocercal. A caudal fin with the vertebral axis slanted dorsally into the fin base, which is also dorsally elevated.

Heterodontoid. A bullhead shark, Horn Shark, or Port Jackson Shark, a member of the order Heterodontiformes, family Heterodontidae.

Heterodonty. In oral teeth, structural differences between teeth in various positions on the jaws, between teeth in the same position during different life stages, or between teeth in the same positions in the two sexes.

Hexanchoid. A cow shark or frilled shark, members of the order Hexanchiformes, and including the sixgill sharks, sevengill sharks, and frilled sharks.

Holotype. Either the only specimen used and mentioned in an original description of a species, with or without a designation of such, or one of two or more specimens used and mentioned in an original description of a species and designated as such. This becomes the 'name-bearer' of the species, and is used to validate the species or scientific name by anchoring it to a single specimen.

Hypaxial web. See page 12.

Hypocercal. A caudal fin with the vertebral axis slanted ventrally into the fin base, which is also ventrally depressed. Found only in angelsharks (Squatiniformes) among living sharks.

ICES. International Council for the Exploration of the Seas.

Incurrent apertures. See page 13.

Indo-Pacific. An area covering the Indian Ocean and the western Pacific Ocean.

Inner margin. See page 12.

Insertion. See page 12.

Inshore. Shallow waters seaward side of the surf zone.

Insular shelf. See Shelf.

Interdorsal ridge. A ridge of skin on the midback of sharks, in a line between the first and second dorsal fins; particularly important in identifying grey sharks (genus Carcharhinus, family Carcharhinidae).

Intermediate teeth. Small oral teeth between the laterals and anteriors of the upper jaw, found in most lamnoids.

Intertidal zone. Shoreline between high and low tide marks that is diurnally exposed to the air by tidal movement. (See page 229)

Island slope. See Slope.

IUCN. The World Conservation Union. A union of sovereign states, government agencies and non-governmental organisations. www.iucn.org.

Jaws. See mandibular arch.

Juvenile. The life stage between hatching from egg or birth to sexual maturity and adulthood.

Keel. See Caudal keel.

Labial cartilages. Paired internal cartilages that support the labial folds at the lateral angles of the mouth. Living neoselachians typically have two pairs of upper labial cartilages, the anterodorsal and posterodorsal labial cartilages, and one pair of ventral labial cartilages, but these are variably reduced and sometimes absent in many sharks.

Labial folds. Lobes of skin at the lateral angles of the mouth, usually with labial cartilages inside them, separated from the sides of the jaws by pockets of skin (labial grooves or furrows).

Labial furrows or labial grooves. See page 13.

Lamnoid. A mackerel shark, a member of the order Lamniformes, and including the sandtiger sharks, Goblin Shark, Crocodile Shark, Megamouth Shark, thresher sharks, Basking Shark, and the makos, Porbeagle, Salmon Shark, and White Shark.

Lateral. Outwards, in the transverse direction towards the periphery of the body. See medial.

Lateral keel. See Caudal keel.

Lateral line. A sensory canal system of pressure-sensitive cells, that run along the sides of the body, often branching at the head, which detect water movements, disturbances and vibrations.

Lateral ridges. Reinforced ridges along the side of the body one of which is often an extension of the caudal keel.

Lateral teeth. Large broad-rooted, compressed, high-crowned oral teeth on the sides of the jaws between the anteriors and laterals.

Lateral trunk denticle. A dermal denticle from the dorsolateral surface of the back below the first dorsal fin base.

Littoral zone. That part of the oceans over the continental and insular shelves, from the intertidal to 200m. See page 229.

Live-bearing. A mode of reproduction in which female sharks give birth to young sharks, which are miniatures of the adults. See Vivipary.

Longevity. The maximum expected age, on average, for a species or population in the absence of human-induced or fishing mortality.

Lower origin. See page 12.

Lower postventral margin. See page 12.

Medial. Inwards, in the transverse direction towards the middle of the body. See lateral.

Medial teeth. Small oral teeth, generally symmetrical and with narrow roots, in one row at the symphysis and often in additional paired rows on either side of the symphysial one.

Migratory. The systematic (as opposed to random) movement of individuals from one place to another, often related to season and breeding or feeding. Knowledge of migratory patterns helps to manage shared stocks and to target aggregations of fish.

Molariform. In oral teeth, referring to a tooth with a broad flat crown with low cusps or none, for crushing hard-shelled invertebrate prey.

Monospecific. Genus containing only one known extant species.

MPA. Marine Protected Area. Any area of the intertidal or subtidal terrain, together with its overlying water and associated flora, fauna, historical and cultural features, which has been reserved by law or other effective means to protect part or all of the enclosed environment.

Nares. See Nostrils.

Nasal aperture. On the neurocranium, an aperture in the anteroventral surface or floor of each nasal capsule, through which the nostril directs water into and out of the nasal organ.

Nasal flap. One of a set of dermal flaps associated with the nostrils, and serving to direct water into and out of them, including the anterior, posterior, and mesonarial flaps.

Nasoral grooves. Many bottom-dwelling, relatively inactive sharks have nasoral grooves, shallow or deep grooves on the ventral surface of the snout between the excurrent apertures and the mouth. The nasoral grooves are covered by expanded anterior nasal flaps that reach the mouth, and form water channels that allow the respiratory current to pull water by partial pressure into and out of the nostrils and into the mouth. This allows the shark to actively irrigate its nasal cavities while sitting still or when slowly moving. Nasoral grooves occur in heterodontoids, orectoloboids, chimaeroids, some carcharhinoids, and most batoids.

Nictitating lower eyelid. In the ground sharks (order Carcharhiniformes), a movable lower eyelid that has special posterior eyelid muscles that lift it and, in some species, completely close the eye opening.

Nictitating upper eyelid. In parascylliid orectoloboids, the upper eyelid has anterior eyelid muscles that pull it down and close the eye opening, analogous to the nictitating lower eyelids of carcharhinoids.

Nomenclature. In biology, the application of distinctive names to groups of organisms.

Non-target species. Species which are not the subject

Nostrils. The external openings of the cavities of the nasal organs, or organs of smell.

Nursery ground. Area (often inshore and in sheltered waters and with abundant food organisms) where newborn sharks live and feed and grow to a certain size in their life cycle, then move elsewhere.

Oceanic. Referring to organisms inhabiting those parts of the oceans beyond the continental and insular shelves, over the continental slopes, ocean floor, sea mounts and abyssal trenches. The open ocean.

Oceanic ridge. Part of the ocean floor where new material is added to plate margins by magma eruptions forming an ever expanding parallel line of deepwater ridges.

Ocellus (plural Ocelli). Eye-like marking in which the central colour is bordered in a full or broken ring of another colour.

Ocular. Of or associated with the eye.

Olfactory. Parts of the body that are associated with the sense of smell.

Order. One of the taxonomic groups of organisms, containing related families; related orders are grouped into classes.

Orectoloboid. A carpet shark, a member of the order Orectolobiformes, including barbelthroat carpet sharks, blind sharks, wobbegongs, bamboosharks, epaulette sharks, nurse sharks, Zebra Shark, and Whale Shark.

Origin. The anterior or front end of the fin base in all fins. The caudal fin has upper and lower origins but no insertion. See insertion.

Paired fins. The pectoral and pelvic fins.

Paratype. Each specimen of a type series other than the holotype. Specimens other than the holotype automatically become paratypes unless the author designates them as referred specimens that are not part of the type series.

Pectoral fins. See page 11.

Pelagic. Referring to organisms that live in the water column, not on the sea bottom.

Pelvic fin. See page 11.

Photophores. Conspicuously pigmented small spots on the bodies of most lanternsharks (family Etmopteridae) and some kitefin sharks (family Dalatiidae). These are tiny round organs that are covered with a conspicuous dark pigment (melanin) and produce light by a low-temperature chemical reaction.

Phylum. In animal taxonomy it is one of the major groupings dividing organisms into superclasses, classes and all other lower groupings.

Placoid scale. See dermal denticle.

Population. A group of individuals of a species living in a particular area. (This is defined by IUCN (2001) as the total number of mature individuals of the taxon, with subpopulations defined as geographically or otherwise distinct groups in the population between which there is little demographic or genetic exchange (typically one successful migrant individual or gamete per year or less).)

Pores, pigmented. In a few sharks and skates, the pores for the lateral line and ampullae of Lorenzini are conspicuously black-pigmented, and look like little black specks.

Posterior. Rearwards, in the longitudinal direction of the caudal fin tip or tail filament. Also caudad.

Posterior margin. See page 12.

Posterior nasal flaps. See page 13.

Posterior notch. See page 12.

Posterior tip. See page 12.

Postventral margin. See page 12.

Preanal ridges. A pair of low, short to long, narrow ridges on the midline of the caudal peduncle entending anteriorly from the anal fin base.

Precaudal fins. All fins in front of the caudal fin.

Precaudal pit. See page 11.

Precaudal tail. See page 11.

Predorsal ridge. A low narrow ridge of skin on the midline of the back anterior to the first dorsal fin base.

Preventral margin. In the caudal fin, the margin from the lower origin to the ventral tip of the caudal fin.

Pristiophoroid. A saw shark, order Pristiophoriformes, family Pristiophoridae.

Productivity. Relates to the birth, growth and mortality rates of a fish stock. Highly productive stocks are characterised by high birth, growth and mortality rates and can usually sustain higher exploitation rates and, if depleted, could recover more rapidly than comparatively less productive stocks.

Protrusible. Capable of being thrust forward, term normally applied to jaws.

Proximal. In any direction, at the near end of a structure.

Pupping ground. Area favoured for giving birth and depositing young.

Red List of Threatened Species. Listing of the conservation status of the world's flora and fauna administered by IUCN. www.redlist.org

Rostral keel. In squaloids, a large vertical plate on the underside of the rostrum and internasal septum, sometimes reduced, and with the cavities of the subnasal fenestrae on either side of the keel.

Rostrum. The cartilaginous anteriormost structure that supports the prenasal snout including lateral line canals and masses of ampullae. It is absent in a few nonbatoid sharks and in many batoids.

Row. In teeth, a single replicating line of teeth, running parallel with the jaw, which includes functional teeth and their replacements, derived from one tooth-producing area on the jaw.

Saddle. Darker dorsal marking that extends downwards either side of the shark but does not meet on the ventral surface.

Scientific name. The formal binomial name of a particular organism, consisting of the genus and specific names; a species only has one valid scientific name.

Second dorsal fin. See page 11.

Secondary caudal keels. Low horizontal dermal keels on the ventral base of the caudal fin in mackerel sharks (Lamnidae) and some somniosids.

Secondary lower eyelid. The eyelid below or lateral to the nictitating lower eyelid, separated from it by a subocular groove or pocket, and, in many carcharhinoids with internal nictitating lower eyelids, functionally replacing them as lower eyelids.

Series. In teeth, a line of teeth running from the front of the jaw inward.

Serrations. In oral teeth, minute teeth formed by the cutting edge of the crown that enhance the slicing abilities of the teeth.

Shark. Generally used for cylindrical or flattened cartilaginous fishes with five to seven external gill openings on the sides of their heads, pectoral fins that are not attached to the head above the gill openings, and a large, stout tail with a large caudal fin; that is, all living elasmobranchs except the rays or batoids. Living sharks in this sense are all members of the Neoselachii, the modern sharks and rays. Rays are essentially flattened sharks with the pectoral fins attached to their heads, while living chimaeras are also called ghost sharks or silver sharks. Hence shark is used here in an alternate and broader sense to include the rays and chimaeras.

Snout. See page 11.

Species. A group of interbreeding individuals with common characteristics that produce fertile (capable of reproducing) offspring and which are not able to interbreed with other such groups, that is, a population that is reproductively isolated from others; related species are grouped into genera.

Spiracle. A small to large opening between the eye and first gill opening of most sharks and rays, representing the modified gill opening between the jaws and hyoid (tongue) arch. Lost in chimaeras and some sharks.

Squalene. A long-chain oily hydrocarbon present in the liver oil of deepwater cartilaginous fishes. It is highly valued for industrial and medicinal use.

Squaloid. A dogfish shark, a member of the order Squaliformes, including bramble sharks, spiny dogfish, gulper sharks, lanternsharks, viper sharks, rough sharks, sleeper sharks, kitefin sharks, and cookiecutter sharks.

Squatinoid. An angelshark, order Squatiniformes, family Squatinidae.

Stock. A group of individuals in a species, which are under consideration from the point of view of actual or potential utilisation, and which occupy a well defined geographical range independent of other stocks of the same species. A stock is often regarded as an entity for management and assessment purposes.

Subcaudal keel. In a few dogfish sharks (family Centrophoridae), a single longitudinal dermal keel on the underside of the caudal peduncle.

Subterminal margin. See page 12.

Subterminal mouth or ventral mouth. Mouth located on the underside of the head, behind the snout.

Subterminal notch. See page 12.

Subtropical region. The intermediate region between the tropical and temperate zones.

Supraorbital crest. On the neurocranium, an arched horizontal plate of cartilage forming the dorsal edge of the orbit on each side; it arises from the medial orbital wall and the cranial roof and extends horizontally from the preorbital process to the postorbital process. It is apparently primitive for shark-like fishes but is variably reduced or absent in some living elasmobranchs.

Supraorbital or brow ridge. A dermal ridge above each eye, particularly well-developed in heterodontoids and some orectoloboids.

Symphyseal or symphysial groove. A longitudinal groove on the ventral surface of the lower jaw of some orectoloboid sharks, extending posteriorly from the lower symphysis.

Symphysial teeth. Larger oral teeth in one row on either side of the symphysis, distal to medials or alternates where present. Symphysials are broader than medials and usually have asymmetrical roots.

Symphysis. The midline of the upper and lower jaws, where the paired jaw cartilages articulate with each other.

Systematics. Scientific study of the kinds and diversity of organisms, including relationships between them.

Tail. See page 11.

Target catch. The catch which is the subject of directed fishing effort within a fishery; the catch consisting of the species primarily sought by fishers.

Taxon, plural taxa. A taxonomic group at any level in a classification. Thus the taxon Chondrichthyes is a class with two taxa as subclasses, Elasmobranchii and Holocephali, and the taxon *Galeorhinus*, a genus, has one taxon as a species, *G. galeus*.

Taxonomy. Often used as a synonym of systematics or classification, but narrowed by some researchers to the theoretical study of the principles of classification.

Temperate. Two circumglobal bands of moderate ocean temperatures usually ranging between 10° and 22°C at the surface, but highly variable due to currents and upwelling. Including the north temperate zone between the Tropic of Cancer, 23°27′N latitude, to the Arctic Circle, 66°30′N; and the south temperate zone between the Tropic of Capricorn, 23°27′S latitude, to the Antarctic Circle, 66°30′N.

Terminal lobe. See page 12.

Terminal margin. See page 12.

Terminal mouth. Mouth located at the very front of the animal. Most cartilaginous fishes have subterminal mouths, but some species (Viper Shark, wobbegongs, angelsharks, frilled sharks, Whale Shark, Megamouth Shark, and mantas) have it terminal or nearly so.

Thorn. In many batoids, most angel sharks and the Bramble Shark (*Echinorhinus brucus*), enlarged, flat conical denticles with a sharp, erect crown and a flattened base (which may grow as the shark grows).

TL. Total length. A standard morphometric measurement for sharks and some batoids, from the tip of snout or rostrum to the end of the upper lobe of the caudal fin.

Transverse. Across the long access of the body.

Tropical. Circumglobal band of warm coastal and oceanic water, usually above 22°C at the surface (but varying because of currents and upwelling), between the latitudes of 23°27′N (Tropic of Cancer) and 23°27′S (Tropic of Capricorn) and including the Equator. .

Truncate. Blunt, abbreviated.

Trunk. See page 11.

Umbilical cord. A modified yolk stalk in placental viviparous sharks, carrying nutrients from the placenta to the foetus.

Undescribed species. An organism not yet formally described by science and so does not yet a have a formal binomial scientific name. Usually assigned a letter or number designation after the generic name, for example, *Gollum* sp. A is an undescribed species of false catshark belonging to the genus *Gollum*.

Unpaired fins. The dorsal, anal, and caudal fins.

Upper eyelid. The dorsal half of the eyelid, separated by a deep pocket (conjunctival fornix) from the eyeball. The upper eyelid fuses with the eyeball and the pocket is lost in all batoids.

Upper origin. See page 12.

Upper postventral margin. See page 12.

Vent. The opening of the cloaca on the ventral surface of the body between the inner margins and at the level of the pelvic fin insertions.

Ventral. Downwards, in the vertical direction of the abdomen. See dorsal.

Ventral fin. See pelvic fin.

Ventral lobe. See page 12.

Ventral margin. See page 12.

Ventral tip. See page 12.

Oceans and seas

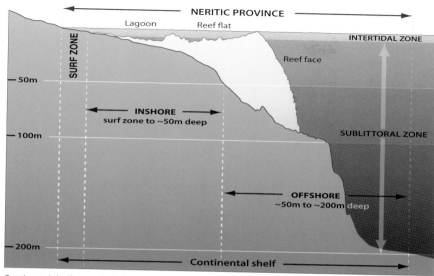

Continental shelf zones, including reef zones.

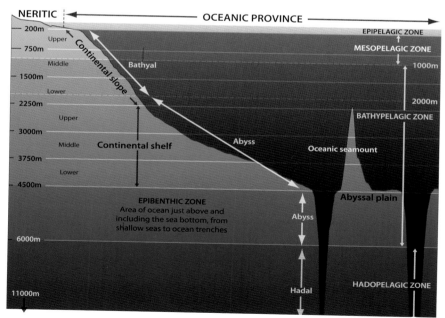

Oceanic zones.

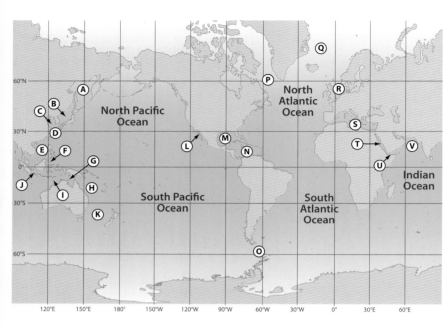

	Body of water	sea area	mean depth
A	Sea of Okhotsk	1,583,000km²	859m
B	Sea of Japan	978,000km²	1752m
C	Yellow Sea	380,000km²	44m
D	East China Sea	1,249,000km²	188m
E	South China Sea	3,500,000km²	1212m
F	Celebes Sea	280,000km²	
G	Arafura Sea	650,000km²	
H	Coral Sea	4,791,000km²	2394m
I	Timor Sea	610,000km²	406m
J	Java Sea	310,000km²	46m
K	Tasman Sea	2,300,000km²	

	Body of water	sea area	mean depth
L	Gulf of California	160,000km²	818m
M	Gulf of Mexico	1,600,000km²	1615m
N	Caribbean Sea	2,754,000km²	2200m
O	Scotia Sea	900,000km²	3500m
P	Labrador Sea	841,000km²	1898m
Q	Greenland Sea	1,205,000km²	1444m
R	North Sea	750,000km²	95m
S	Mediterranean Sea	970,000km²	1500m
T	Red Sea	438,000km²	490m
U	Gulf of Aden	530,000km²	1800m
V	Arabian Sea	3,862,000km²	4652m

Large bodies of water referred to in this book.

Field observations

Many readers will use this book for identifying sharks that they see while diving or fishing and will probably mainly come across fairly common and widely distributed species. Even so, it is worth keeping good records of your observations because scientific knowledge of even some of the most widespread species is lacking. Anyone may be able to contribute important new information, particularly if they are in a part of the world where little research is underway.

Before handling a live shark, please remember that these animals live supported by water. Their internal organs (gut, liver etc.) do not have the surrounding protection and support provided by the ribs and abdominal muscles of land animals. They can, therefore, be extremely easily damaged if lifted out of the water without good abdominal support (i.e. in a sling). Please take as many measurements as possible in the water alongside the boat, do not take your shark out to hug it, and try to ensure that it is released in good condition. You may need to spend some time helping the shark to get oxygenated water flowing over the gills again, if it has been motionless for a while. Pushing or pulling it gently through the water (headfirst, naturally) should help.

Fish markets, particularly (but not exclusively) in tropical countries, are some of the best hunting grounds for poorly known or even completely unknown sharks. One of the authors collected an undescribed (but relatively common) species of houndshark on her very first visit to a small fish market in Borneo. You may have to get up extremely early in the morning to see the fish as they are landed and before they are chopped up and sold and are advised to wear old clothes and shoes that can be washed (or thrown away) afterwards, but the experience can be really memorable. With luck, stallholders will be enthusiastic and helpful if you show a keen interest in their stock.

Where possible the following information should be recorded, whether from live sharks in the water, on hook and line alongside a boat, onboard or onshore, or from dead specimens.

i.   Name and address of observer or collector.

ii.   Date, time, location, habitat and water depth (where available).

iii. Other relevant observations (e.g. behaviour).

iv.   Photographs of the whole specimen, particularly if it is an uncommon record or outside its usual geographic range. These should be taken from the side (standard scientific procedure is to illustrate the left side of the shark), from above, and from below, with close-ups of the underside of the head and pectoral fins. Put something in the photograph to provide a known measurement scale.

v.   Measurements. Anglers like to record weights, but since these are very variable, depending upon time of year, point in the reproductive cycle etc., scientists prefer to record length as well, if not instead of weight. Total length should be recorded as a straight point-to-point distance, not over the curve of the body (which produces an overestimate of length). Precaudal length, from tip of snout to the tail fork, is another important measurement and can be easier to record than total length. Other useful measurements are illustrated opposite.

vi.   Record whether male (a photograph of the claspers may be useful in judging maturity) or female, and whether there are any signs of pregnancy.

vii. If the specimen is dead, remove and dry a strip of teeth from each of the upper and lower jaws (label them) or keep the entire jaws. The latter should be pinned to a board to dry in order to prevent distortion. If it is also possible to keep and dry the fins and the vertebral column, these can be very useful in confirming identification of species that are difficult to identify. DNA can also be extracted from dried tissue for scientific studies.

viii. If the specimen is dead, small and apparently unusual, it can be useful to keep the whole animal. Freezing is the easiest way to do this in the short term. In the longer term, it will be necessary to fix and preserve the specimen, using formalin and alcohol, but these procedures are usually undertaken in museums because of the difficulties of safely storing these toxic and flammable chemicals. For more information, see Compagno 2001.

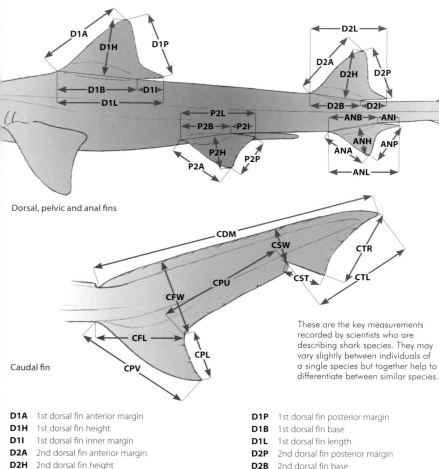

Dorsal, pelvic and anal fins

Caudal fin

These are the key measurements recorded by scientists who are describing shark species. They may vary slightly between individuals of a single species but together help to differentiate between similar species.

D1A 1st dorsal fin anterior margin
D1H 1st dorsal fin height
D1I 1st dorsal fin inner margin
D2A 2nd dorsal fin anterior margin
D2H 2nd dorsal fin height
D2I 2nd dorsal fin inner margin

P2A Pelvic fin anterior margin
P2H Pelvic fin height
P2I Pelvic fin inner margin

ANA Anal fin anterior margin
ANH Anal fin height
ANI Anal fin inner margin

CDM Caudal fin dorsal margin
CFW Caudal fin fork width
CFL Caudal fin fork length
CPL Caudal fin lower postventral margin
CTR Caudal fin terminal margin

D1P 1st dorsal fin posterior margin
D1B 1st dorsal fin base
D1L 1st dorsal fin length
D2P 2nd dorsal fin posterior margin
D2B 2nd dorsal fin base
D2L 2nd dorsal fin length

P2P Pelvic fin posterior margin
P2B Pelvic fin base
P2L Pelvic fin length

ANP Anal fin posterior margin
ANB Anal fin base
ANL Anal fin length

CPU Caudal fin upper postventral margin
CSW Caudal fin subterminal width
CPV Caudal fin preventral margin
CST Caudal fin subterminal margin
CTL Caudal fin terminal lobe

Fin measurements.

Remember that many of the species described in this field guide may well turn out to be two or more very similar species. They may be distinguished by careful examination and measurements, by differences in size (they may mature at quite different lengths), by their use of different habitats and prey species, or because of different (but sometimes overlapping) distribution. Confusion between such similar species makes it very hard to understand their distribution, habitat, life history and other biological characters. Good records can help to overcome these problems.

Records of sharks, particularly of unusual species or species recorded outside their usual range, should be sent to the relevant national or state museum, or fishery department, of the country in whose waters they were recorded. County biological records centres may be interested in receiving UK records. At minimum, a good photograph, ideally the specimen itself, should accompany unusual records, particularly if it is the first record from that country or region, but please contact the curator with details before sending in any specimens (particularly if these are large). While every country needs a national fish collection for reference purposes, to help train its fisheries staff and researchers and for the use of visiting scientists, and should be offered new specimens, some institutes may not have the necessary facilities to curate and keep them in good condition. In these cases, or if more than one important specimen has been collected, it may be necessary to send them to one of the major international fish collections as well, or instead.

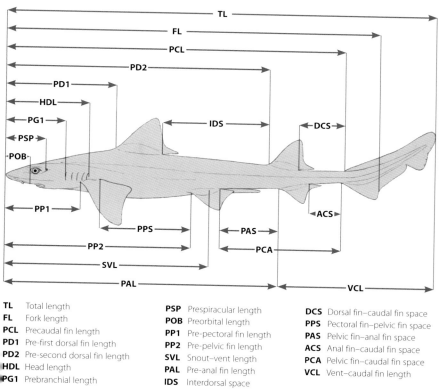

TL	Total length	**PSP**	Prespiracular length	**DCS**	Dorsal fin–caudal fin space
FL	Fork length	**POB**	Preorbital length	**PPS**	Pectoral fin–pelvic fin space
PCL	Precaudal fin length	**PP1**	Pre-pectoral fin length	**PAS**	Pelvic fin–anal fin space
PD1	Pre-first dorsal fin length	**PP2**	Pre-pelvic fin length	**ACS**	Anal fin–caudal fin space
PD2	Pre-second dorsal fin length	**SVL**	Snout–vent length	**PCA**	Pelvic fin–caudal fin length
HDL	Head length	**PAL**	Pre-anal fin length	**VCL**	Vent–caudal fin length
PG1	Prebranchial length	**IDS**	Interdorsal space		

Main longitudinal measurements.

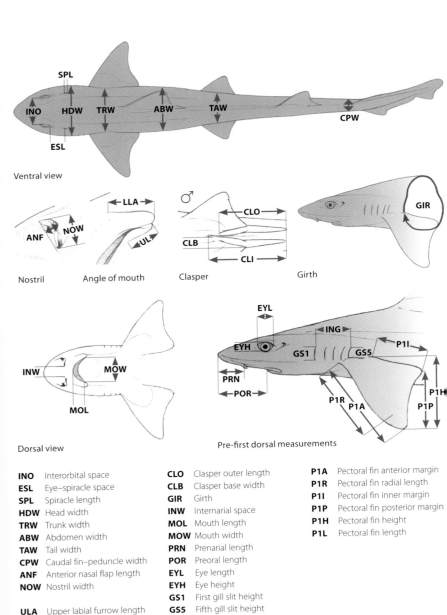

Ventral view

Nostril Angle of mouth Clasper Girth

Dorsal view

Pre-first dorsal measurements

INO	Interorbital space	**CLO**	Clasper outer length	**P1A**	Pectoral fin anterior margin
ESL	Eye–spiracle space	**CLB**	Clasper base width	**P1R**	Pectoral fin radial length
SPL	Spiracle length	**GIR**	Girth	**P1I**	Pectoral fin inner margin
HDW	Head width	**INW**	Internarial space	**P1P**	Pectoral fin posterior margin
TRW	Trunk width	**MOL**	Mouth length	**P1H**	Pectoral fin height
ABW	Abdomen width	**MOW**	Mouth width	**P1L**	Pectoral fin length
TAW	Tail width	**PRN**	Prenarial length		
CPW	Caudal fin–peduncle width	**POR**	Preoral length		
ANF	Anterior nasal flap length	**EYL**	Eye length		
NOW	Nostril width	**EYH**	Eye height		
		GS1	First gill slit height		
ULA	Upper labial furrow length	**GS5**	Fifth gill slit height		
LLA	Lower labial furrow length	**ING**	Intergill length		

Other measurements.

Further reading

Bigelow, H.B. and Schroeder W.C. 1948. Chapter three, Sharks. In: Fishes of the Western North Atlantic. *Mem. Sears Fnd. Mar. Res.* (1) 1: 56-576, figs. 6-106.

Camhi, M.D., Pikitch E.K. and Babcock E.A. (Eds). 2007. *Sharks of the Open Ocean: Biology, Fisheries and Conservation.* Blackwell Publishing, Oxford, UK.

Castro, J.I. 2011. *The sharks of North America.* Oxford University Press, USA.

Carrier, J.C., Musick J.A. and Heithaus M.R. (Eds). 2010. *Sharks and their relatives II: biodiversity, adaptive physiology, and conservation.* CRC Press, Boca Raton, USA.

Carrier, J.C., Musick J.A. and Heithaus M.R. (Eds). 2012. *The biology of sharks and their relatives.* 2nd Edition. CRC Press, Boca Raton, USA.

Compagno, L.J.V. 1984. *Sharks of the World. An annotated and illustrated catalogue of shark species known to date.* FAO Species Catalogue Vol. 4 (1 & 2). *FAO Fish. Synop.* FAO, Rome, Italy.

Compagno, L.J.V. 1988. *Sharks of the Order Carcharhiniformes.* Princeton University Press, Princeton, New Jersey, USA.

Compagno, L.J.V. 1998. Sharks. *In:* Carpenter, K.E. and Niem V.H. (Eds) *The living marine resources of the Western Central Pacific. FAO species identification guide for fishery purposes.* 2: 1195-1368. FAO, Rome, Italy.

Compagno, L.J.V. 2001. *Sharks of the World. An annotated and illustrated catalogue of shark species known to date.* Volume 2. Bullhead, mackerel and carpet sharks (Heterodontiformes, Lamniformes and Orectolobiformes). *FAO Species Catalogue for Fisheries Purposes.* No. 1, Vol. 2. FAO, Rome, Italy.

Compagno, L.J.V. 2002. Sharks. *In:* Carpenter, K.E.: *(ed.).* The living marine resources of the Western Central Atlantic. Volume 1: Introduction, mollusks, crustaceans, hagfishes, sharks, batoid fishes, and chimaeras. *FAO species identification guide for fishery purposes and American Society of Ichthyologists and Herpetologists Special Publication No. 5.* Rome. FAO, Rome, Italy.

Compagno, L.J.V., Dando, M. and Fowler, S. 2005. *A Field Guide to the Sharks of the World.* HarperCollins, London, UK.

Compagno, L.J.V., Ebert D.A. and Smale M.J. 1989. *Guide to the sharks and rays of southern Africa.* Struik Publishers, Cape Town, South Africa.

Ebert, D.A. 2003. *Sharks, Rays, and Chimaeras of California.* University of California Press, California, USA.

Ebert, D.A. 2013. Deepsea sharks of the Indian Ocean. *FAO Species Catalogue for Fishery Purposes.* FAO, Rome, Italy.

Ebert, D.A. and Compagno L.J.V. in press. *Sharks of the world. An annotated and illustrated catalogue of shark species known to date.* Volume 1. Cow, frilled, dogfish, saw, and angel sharks (Hexanchiformes, Squaliformes, Pristiophoriformes, and Squatiniformes). *FAO Species Catalogue for Fishery Purposes.* FAO, Rome, Italy.

Ebert, D.A. and Stehmann M.F.W. 2013. *Sharks, batoids, and chimaeras of the North Atlantic. FAO Species Catalogue for Fishery Purposes.* No. 7. FAO, Rome, Italy.

Ebert, D.A., Fowler, S. and Compagno L.J.V. 2013. *Sharks of the World: a fully illustrated guide.* Wild Nature Press, Plymouth, UK.

Eilperin, J. 2011. *Demon fish: Travels through the hidden world of sharks.* Pantheon. New York, USA.

Eschmeyer, W.N. 2013. The catalogue of fishes on-line. California Academy of Sciences: San Francisco. Available from: www.calacademy.org/research/ichthyology/catalogue/fishcatmain.asp

Last, P.R. and Stevens J.D. 2009. *Sharks and rays of Australia.* CSIRO, Australia.

Last, P.R., White W.T. and Pogonoski J.J. (Eds). 2007. Descriptions of new dogfishes of the genus *Squalus* (Squaloidea: Squalidae). *CSIRO Marine and Atmospheric Research Paper* No. 014, 130 pp.

Last, P.R., White W.T. and Pogonoski J.J. (Eds). 2008. Descriptions of new Australian Chondrichthyans. *CSIRO Marine and Atmospheric Research Paper* No. 022, 358 pp.

Last, P.R., White W.T. and Pogonoski J.J. (Eds). 2010. Descriptions of new sharks and rays from Borneo. *CSIRO Marine and Atmospheric Research Paper* No. 032, 165 pp.

Nakabo, T. (Ed.). 2002. *Fishes of Japan with pictorial keys to the species.* English edition. Tokai University Press, Tokyo.

White, W.T., Last, P.R., Stevens, J.D., Yearsley, G.K., Fahmi and Dharmadi. 2006. *Economically important sharks and rays of Indonesia.* Australian Center for International Agriculture Research Monograph Series, no. 124, p. 329.

Scientific societies and conservation organisations

American Elasmobranch Society www.elasmo.org

Convention on International Trade in Endangered Species www.cites.org

Convention on Migratory Species (CMS) www.cms.int

Convention on Migratory Species Sharks Memorandum of Understanding (CMS Sharks MOU)
    www.sharksmou.org

European Elasmobranch Association (with links to many member bodies)
    www.eulasmo.org

IUCN Red List of Threatened Species on line data base www.iucnredlist.org

IUCN Shark Specialist Group www.iucnssg.org

Oceania Chondrichthyan Society www.oceaniasharks.org.au

Pew Charitable Trusts www.pewenvironment.org

Project AWARE Foundation www.projectaware.org

Save our Seas Foundation www.saveourseas.com

Shark Alliance www.sharkalliance.org

Shark Foundation www.shark.ch

Shark Research Institute www.sharks.org

Shark Trust www.sharktrust.org

South African Shark Conservancy www.sharkconservancy.org

TRAFFIC, the wildlife trade monitoring network www.traffic.org/fish

Other sources of online information

Australian Museum www.australianmuseum.net.au/fishes

Catalogue of Fishes research.calacademy.org/ichthyology/catalog

FAO Fisheries and Aquaculture Department www.fao.org/fi

Fish Base www.fishbase.org

Florida Museum of Natural History www.flmnh.ufl.edu/fish/sharks

Shark References online database www.shark-references.com

Smithsonian National Museum of Natural History www.ocean.si.edu/ocean-life-ecosystems/sharks-rays

Species checklist

	Order/Family	Scientific name	English name	Page	
	Hexanchiformes – frilled and cow sharks			42	
1	Chlamydoselachidae – frilled sharks	*Chlamydoselachus africana*	Southern African Frilled Shark	44	
2		*Chlamydoselachus anguineus*	Frilled Shark	44	
3	Hexanchidae – cow sharks	*Heptranchias perlo*	Sharpnose Sevengill Shark	44	
4		*Hexanchus griseus*	Bluntnose Sixgill Shark	44	
5		*Hexanchus nakamurai*	Bigeye Sixgill Shark	44	
6		*Notorynchus cepedianus*	Broadnose Sevengill Shark	44	
	Echinorhiniformes – bramble sharks			46	
7	Echinorhinidae – bramble sharks	*Echinorhinus brucus*	Bramble Shark	48	
8		*Echinorhinus cookei*	Prickly Shark	48	
	Squaliformes – dogfish sharks			46	
9	Squalidae – dogfish sharks	*Cirrhigaleus asper*	Roughskin Spurdog	50	
10		*Cirrhigaleus australis*	Southern Mandarin Dogfish	50	
11		*Cirrhigaleus barbifer*	Mandarin Dogfish	50	
12		*Squalus acanthias*	Piked Dogfish	48	
13		*Squalus albifrons*	Eastern Highfin Spurdog	50	
14		*Squalus altipinnis*	Western Highfin Spurdog	50	
15		*Squalus blainville*	Longnose Spurdog	54	
16		*Squalus brevirostris*	Japanese Shortnose Spurdog	54	
17		*Squalus bucephalus*	Bighead Spurdog	52	
18		*Squalus chloroculus*	Greeneye Spurdog	52	
19		*Squalus crassispinus*	Fatspine Spurdog	50	
20		*Squalus cubensis*	Cuban Dogfish	54	
21		*Squalus edmundsi*	Edmund's Spurdog	52	
22		*Squalus formosus*	Taiwan Spurdog	52	
23		*Squalus grahami*	Eastern Longnose Spurdog	50	
24		*Squalus griffini*	New Zealand Dogfish	52	
25		*Squalus hemipinnis*	Indonesian Shortsnout Dogfish	52	
26		*Squalus japonicus*	Japanese Spurdog	54	
27		*Squalus lalannei*	Seychelles Spurdog	52	
28		*Squalus megalops*	Shortnose Spurdog	54	
29		*Squalus melanurus*	Blacktail Spurdog	54	
30		*Squalus mitsukurii*	Shortspine Spurdog	48	
31		*Squalus montalbani*	Philippines Spurdog	52	
32		*Squalus nasutus*	Western Longnose Spurdog	50	
33		*Squalus notocaudatus*	Bartail Spurdog	50	
34		*Squalus rancureli*	Cyrano Spurdog	54	
35		*Squalus raoulensis*	Kermadec Spiny Dogfish	54	
36		*Squalus suckleyi*	North Pacific Spiny Dogfish	48	
37	Centrophoridae – gulper sharks	*Centrophorus acus*	Needle Dogfish	56	

	Order/Family	Scientific name	English name	Page
38		*Centrophorus atromarginatus*	Dwarf Gulper Shark	58
39		*Centrophorus granulosus*	Gulper Shark	56
40		*Centrophorus harrissoni*	Longnose Gulper Shark	56
41		*Centrophorus isodon*	Blackfin Gulper Shark	58
42		*Centrophorus lusitanicus*	Lowfin Gulper Shark	56
43		*Centrophorus moluccensis*	Smallfin Gulper Shark	56
44		*Centrophorus niaukang*	Taiwan Gulper Shark	56
45		*Centrophorus seychellorum*	Seychelles Gulper Shark	58
46		*Centrophorus squamosus*	Leafscale Gulper Shark	56
47		*Centrophorus tesselatus*	Mosaic Gulper Shark	56
48		*Centrophorus westraliensis*	Western Gulper Shark	58
49		*Centrophorus zeehaani*	Southern Dogfish	58
50		*Deania calcea*	Birdbeak Dogfish	58
51		*Deania hystricosa*	Rough Longnose Dogfish	58
52		*Deania profundorum*	Arrowhead Dogfish	58
53		*Deania quadrispinosa*	Longsnout Dogfish	58
54	Etmopteridae – lanternsharks	*Aculeola nigra*	Hooktooth Dogfish	62
55		*Centroscyllium excelsum*	Highfin Dogfish	62
56		*Centroscyllium fabricii*	Black Dogfish	62
57		*Centroscyllium granulatum*	Granular Dogfish	62
58		*Centroscyllium kamoharai*	Bareskin Dogfish	62
59		*Centroscyllium nigrum*	Combtooth Dogfish	62
60		*Centroscyllium ornatum*	Ornate Dogfish	62
61		*Centroscyllium ritteri*	Whitefin Dogfish	62
62		*Etmopterus baxteri*	Giant Lanternshark	72
63		*Etmopterus bigelowi*	Blurred Smooth Lanternshark	66
64		*Etmopterus brachyurus*	Shorttail Lanternshark	70
65		*Etmopterus bullisi*	Lined Lanternshark	64
66		*Etmopterus burgessi*	Broadsnout Lanternshark	70
67		*Etmopterus carteri*	Cylindrical Lanternshark	66
68		*Etmopterus caudistigmus*	Tailspot Lanternshark	72
69		*Etmopterus compagnoi*	Brown Lanternshark	66
70		*Etmopterus decacuspidatus*	Combtooth Lanternshark	68
71		*Etmopterus dianthus*	Pink Lanternshark	70
72		*Etmopterus dislineatus*	Lined Lanternshark	72
73		*Etmopterus evansi*	Blackmouth Lanternshark	68
74		*Etmopterus fusus*	Pygmy Lanternshark	68
75		*Etmopterus gracilispinis*	Broadband Lanternshark	66
76		*Etmopterus granulosus*	Southern Lanternshark	72
77		*Etmopterus hillianus*	Caribbean Lanternshark	64
78		*Etmopterus joungi*	Shortfin Smooth Lanternshark	70
79		*Etmopterus litvinovi*	Smalleye Lanternshark	70
80		*Etmopterus lucifer*	Blackbelly Lanternshark	70

	Order/Family	Scientific name	English name	Page
81		*Etmopterus molleri*	Slendertail Lanternshark	70
82		*Etmopterus perryi*	Dwarf Lanternshark	66
83		*Etmopterus polli*	African Lanternshark	64
84		*Etmopterus princeps*	Great Lanternshark	64
85		*Etmopterus pseudosqualiolus*	False Lanternshark	72
86		*Etmopterus pusillus*	Smooth Lanternshark	64
87		*Etmopterus pycnolepis*	Densescale Lanternshark	72
88		*Etmopterus robinsi*	West Indian Lanternshark	66
89		*Etmopterus schultzi*	Fringefin Lanternshark	64
90		*Etmopterus sculptus*	Sculptured Lanternshark	66
91		*Etmopterus sentosus*	Thorny Lanternshark	68
92		*Etmopterus sheikoi*	Rasptooth Dogfish	68
93		*Etmopterus spinax*	Velvet Belly	64
94		*Etmopterus splendidus*	Splendid Lanternshark	68
95		*Etmopterus unicolor*	Brown Lanternshark	66
96		*Etmopterus viator*	Traveller Lanternshark	72
97		*Etmopterus villosus*	Hawaiian Lanternshark	68
98		*Etmopterus virens*	Green Lanternshark	64
99		*Trigonognathus kabeyai*	Viper Dogfish	68
100	Somniosidae – sleeper sharks	*Centroscymnus coelolepis*	Portuguese Dogfish	74
101		*Centroscymnus owstoni*	Roughskin Dogfish	74
102		*Centroselachus crepidater*	Longnose Velvet Dogfish	74
103		*Proscymnodon macracanthus*	Largespine Velvet Dogfish	74
104		*Proscymnodon plunketi*	Plunket Shark	74
105		*Scymnodalatias albicauda*	Whitetail Dogfish	76
106		*Scymnodalatias garricki*	Azores Dogfish	76
107		*Scymnodalatias oligodon*	Sparsetooth Dogfish	76
108		*Scymnodalatias sherwoodi*	Sherwood Dogfish	76
109		*Scymnodon ringens*	Knifetooth Dogfish	76
110		*Somniosus antarcticus*	Southern Sleeper Shark	78
111		*Somniosus longus*	Frog Shark	78
112		*Somniosus microcephalus*	Greenland Shark	78
113		*Somniosus pacificus*	Pacific Sleeper Shark	78
114		*Somniosus rostratus*	Little Sleeper Shark	78
115		*Zameus ichiharai*	Japanese Velvet Dogfish	76
116		*Zameus squamulosus*	Velvet Dogfish	76
117	Oxynotidae – roughsharks	*Oxynotus bruniensis*	Prickly Dogfish	80
118		*Oxynotus caribbaeus*	Caribbean Roughshark	80
119		*Oxynotus centrina*	Angular Roughshark	80
120		*Oxynotus japonicus*	Japanese Roughshark	80
121		*Oxynotus paradoxus*	Sailfin Roughshark	80
122	Dalatiidae – kitefin sharks	*Dalatias licha*	Kitefin Shark	80
123		*Euprotomicroides zantedeschia*	Taillight Shark	82

	Order/Family	Scientific name	English name	Page
124		*Euprotomicrus bispinatus*	Pygmy Shark	82
125		*Heteroscymnoides marleyi*	Longnose Pygmy Shark	82
126		*Isistius brasiliensis*	Cookiecutter Shark	82
127		*Isistius labialis*	South China Cookiecutter Shark	82
128		*Isistius plutodus*	Largetooth Cookiecutter Shark	82
129		*Mollisquama parini*	Pocket Shark	82
130		*Squaliolus aliae*	Smalleye Pygmy Shark	82
131		*Squaliolus laticaudus*	Spined Pygmy Shark	82
	Pristiophoriformes – sawsharks			84
132	Pristiophoridae – sawsharks	*Pliotrema warreni*	Sixgill Sawshark	86
133		*Pristiophorus cirratus*	Longnose Sawshark	86
134		*Pristiophorus delicatus*	Tropical Sawshark	88
135		*Pristiophorus japonicus*	Japanese Sawshark	86
136		*Pristiophorus lanae*	Lana's Sawshark	88
137		*Pristiophorus nancyae*	African Dwarf Sawshark	88
138		*Pristiophorus nudipinnis*	Shortnose Sawshark	86
139		*Pristiophorus schroederi*	Bahamas Sawshark	88
	Squatiniformes – angelsharks			85
140	Squatinidae – angelsharks	*Squatina aculeata*	Sawback Angelshark	90
141		*Squatina africana*	African Angelshark	90
142		*Squatina albipunctata*	Eastern Angelshark	94
143		*Squatina argentina*	Argentine Angelshark	90
144		*Squatina armata*	Chilean Angelshark	92
145		*Squatina australis*	Australian Angelshark	92
146		*Squatina caillieti*	Philippines Angelshark	92
147		*Squatina californica*	Pacific Angelshark	92
148		*Squatina dumeril*	Sand Devil	90
149		*Squatina formosa*	Taiwan Angelshark	92
150		*Squatina guggenheim*	Angular Angelshark	90
151		*Squatina japonica*	Japanese Angelshark	92
152		*Squatina legnota*	Indonesian Angelshark	92
153		*Squatina nebulosa*	Clouded Angelshark	94
154		*Squatina occulta*	Hidden Angelshark	94
155		*Squatina oculata*	Smoothback Angelshark	94
156		*Squatina pseudocellata*	Western Angelshark	94
157		*Squatina squatina*	Angelshark	90
158		*Squatina tergocellata*	Ornate Angelshark	94
159		*Squatina tergocellatoides*	Ocellated Angelshark	94
	Heterodontiformes – bullhead sharks			96
160	Heterodontidae – bullhead sharks	*Heterodontus francisci*	Horn Shark	100
161		*Heterodontus galeatus*	Crested Bullhead Shark	100
162		*Heterodontus japonicus*	Japanese Bullhead Shark	100
163		*Heterodontus mexicanus*	Mexican Hornshark	102

	Order/Family	Scientific name	English name	Page
164		*Heterodontus omanensis*	Oman Bullhead Shark	102
165		*Heterodontus portusjacksoni*	Port Jackson Shark	100
166		*Heterodontus quoyi*	Galapagos Bullhead Shark	102
167		*Heterodontus ramalheira*	Whitespotted Bullhead Shark	102
168		*Heterodontus zebra*	Zebra Bullhead Shark	102
	Lamniformes – mackerel sharks			97
169	Mitsukurinidae – goblin sharks	*Mitsukurina owstoni*	Goblin Shark	104
170	Odontaspididae – sandtiger sharks	*Carcharias taurus*	Sandtiger Shark	104
171		*Odontaspis ferox*	Smalltooth Sandtiger	104
172		*Odontaspis noronhai*	Bigeye Sandtiger	104
173	Pseudocarchariidae – crocodile sharks	*Pseudocarcharias kamoharai*	Crocodile Shark	104
174	Megachasmidae – megamouth sharks	*Megachasma pelagios*	Megamouth Shark	106
175	Cetorhinidae – basking sharks	*Cetorhinus maximus*	Basking Shark	106
176	Alopiidae – thresher sharks	*Alopias pelagicus*	Pelagic Thresher	108
177		*Alopias superciliosus*	Bigeye Thresher	108
178		*Alopias vulpinus*	Thresher Shark	108
179	Lamnidae – mackerel sharks	*Carcharodon carcharias*	White Shark	110
180		*Isurus oxyrinchus*	Shortfin Mako	110
181		*Isurus paucus*	Longfin Mako	110
182		*Lamna ditropis*	Salmon Shark	110
183		*Lamna nasus*	Porbeagle Shark	110
	Orectolobiformes – carpetsharks			112
184	Parascylliidae – collared carpetsharks	*Cirrhoscyllium expolitum*	Barbelthroat Carpetshark	116
185		*Cirrhoscyllium formosanum*	Taiwan Saddled Carpetshark	116
186		*Cirrhoscyllium japonicum*	Saddled Carpetshark	116
187		*Parascyllium collare*	Collared Carpetshark	114
188		*Parascyllium elongatum*	Elongate Carpetshark	114
189		*Parascyllium ferrugineum*	Rusty Carpetshark	114
190		*Parascyllium sparsimaculatum*	Ginger Carpetshark	114
191		*Parascyllium variolatum*	Necklace Carpetshark	114
192	Brachaeluridae – blind sharks	*Brachaelurus colcloughi*	Bluegrey Carpetshark	116
193		*Brachaelurus waddi*	Blind Shark	116
194	Orectolobidae – wobbegongs	*Eucrossorhinus dasypogon*	Tasselled Wobbegong	118
195		*Orectolobus floridus*	Floral Banded Wobbegong	122
196		*Orectolobus halei*	Gulf Wobbegong	122
197		*Orectolobus hutchinsi*	Western Wobbegong	120
198		*Orectolobus japonicus*	Japanese Wobbegong	118
199		*Orectolobus leptolineatus*	False Cobbler Wobbegong	120
200		*Orectolobus maculatus*	Spotted Wobbegong	120
201		*Orectolobus ornatus*	Ornate Wobbegong	120
202		*Orectolobus parvimaculatus*	Dwarf Spotted Wobbegong	122
203		*Orectolobus reticulatus*	Network Wobbegong	122
204		*Orectolobus wardi*	Northern Wobbegong	118

	Order/Family	Scientific name	English name	Page
205		*Sutorectus tentaculatus*	Cobbler Wobbegong	118
206	Hemiscylliidae – longtailed carpetsharks	*Chiloscyllium arabicum*	Arabian Carpetshark	124
207		*Chiloscyllium burmensis*	Burmese Bambooshark	124
208		*Chiloscyllium griseum*	Grey Bambooshark	124
209		*Chiloscyllium hasselti*	Indonesian Bambooshark	124
210		*Chiloscyllium indicum*	Slender Bambooshark	124
211		*Chiloscyllium plagiosum*	Whitespotted Bambooshark	124
212		*Chiloscyllium punctatum*	Brownbanded Bambooshark	124
213		*Hemiscyllium freycineti*	Indonesian Speckled Carpetshark	126
214		*Hemiscyllium galei*	Gale's Epaulette Shark	126
215		*Hemiscyllium hallstromi*	Papuan Epaulette Carpetshark	126
216		*Hemiscyllium henryi*	Henry's Epaulette Shark	126
217		*Hemiscyllium michaeli*	Michael's Epaulette Shark	126
218		*Hemiscyllium ocellatum*	Epaulette Shark	126
219		*Hemiscyllium strahani*	Hooded Carpetshark	126
220		*Hemiscyllium trispeculare*	Speckled Carpetshark	126
221	Stegostomatidae – zebra sharks	*Stegostoma fasciatum*	Zebra Shark	130
222	Ginglymostomatidae – Nurse sharks	*Ginglymostoma cirratum*	Nurse Shark	130
223		*Nebrius ferrugineus*	Tawny Nurse Shark	130
224		*Pseudoginglymostoma brevicaudatum*	Shorttail Nurse Shark	130
225	Rhincodontidae – whale sharks	*Rhincodon typus*	Whale Shark	106
	Carcharhiniformes – ground sharks			128
226	Scyliorhinidae – catsharks	*Apristurus albisoma*	White-bodied Catshark	140
227		*Apristurus ampliceps*	Roughskin Catshark	138
228		*Apristurus aphyodes*	White Ghost Catshark	134
229		*Apristurus australis*	Pinocchio Catshark	138
230		*Apristurus brunneus*	Brown Catshark	140
231		*Apristurus bucephalus*	Bighead Catshark	138
232		*Apristurus canutus*	Hoary Catshark	134
233		*Apristurus exsanguis*	Flaccid Catshark	138
234		*Apristurus fedorovi*	Stout Catshark	138
235		*Apristurus gibbosus*	Humpback Catshark	140
236		*Apristurus herklotsi*	Longfin Catshark	140
237		*Apristurus indicus*	Smallbelly Catshark	136
238		*Apristurus internatus*	Shortnose Demon Catshark	136
239		*Apristurus investigatoris*	Broadnose Catshark	140
240		*Apristurus japonicus*	Japanese Catshark	140
241		*Apristurus kampae*	Longnose Catshark	140
242		*Apristurus laurussoni*	Iceland Catshark	134
243		*Apristurus longicephalus*	Longhead Catshark	136
244		*Apristurus macrorhynchus*	Flathead Catshark	136
245		*Apristurus macrostomus*	Broadmouth Catshark	140
246		*Apristurus manis*	Ghost Catshark	134

	Order/Family	Scientific name	English name	Page
247		Apristurus melanoasper	Fleshynose Catshark	138
248		Apristurus microps	Smalleye Catshark	134
249		Apristurus micropterygeus	Smalldorsal Catshark	140
250		Apristurus nasutus	Largenose Catshark	136
251		Apristurus parvipinnis	Smallfin Catshark	134
252		Apristurus pinguis	Bulldog Catshark	138
253		Apristurus platyrhynchus	Bigfin Catshark	138
254		Apristurus profundorum	Deepwater Catshark	134
255		Apristurus riveri	Broadgill Catshark	134
256		Apristurus saldanha	Saldanha Catshark	134
257		Apristurus sibogae	Pale Catshark	136
258		Apristurus sinensis	South China Catshark	136
259		Apristurus spongiceps	Spongehead Catshark	136
260		Apristurus stenseni	Panama Ghost Catshark	136
261		Asymbolus analis	Grey Spotted Catshark	142
262		Asymbolus funebris	Blotched Catshark	142
263		Asymbolus galacticus	Starry Catshark	142
264		Asymbolus occiduus	Western Spotted Catshark	142
265		Asymbolus pallidus	Pale Spotted Catshark	142
266		Asymbolus parvus	Dwarf Catshark	142
267		Asymbolus rubiginosus	Orange Spotted Catshark	142
268		Asymbolus submaculatus	Variegated Catshark	142
269		Asymbolus vincenti	Gulf Catshark	142
270		Atelomycterus baliensis	Bali Catshark	144
271		Atelomycterus fasciatus	Banded Sand Catshark	144
272		Atelomycterus macleayi	Australian Marbled Catshark	144
273		Atelomycterus marmoratus	Coral Catshark	144
274		Atelomycterus marnkalha	Whitespotted Sand Catshark	144
275		Aulohalaelurus kanakorum	New Caledonia Catshark	144
276		Aulohalaelurus labiosus	Blackspotted Catshark	144
277		Bythaelurus canescens	Dusky Catshark	146
278		Bythaelurus clevai	Broadhead Catshark	146
279		Bythaelurus dawsoni	New Zealand Catshark	146
280		Bythaelurus giddingsi	Jaguar Catshark	146
281		Bythaelurus hispidus	Bristly Catshark	146
282		Bythaelurus immaculatus	Spotless Catshark	146
283		Bythaelurus incanus	Dusky Catshark	146
284		Bythaelurus lutarius	Mud Catshark	146
285		Cephaloscyllium albipinnum	Whitefin Swellshark	148
286		Cephaloscyllium cooki	Cook's Swellshark	150
287		Cephaloscyllium fasciatum	Reticulated Swellshark	148
288		Cephaloscyllium hiscosellum	Australian Reticulated Swellshark	150
289		Cephaloscyllium isabellum	Draughtsboard Shark	148

	Order/Family	Scientific name	English name	Page	
290		*Cephaloscyllium laticeps*	Australian Swellshark	148	
291		*Cephaloscyllium maculatum*	Spotted Swellshark	150	
292		*Cephaloscyllium pardelotum*	Leopard-spotted Swellshark	150	
293		*Cephaloscyllium pictum*	Painted Swellshark	150	
294		*Cephaloscyllium sarawakensis*	Sarawak Swellshark	150	
295		*Cephaloscyllium signourum*	Flagtail Swellshark	150	
296		*Cephaloscyllium silasi*	Indian Swellshark	150	
297		*Cephaloscyllium speccum*	Speckled Swellshark	148	
298		*Cephaloscyllium stevensi*	Steven's Swellshark	150	
299		*Cephaloscyllium sufflans*	Balloon Shark	148	
300		*Cephaloscyllium umbratile*	Japanese Swellshark	148	
301		*Cephaloscyllium variegatum*	Saddled Swellshark	148	
302		*Cephaloscyllium ventriosum*	Swellshark	148	
303		*Cephaloscyllium zebrum*	Narrowbar Swellshark	148	
304		*Cephalurus cephalus*	Lollipop Catshark	164	
305		*Figaro boardmani*	Australian Sawtail Catshark	154	
306		*Figaro striatus*	Northern Sawtail Catshark	154	
307		*Galeus antillensis*	Antilles Catshark	152	
308		*Galeus arae*	Roughtail Catshark	152	
309		*Galeus atlanticus*	Atlantic Sawtail Catshark	152	
310		*Galeus cadenati*	Longfin Sawtail Catshark	154	
311		*Galeus eastmani*	Gecko Catshark	154	
312		*Galeus gracilis*	Slender Sawtail Catshark	154	
313		*Galeus longirostris*	Longnose Sawtail Catshark	154	
314		*Galeus melastomus*	Blackmouth Catshark	152	
315		*Galeus mincaronei*	Southern Sawtail Catshark	152	
316		*Galeus murinus*	Mouse Catshark	152	
317		*Galeus nipponensis*	Broadfin Sawtail Catshark	152	
318		*Galeus piperatus*	Peppered Catshark	152	
319		*Galeus polli*	African Sawtail Catshark	152	
320		*Galeus priapus*	Phallic Catshark	154	
321		*Galeus sauteri*	Blacktip Sawtail Catshark	152	
322		*Galeus schultzi*	Dwarf Sawtail Catshark	154	
323		*Galeus springeri*	Springer's Sawtail Catshark	154	
324		*Halaelurus boesemani*	Speckled Catshark	156	
325		*Halaelurus buergeri*	Blackspotted Catshark	156	
326		*Halaelurus lineatus*	Lined Catshark	156	
327		*Halaelurus maculosus*	Indonesian Speckled Catshark	156	
328		*Halaelurus natalensis*	Tiger Catshark	156	
329		*Halaelurus quagga*	Quagga Catshark	156	
330		*Halaelurus sellus*	Rusty Catshark	156	
331		*Haploblepharus edwardsii*	Puffadder Shyshark	158	
332		*Haploblepharus fuscus*	Brown Shyshark	158	

	Order/Family	Scientific name	English name	Page
333		*Haploblepharus kistnasamyi*	Natal Shyshark	158
334		*Haploblepharus pictus*	Dark Shyshark	158
335		*Holohalaelurus favus*	Honeycomb Izak Catshark	160
336		*Holohalaelurus grennian*	Grinning Izak	160
337		*Holohalaelurus melanostigma*	Crying Izak Catshark	160
338		*Holohalaelurus punctatus*	African Spotted Catshark	160
339		*Holohalaelurus regani*	Izak Catshark	160
340		*Parmaturus albimarginatus*	Whitetip Catshark	162
341		*Parmaturus albipenis*	White-clasper Catshark	162
342		*Parmaturus bigus*	Beige Catshark	162
343		*Parmaturus campechiensis*	Campeche Catshark	162
344		*Parmaturus lanatus*	Velvet Catshark	162
345		*Parmaturus macmillani*	New Zealand Filetail	162
346		*Parmaturus melanobranchius*	Blackgill Catshark	164
347		*Parmaturus pilosus*	Salamander Catshark	164
348		*Parmaturus xaniurus*	Filetail Catshark	162
349		*Pentanchus profundicolus*	Onefin Catshark	164
350		*Poroderma africanum*	Pyjama Shark	158
351		*Poroderma pantherinum*	Leopard Catshark	158
352		*Schroederichthys bivius*	Narrowmouth Catshark	166
353		*Schroederichthys chilensis*	Redspotted Catshark	166
354		*Schroederichthys maculatus*	Narrowtail Catshark	166
355		*Schroederichthys saurisqualus*	Lizard Catshark	166
356		*Schroederichthys tenuis*	Slender Catshark	166
357		*Scyliorhinus besnardi*	Polkadot Catshark	170
358		*Scyliorhinus boa*	Boa Catshark	168
359		*Scyliorhinus canicula*	Smallspotted Catshark	168
360		*Scyliorhinus capensis*	Yellowspotted Catshark	168
361		*Scyliorhinus cervigoni*	West African Catshark	168
362		*Scyliorhinus comoroensis*	Comoro Catshark	168
363		*Scyliorhinus garmani*	Brownspotted Catshark	170
364		*Scyliorhinus haeckelii*	Freckled Catshark	170
365		*Scyliorhinus hesperius*	Whitesaddled Catshark	170
366		*Scyliorhinus meadi*	Blotched Catshark	170
367		*Scyliorhinus retifer*	Chain Catshark	170
368		*Scyliorhinus stellaris*	Nursehound	168
369		*Scyliorhinus tokubee*	Izu Catshark	170
370		*Scyliorhinus torazame*	Cloudy Catshark	170
371		*Scyliorhinus torrei*	Dwarf Catshark	170
372	Proscylliidae – finback catsharks	*Ctenacis fehlmanni*	Harlequin Catshark	172
373		*Eridacnis barbouri*	Cuban Ribbontail Catshark	172
374		*Eridacnis radcliffei*	Pygmy Ribbontail Catshark	172
375		*Eridacnis sinuans*	African Ribbontail Catshark	172

	Order/Family	Scientific name	English name	Page
376		*Proscyllium habereri*	Graceful Catshark	172
377		*Proscyllium magnificum*	Magnificent Catshark	172
378	Pseudotriakidae – false catsharks	*Gollum attenuatus*	Slender Smoothhound	172
379		*Gollum suluensis*	Sulu Gollumshark	172
380		*Gollum sp. B*	Whitemarked Gollumshark	172
381		*Pseudotriakis microdon*	False Catshark	176
382		*Planonasus parini*	Pygmy False Catshark	176
383	Leptochariidae – barbeled houndsharks	*Leptocharias smithii*	Barbeled Houndshark	176
384	Triakidae – houndsharks	*Furgaleus macki*	Whiskery Shark	176
385		*Galeorhinus galeus*	Tope	176
386		*Gogolia filewoodi*	Sailback Houndshark	176
387		*Hemitriakis abdita*	Deepwater Sicklefin Houndshark	178
388		*Hemitriakis complicofasciata*	Striped Topeshark	178
389		*Hemitriakis falcata*	Sicklefin Houndshark	178
390		*Hemitriakis indroyonoi*	Indonesian Houndshark	178
391		*Hemitriakis japanica*	Japanese Topeshark	178
392		*Hemitriakis leucoperiptera*	Whitefin Topeshark	178
393		*Hypogaleus hyugaensis*	Blacktip Topeshark	176
394		*Iago garricki*	Longnose Houndshark	180
395		*Iago mangalorensis*	Mangalore Houndshark	180
396		*Iago omanensis*	Bigeye Houndshark	180
397		*Mustelus albipinnis*	White-margin Fin Houndshark	186
398		*Mustelus antarcticus*	Gummy Shark	188
399		*Mustelus asterias*	Starry Smoothhound	182
400		*Mustelus californicus*	Grey Smoothhound	184
401		*Mustelus canis*	Dusky Smoothhound	182
402		*Mustelus dorsalis*	Sharptooth Smoothhound	184
403		*Mustelus fasciatus*	Striped Smoothhound	186
404		*Mustelus griseus*	Spotless Smoothhound	184
405		*Mustelus henlei*	Brown Smoothhound	184
406		*Mustelus higmani*	Smalleye Smoothhound	186
407		*Mustelus lenticulatus*	Rig	188
408		*Mustelus lunulatus*	Sicklefin Smoothhound	186
409		*Mustelus manazo*	Starspotted Smoothhound	184
410		*Mustelus mento*	Speckled Smoothhound	184
411		*Mustelus minicanis*	Venezuelan Dwarf Smoothhound	186
412		*Mustelus mosis*	Arabian Smoothhound	184
413		*Mustelus mustelus*	Smoothhound	182
414		*Mustelus norrisi*	Narrowfin Smoothhound	186
415		*Mustelus palumbes*	Whitespot Smoothhound	182
416		*Mustelus punctulatus*	Blackspot Smoothhound	182
417		*Mustelus ravidus*	Australian Grey Smoothhound	188
418		*Mustelus schmitti*	Narrownose Smoothhound	182

	Order/Family	Scientific name	English name	Page
419		*Mustelus sinusmexicanus*	Gulf of Mexico Smoothhound	186
420		*Mustelus stevensi*	Whitespotted Gummy Shark	188
421		*Mustelus walkeri*	Eastern Spotted Gummy Shark	188
422		*Mustelus whitneyi*	Humpback Smoothhound	186
423		*Mustelus widodoi*	Whitefin Smoothhound	188
424		*Scylliogaleus quecketti*	Flapnose Houndshark	180
425		*Triakis acutipinna*	Sharpfin Houndshark	180
426		*Triakis maculata*	Spotted Houndshark	180
427		*Triakis megalopterus*	Spotted Gully Shark	180
428		*Triakis scyllium*	Banded Houndshark	180
429		*Triakis semifasciata*	Leopard Shark	180
430	Hemigaleidae – weasel sharks	*Chaenogaleus macrostoma*	Hooktooth Shark	190
431		*Hemigaleus australiensis*	Australian Weasel Shark	190
432		*Hemigaleus microstoma*	Sicklefin Weasel Shark	190
433		*Hemipristis elongatus*	Snaggletooth Shark	190
434		*Paragaleus leucolomatus*	Whitetip Weasel Shark	190
435		*Paragaleus pectoralis*	Atlantic Weasel Shark	190
436		*Paragaleus randalli*	Slender Weasel Shark	190
437		*Paragaleus tengi*	Straighttooth Weasel Shark	190
438	Carcharhinidae – requiem sharks	*Carcharhinus acronotus*	Blacknose Shark	208
439		*Carcharhinus albimarginatus*	Silvertip Shark	198
440		*Carcharhinus altimus*	Bignose Shark	204
441		*Carcharhinus amblyrhynchoides*	Graceful Shark	200
442		*Carcharhinus amblyrhynchos*	Grey Reef Shark	198
443		*Carcharhinus amboinensis*	Pigeye Shark	212
444		*Carcharhinus borneensis*	Borneo Shark	218
445		*Carcharhinus brachyurus*	Bronze Whaler	206
446		*Carcharhinus brevipinna*	Spinner Shark	204
447		*Carcharhinus cautus*	Nervous Shark	216
448		*Carcharhinus coatesi*	Coate's Shark	216
449		*Carcharhinus dussumieri*	Whitecheek Shark	214
450		*Carcharhinus falciformis*	Silky Shark	196
451		*Carcharhinus fitzroyensis*	Creek Whaler	216
452		*Carcharhinus galapagensis*	Galapagos Shark	202
453		*Carcharhinus hemiodon*	Pondicherry Shark	214
454		*Carcharhinus isodon*	Finetooth Shark	208
455		*Carcharhinus leiodon*	Smoothtooth Blacktip	208
456		*Carcharhinus leucas*	Bull Shark	194
457		*Carcharhinus limbatus*	Blacktip Shark	204
458		*Carcharhinus longimanus*	Oceanic Whitetip Shark	194
459		*Carcharhinus macloti*	Hardnose Shark	218
460		*Carcharhinus melanopterus*	Blacktip Reef Shark	198
461		*Carcharhinus obscurus*	Dusky Shark	202

	Order/Family	Scientific name	English name	Page
462		*Carcharhinus perezi*	Caribbean Reef Shark	206
463		*Carcharhinus plumbeus*	Sandbar Shark	202
464		*Carcharhinus porosus*	Smalltail Shark	212
465		*Carcharhinus sealei*	Blackspot Shark	218
466		*Carcharhinus signatus*	Night Shark	208
467		*Carcharhinus sorrah*	Spottail Shark	216
468		*Carcharhinus tjujot*	Indonesian Whaler Shark	216
469		*Carcharhinus tilsoni*	Australian Blacktip Shark	208
470		*Galeocerdo cuvier*	Tiger Shark	194
471		*Glyphis fowlerae*	Borneo River Shark	210
472		*Glyphis gangeticus*	Ganges Shark	210
473		*Glyphis garricki*	New Guinea River Shark	210
474		*Glyphis glyphis*	Speartooth Shark	210
475		*Glyphis siamensis*	Irrawaddy River Shark	210
476		*Isogomphodon oxyrhynchus*	Daggernose Shark	212
477		*Lamiopsis temmincki*	Broadfin Shark	216
478		*Lamiopsis tephrodes*	Boneo Broadfin Shark	216
479		*Loxodon macrorhinus*	Sliteye Shark	218
480		*Nasolamia velox*	Whitenose Shark	216
481		*Negaprion acutidens*	Sharptooth Lemon Shark	200
482		*Negaprion brevirostris*	Lemon Shark	206
483		*Prionace glauca*	Blue Shark	196
484		*Rhizoprionodon acutus*	Milk Shark	214
485		*Rhizoprionodon lalandei*	Brazilian Sharpnose Shark	218
486		*Rhizoprionodon longurio*	Pacific Sharpnose Shark	214
487		*Rhizoprionodon oligolinx*	Grey Sharpnose Shark	218
488		*Rhizoprionodon porosus*	Caribbean Sharpnose Shark	212
489		*Rhizoprionodon taylori*	Australian Sharpnose Shark	218
490		*Rhizoprionodon terraenovae*	Atlantic Sharpnose Shark	212
491		*Scoliodon laticaudus*	Spadenose Shark	218
492		*Scoliodon macrorhynchos*	New Spadenose Shark	218
493		*Triaenodon obesus*	Whitetip Reef Shark	200
494	Sphyrnidae – hammerhead sharks	*Eusphyra blochii*	Winghead Shark	220
495		*Sphyrna corona*	Scalloped Bonnethead	220
496		*Sphyrna lewini*	Scalloped Hammerhead	222
497		*Sphyrna media*	Scoophead Shark	220
498		*Sphyrna mokarran*	Great Hammerhead	222
499		*Sphyrna tiburo*	Bonnethead Shark	220
500		*Sphyrna tudes*	Smalleye Hammerhead	220
501		*Sphyrna zygaena*	Smooth Hammerhead	222

Index